Introduction to Theoretical Physics

Introduction to

Theoretical

Classical Mechanics

Roald K. Wangsness

Professor of Physics, University of Arizona

John Wiley and Sons, Inc., New York and London

Physics

and Electrodynamics

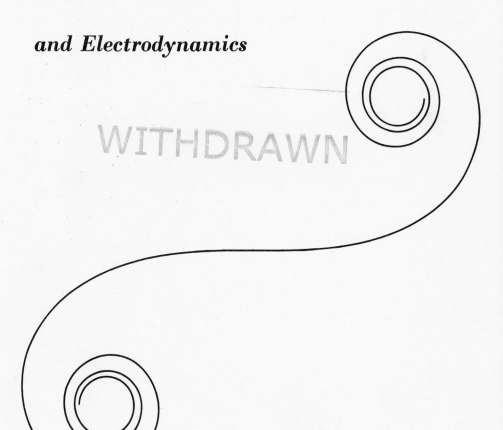

Library of Congress Catalog Card Number: 63–14070
Printed in the United States of America

For Steven and Peter

Preface

Modern developments in science and technology have made it desirable, and almost mandatory in some cases, that students of chemistry, electrical engineering, metallurgy, and similar subjects take more advanced courses in contemporary physics than they have in the past, particularly courses in quantum mechanics and solid state physics. In addition, many of these students have found it desirable to minor in physics, especially on the graduate level. Unfortunately, their preparation in classical theoretical physics is not always sufficient to enable them to study these other subjects as profitably as they might. Often the usual graduate courses in physics are too long, too detailed, and too involved to be suitable for their purposes.

My principal purpose in writing this book is to provide for the needs of these students by giving them the essential, although limited, background in classical mechanics and electromagnetism that they require, particularly as preparation for quantum mechanics. The greatest problem in constructing such a book is in deciding what may be omitted so that the final material can be covered in the usual two-semester course. Accordingly, I have omitted many detailed examples and special mathematical methods and have relied on fewer samples of theoretical calculations to demonstrate and to clarify the important conceptual features under discussion. Nevertheless, the material has been developed to where it is useful, and not merely superficial. As a result, this book can be profitably used as a text for undergraduate physics majors. I have assumed a minimal amount of previous preparation: calculus through partial differentiation, and an introductory physics course. Whatever other mathematical methods and tools are required are developed within the text, so that it is self-contained in this respect. In any event, my aim is less to stress the purely mathematical aspects of theoretical physics than to emphasize the development and applicability of concepts, including the importance of approximation methods and the limited range of validity of many commonly used descriptions, as in the discussion of linear dielectrics in Chapter 22.

The first part of the book consists of a survey of the principles of classical mechanics. The initial emphasis here, of course, is the development through the Hamiltonian formulation. Then the mechanics of coupled systems of various types is discussed at great length so that the student can become familiar with the normal mode concept and the expansion of mechanical states as linear combinations of the normal modes. Once these concepts are firmly grasped, many of the mathematical operations faced in beginning quantum mechanics offer no real difficulties. In addition, a study of normal modes and frequencies is of obvious value to those interested in the details of molecular structure.

The second and third parts deal with electromagnetic fields as independent entities and with the interactions between these fields and matter. The aim here is to derive Maxwell's equations quite quickly from a few fundamental experimental results and concepts of the structure of matter as reflected in its macroscopic electromagnetic properties. In this way, the physical basis of Maxwell's theory is made very evident, and the rest of electromagnetism can then be treated as a study of the various classes of solutions of Maxwell's equations. To a large extent, particularly in the discussion of units, the last two parts are independent of the first part and could be used as a text for a separate survey course in electromagnetic theory. A subsequent volume will deal with the areas of relativity, kinetic theory, thermodynamics, and statistical mechanics.

I have deliberately chosen standard examples for most of the exercises; the primary reasons being that these familiar examples are assumed by everyone to be part of the background of all students of this material, and most of them are of the type that everyone should do at least once in his life. I have not always used the most compact mathematical notation as soon as it was possible since the introduction of a new abbreviated notation often coincides with the introduction of a new concept, and it is better to sacrifice elegance occasionally in order to prevent the possibility of the student's being puzzled by more than one thing at a time. The caret notation for the unit vector, e.g., $\hat{\mathbf{l}}$, $\hat{\mathbf{n}}$, etc., has been used because it is very commonly used in classrooms and is unambiguous in identifying unit vectors as such. The symbols $=$, $\simeq$, $\approx$, $\sim$, $\neq$ always mean, respectively: equal to, approximately equal to, of the order of magnitude of, proportional to, and different from.

The organization and choice of material in this book were developed over a period of years in connection with a theoretical physics course which I taught at the U.S. Naval Ordnance Laboratory for the University of Maryland and, later, at the University of Arizona, and I am indebted to the many students who have contributed to the final formulation. I am also grateful to my wife, Cleo Abbott Wangsness, for her encouragement and invaluable assistance in all phases of the preparation of this book.

ROALD K. WANGSNESS

Tucson, Arizona
March, 1963

Contents

Introduction, 1

Introduction

> This will be a study worthy
> your talent, and by which you will
> become well read in history, in
> love with virtue, knowing in
> goodness, improved in manners,
> brave without rashness, and cau-
> tious without cowardice. . . .
>
> —Cervantes, *Don Quixote*

It would be a rare person, indeed, who would claim that the study of theoretical physics would inevitably lead to all the desirable consequences outlined above, although one could actually devise some very good arguments in support of such a claim.

A more modest consequence which one should hope to see result from a study of theoretical physics is the development of an attitude toward and a way of thinking about physical problems. In many respects, it is easier to illustrate such a mental pattern by successive specific examples than it is to discuss it in abstract terms. One of the purposes of this book is to develop and discuss the principal concepts of an old and highly organized portion of classical theoretical physics in sufficient detail to give a coherent survey of the subject, as well as to provide enough of the principal tools so that one can actually use them in specific applications.

In general terms, the purpose of theoretical physics is to provide a set of concepts which can be used to correlate and describe the results of experiments performed in the past and to predict the numerical results of future experiments. These concepts are represented symbolically so that they can be dealt with by mathematical methods. Accordingly, many of the intermediate stages of theoretical calculations have no immediate experimental counterparts; the ultimate justification of any theoretical scheme can therefore not be experimentally obtained in every detail, but only indirectly by comparison of end results of the theory with experiment.

One quickly finds that many actual problems are too involved to be solved exactly, so that it is important that one be able to idealize a problem by including only the essential features and ignoring, at least temporarily, other features whose effects are much less important. Similarly, in the mathematical steps and in the interpretation of results, it is necessary that one develop a facility in approximating involved quantities or processes, so that again one can concentrate on the essentials of a situation without dissipating one's efforts in dealing with inconsequential complications. The ability to make judicious approximations is justly regarded as the mark of an accomplished theoretical physicist.

Selected references

The following four books cover mechanics and electrodynamics thoroughly, and at a more advanced level than ours. They include many problems and extensive bibliographies.

H. Goldstein, *Classical Mechanics*, Addison-Wesley, 1950.
H. C. Corben and P. Stehle, *Classical Mechanics* (2nd. ed.), Wiley, 1960.
W. K. H. Panofsky and M. Phillips, *Classical Electricity and Magnetism* (2nd. ed.), Addison-Wesley, 1962.
J. D. Jackson, *Classical Electrodynamics*, Wiley, 1962.

The following two books include many similar topics at about the same level as we do.

J. C. Slater and N. H. Frank, (1) *Mechanics*, (2) *Electromagnetism*, McGraw-Hill, 1947.

Some of the subjects we have considered are discussed in a more elementary fashion in

F. W. Constant, *Theoretical Physics* (2 vols.), Addison-Wesley, 1954.

Mathematical methods and results appropriate to the material in this book are well discussed in

H. Margenau and G. M. Murphy, *The Mathematics of Physics and Chemistry* (2nd. ed.), van Nostrand, 1956.

They are covered much more exhaustively in

P. M. Morse and H. Feshbach, *Methods of Theoretical Physics* (2 vols.), McGraw-Hill, 1953.

An excellent book on the more general aspects of the methods and meaning of theoretical physics is

R. B. Lindsay and H. Margenau, *Foundations of Physics*, Wiley, 1936.

Part One

Mechanics

1 Vector analysis

We begin with a discussion of the fundamentals of vector analysis. Our treatment will not be complete but will provide an introduction sufficient for our purposes. The use of vector notation is advantageous because the resulting compactness and clarity of our results will enable us to use these results more effectively and to understand their basic physical significance more easily.

1-1 Definition of a vector

The properties of the *displacement of a point* provide us with the essentials required for our definition. If we start at some point P_1 and move in some arbitrary way to another point P_2, we see from Fig. 1-1 that the *net* effect of the motion is the same as if the point were moved along the straight line D from P_1 to P_2 as indicated by the direction of the arrow. This line D is called the displacement. If we now displace our point along E from P_2 to another point P_3, we see from Fig. 1-2 that the net effect is the same as if the point had been given the single displacement F from P_1 to P_3. Accordingly, we can speak of F as the resultant, or sum, of the successive displacements D and E, and Fig. 1-2 shows, therefore, how displacements are combined to obtain the resultant.

A *vector* is a generalization of these considerations in that it is defined as any quantity which has the same mathematical properties as the displacement of a point. Thus we see that: a vector has a magnitude; has a direction; and the addition of two vectors of the same intrinsic nature follows the rule illustrated in Fig. 1-2 (this rule is often called the parallelogram law of addition). Because of the first two properties, we can represent a vector by a directed line such as those already used for

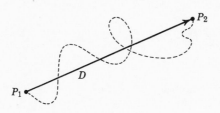

Fig. 1-1

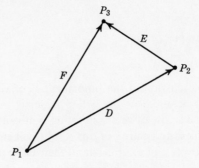

Fig. 1-2

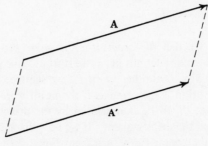

Fig. 1-3

displacements. A vector is generally printed in boldface type, thus, **A**; its magnitude will be represented by $|\mathbf{A}|$ or by A.

A *scalar* is a quantity which has magnitude only. For example, the mass of a body is a scalar, whereas its weight, which is the gravitational force acting on the body, is a vector.

Because of the nature of a vector as a directed quantity, it follows that a parallel displacement of a vector does not alter it, or, in other words, two vectors are equal if they have the same magnitude and direction. This is illustrated in Fig. 1-3, where we see that $\mathbf{A} = \mathbf{A}'$. Now we can turn to the question of what mathematical operations we can perform with and on vectors.

1-2 Addition

From our rule we find that, if we take **A** and add **B**, we obtain the sum **C** shown as the solid line in Fig. 1-4. We also see that, if we take **B** and then add **A**, we get the same vector **C**. Therefore addition of vectors has

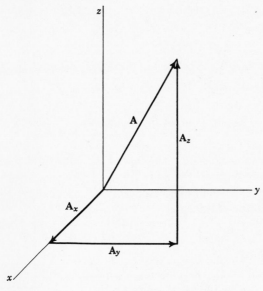

Fig. 1-6

ponents. From Fig. 1-7, we see that the components of the sum
A + B are equal to the sum of the components, i.e., $C_x = A_x + B_x$,

or convenience, we define three unit vectors $\hat{\mathbf{i}}, \hat{\mathbf{j}}, \hat{\mathbf{k}}$ along the directions
he rectangular axes, as shown in Fig. 1-8. Since $\mathbf{A}_x = A_x\hat{\mathbf{i}}$, etc., we can
e a vector in terms of its components as

$$\mathbf{A} = A_x\hat{\mathbf{i}} + A_y\hat{\mathbf{j}} + A_z\hat{\mathbf{k}} \tag{1-4}$$

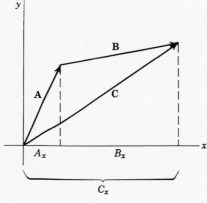

Fig. 1-7

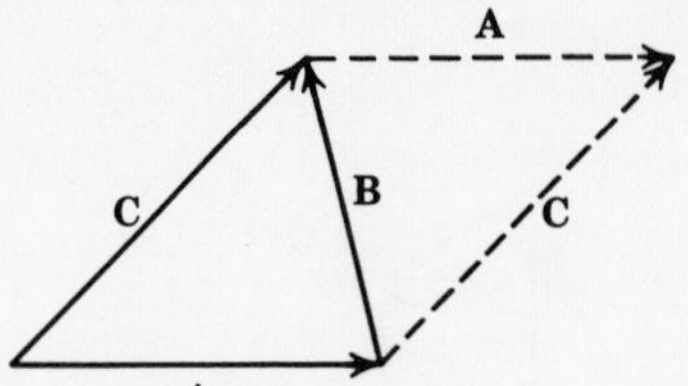

Fig. 1-4 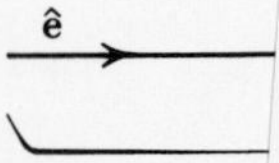   Fi

the property that

$$C = A + B = B + A$$

By proceeding in the same manner, one can estal
property of vector addition:

$$D = (A + B) + C = A + (B + C) = (A + $$

If we reverse a displacement such as D in Fig. 1-1
opposite direction, the net effect is then no displa
appropriate to define the negative of a vector as a vec
nitude but reversed in direction, for then we should ol
as we would want. Then we can easily subtract a
negative.

The product of a scalar and vector, sA, is then
vectors A, or is a vector with a magnitude equal to
of A, and is in the same direction as A if s is positiv
direction to A if s is negative.

A unit vector is defined as a vector of unit magnit
$\hat{e}$; thus $|\hat{e}| = 1$. If $\hat{e}$ is chosen to have the direction
$A = A\hat{e}$; this point is illustrated in Fig. 1-5.

1-3 Components

In Fig. 1-6, we see that we can write a vector
properly chosen vectors each of which is parallel
rectangular coordinate system; that is,

$$A = A_x + A_y + A_z$$

These three vectors are called the components of A
however, usually refers simply to the numerica
hence we see that a vector can be specified by th
The addition of vectors is easily done in t

and, from Fig. 1-6, we see that we can express its magnitude in terms of its components as

$$A = |\mathbf{A}| = (A_x^2 + A_y^2 + A_z^2)^{\frac{1}{2}} \tag{1-5}$$

We further see from Fig. 1-9 that the angle between **A** and the x axis, which we write as $(\mathbf{A}, \hat{\mathbf{i}})$, is given by

$$\cos(\mathbf{A}, \hat{\mathbf{i}}) = \frac{A_x}{A} = \frac{A_x}{(A_x^2 + A_y^2 + A_z^2)^{\frac{1}{2}}} \tag{1-6}$$

Similar expressions hold for the other two direction angles, so we see from (1-5) and (1-6) that, if we know the rectangular components of a vector, we can calculate its magnitude and direction.

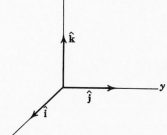

We now turn to multiplication; two types are defined.

1-4 Scalar product

Because of the notation the scalar product is also called the dot product. We define the scalar product of two vectors as the scalar equal to the product of the magnitudes of the vectors and the cosine of the angle between them, or

Fig. 1-8

$$\mathbf{A} \cdot \mathbf{B} = AB \cos(\mathbf{A}, \mathbf{B}) \tag{1-7}$$

We see from Fig. 1-10 that we can get a simple interpretation of the scalar product: $[A \cos(\mathbf{A}, \mathbf{B})]B$ = component of **A** along the direction of **B** times the magnitude of **B** = $[B \cos(\mathbf{A}, \mathbf{B})]A$ = component of **B** along **A** times magnitude of **A**.

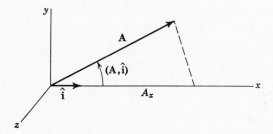

Fig. 1-9

It is clear from (1-7) that the order of the terms does not change the scalar product; i.e.,

$$\mathbf{A} \cdot \mathbf{B} = \mathbf{B} \cdot \mathbf{A} \qquad (1\text{-}8)$$

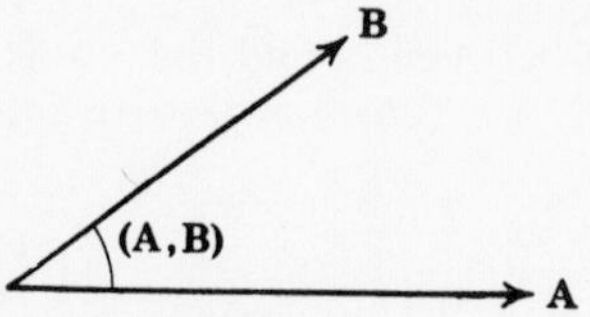

Fig. 1-10

If we knew only the rectangular components of **A** and **B**, it would be inconvenient to calculate **A** · **B** from (1-7) since this would necessitate finding the angle between **A** and **B**. Fortunately, it is possible to express **A** · **B** simply in terms of the rectangular components. Since the angle between each pair of unit vectors defined in Fig. 1-8 is $\pi/2$, we easily find from (1-7) that

$$\hat{\imath} \cdot \hat{\jmath} = \hat{\jmath} \cdot \hat{k} = \hat{k} \cdot \hat{\imath} = 0 \qquad (1\text{-}9)$$

In the same way,

$$\hat{\imath} \cdot \hat{\imath} = \hat{\jmath} \cdot \hat{\jmath} = \hat{k} \cdot \hat{k} = 1 \qquad (1\text{-}10)$$

because the angle involved is zero. If we now write **A** and **B** in the form given by (1-4), multiply them together, use the distributive property together with (1-9) and (1-10) to simplify the resulting nine terms, we find that

$$\mathbf{A} \cdot \mathbf{B} = A_x B_x + A_y B_y + A_z B_z \qquad (1\text{-}11)$$

From (1-7), it follows that if two vectors are perpendicular then **A** · **B** = 0, and conversely.

Also, the square of a vector can be interpreted as the vector dotted with itself; the result is the square of its magnitude. Thus

$$\mathbf{A} \cdot \mathbf{A} = \mathbf{A}^2 = A^2 \qquad (1\text{-}12)$$

1-5 Vector product

This is also called the cross product and is written **A** × **B**. It is a vector perpendicular to *both* **A** and **B**, and its magnitude is defined as

$$|\mathbf{A} \times \mathbf{B}| = AB \sin (\mathbf{A}, \mathbf{B}) \qquad (1\text{-}13)$$

Its direction is given by the following right-hand rule: If the fingers of the right hand are curled in the sense necessary to rotate **A** through the smaller angle into coincidence with **B**, the thumb points in the direction of **A** × **B**. This rule is illustrated in Fig. 1-11.

If we look at the plane containing **A** and **B** shown in Fig. 1-12, we can get a simple interpretation of the cross product. We see from Fig. 1-12 and (1-13), that the magnitude of the cross product is equal to the area of the parallelogram with **A** and **B** as sides.

From the definition of the direction of a cross product shown in Fig. 1-11, it is evident that the order is important, since it is easily seen that

$$\mathbf{B} \times \mathbf{A} = -(\mathbf{A} \times \mathbf{B}) \qquad (1\text{-}14)$$

If **A** and **B** are parallel, then it follows from (1-13) that $\mathbf{A} \times \mathbf{B} = 0$, and conversely. In particular,

$$\mathbf{A} \times \mathbf{A} = 0 \qquad (1\text{-}15)$$

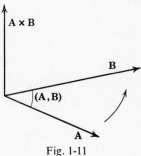

For the unit vectors along the axes shown in Fig. 1-8, if we use (1-13), the right-hand rule, the facts that they are mutually perpendicular and that the cross product is perpendicular to both vectors, we easily find that

Fig. 1-11

$$\hat{\mathbf{i}} \times \hat{\mathbf{j}} = \hat{\mathbf{k}}, \quad \hat{\mathbf{j}} \times \hat{\mathbf{k}} = \hat{\mathbf{i}}, \quad \hat{\mathbf{k}} \times \hat{\mathbf{i}} = \hat{\mathbf{j}} \qquad (1\text{-}16)$$

From (1-15), it follows that

$$\hat{\mathbf{i}} \times \hat{\mathbf{i}} = \hat{\mathbf{j}} \times \hat{\mathbf{j}} = \hat{\mathbf{k}} \times \hat{\mathbf{k}} = 0 \qquad (1\text{-}17)$$

The vector product can also be conveniently written in terms of the rectangular components. We write **A** and **B** in the form (1-4), multiply them together, and use the distributive property with (1-14), (1-16), and (1-17) to simplify the result. We find that

$$\mathbf{A} \times \mathbf{B} = (A_y B_z - A_z B_y)\hat{\mathbf{i}} + (A_z B_x - A_x B_z)\hat{\mathbf{j}} + (A_x B_y - A_y B_x)\hat{\mathbf{k}} \qquad (1\text{-}18)$$

This can be written as an easily remembered determinant:

$$\mathbf{A} \times \mathbf{B} = \begin{vmatrix} \hat{\mathbf{i}} & \hat{\mathbf{j}} & \hat{\mathbf{k}} \\ A_x & A_y & A_z \\ B_x & B_y & B_z \end{vmatrix} \qquad (1\text{-}19)$$

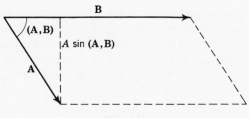

Fig. 1-12

It will be left as exercises to verify that

$$\mathbf{A} \cdot (\mathbf{B} \times \mathbf{C}) = (\mathbf{A} \times \mathbf{B}) \cdot \mathbf{C} = \begin{vmatrix} A_x & A_y & A_z \\ B_x & B_y & B_z \\ C_x & C_y & C_z \end{vmatrix} \qquad (1\text{-}20)$$

and that

$$\mathbf{A} \times (\mathbf{B} \times \mathbf{C}) = \mathbf{B}(\mathbf{A} \cdot \mathbf{C}) - \mathbf{C}(\mathbf{A} \cdot \mathbf{B}) \qquad (1\text{-}21)$$

In (1-20) we see that the dot and the cross can be interchanged without affecting the value of this triple scalar product; hence the parentheses are not really needed. The triple vector product formula (1-21) can be easily remembered from the phrase "back minus cab"; however, the parentheses are important because $(\mathbf{A} \times \mathbf{B}) \times \mathbf{C} = -\mathbf{C} \times (\mathbf{A} \times \mathbf{B})$ from (1-14).

Division of vectors is not defined.

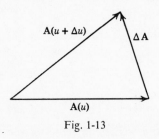

$\mathbf{A}(u + \Delta u)$
$\Delta \mathbf{A}$
$\mathbf{A}(u)$

Fig. 1-13

1-6 Differentiation with respect to a scalar

Suppose that $\mathbf{A}$ is a continuous function of some scalar variable u, so that we can write $\mathbf{A} = \mathbf{A}(u)$. This is equivalent to the three equations: $A_x = A_x(u)$, $A_y = A_y(u)$, $A_z = A_z(u)$. If u is changed to $u + \Delta u$, $\mathbf{A}$ will change by the amount $\Delta \mathbf{A}$, where $\Delta \mathbf{A} = \mathbf{A}(u + \Delta u) - \mathbf{A}(u)$, as illustrated in Fig. 1-13. We can then define the derivative of the vector $\mathbf{A}$ with respect to the scalar u as follows:

$$\frac{d\mathbf{A}}{du} = \lim_{\Delta u \to 0} \frac{\Delta \mathbf{A}}{\Delta u} = \lim_{\Delta u \to 0} \frac{\mathbf{A}(u + \Delta u) - \mathbf{A}(u)}{\Delta u} \qquad (1\text{-}22)$$

This process has yielded another vector from a vector.

1-7 Gradient of a scalar

In this differentiating process, we get a vector from a scalar. Suppose we have a scalar u which is a function of position so that we can write $u = u(x, y, z)$. An example of this would be the temperature at each point in a room. At some other point, which is displaced by $d\mathbf{s}$ from the first, the value of the scalar will have changed from u to $u + du$ (Fig. 1-14). In fact,

$$du = \frac{\partial u}{\partial x} dx + \frac{\partial u}{\partial y} dy + \frac{\partial u}{\partial z} dz \qquad (1\text{-}23)$$

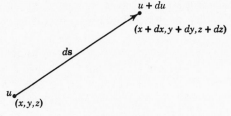

Fig. 1-14

and we also have

$$ds = dx\hat{\mathbf{i}} + dy\hat{\mathbf{j}} + dz\hat{\mathbf{k}} \tag{1-24}$$

Comparing (1-23) and (1-24) with (1-11), we see that we can also write du as the scalar product of $d\mathbf{s}$ and the vector:

$$\text{grad } u = \frac{\partial u}{\partial x}\hat{\mathbf{i}} + \frac{\partial u}{\partial y}\hat{\mathbf{j}} + \frac{\partial u}{\partial z}\hat{\mathbf{k}} \tag{1-25}$$

so that

$$du = \text{grad } u \cdot d\mathbf{s} \tag{1-26}$$

The vector which is written in terms of its rectangular components in (1-25) is called the gradient of u; we can regard (1-26) as the general definition of grad u since it is written in a form which is independent of a particular coordinate system.

In order to understand the meaning of the gradient, let us consider Fig. 1-15, in which we indicate the surfaces made up of the points for which u has the equal values u_1, u_2, u_3, ... Now a displacement such as $d\mathbf{s}_1$ which is completely on one of these surfaces does *not* take one to a point where u is changed. Therefore $du_1 = \text{grad } u \cdot d\mathbf{s}_1 = 0$. Comparing this

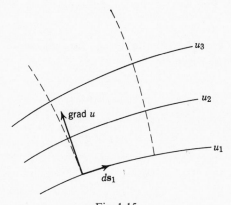

Fig. 1-15

with (1-7), we see that grad u and $d\mathbf{s}_1$ are perpendicular; in other words, grad u is perpendicular to the surfaces of constant u, as shown in Fig. 1-15.

Let us also consider a displacement $d\mathbf{s}'$, of constant magnitude but varying direction. We see from (1-26) that the change in u resulting from this displacement is $du = |\text{grad } u| \, ds' \cos (\text{grad } u, d\mathbf{s}')$. We now see that du will be a maximum when the angle between grad u and $d\mathbf{s}'$ is zero so that they are parallel. In other words, the direction of the gradient is also the direction in which the scalar has its maximum rate of change.

1-8 Other differential operations

We see that (1-25) can also be formally written

$$\text{grad } u = \nabla u \tag{1-27}$$

if we introduce the operator "del,"

$$\nabla = \hat{\imath}\frac{\partial}{\partial x} + \hat{\jmath}\frac{\partial}{\partial y} + \hat{k}\frac{\partial}{\partial z} \tag{1-28}$$

If we treat ∇ as a legitimate vector (which it can be proved to be), we can now perform two other differential operations of interest by using our two forms of multiplication.

The scalar product is called the *divergence*. Using (1-11) and (1-28), we obtain

$$\text{div } \mathbf{A} = \nabla \cdot \mathbf{A} = \frac{\partial A_x}{\partial x} + \frac{\partial A_y}{\partial y} + \frac{\partial A_z}{\partial z} \tag{1-29}$$

This has given us a scalar from a vector.

The vector product is called the *curl*. Using (1-18) and (1-28), we find that

$$\text{curl } \mathbf{A} = \nabla \times \mathbf{A} = \left(\frac{\partial A_z}{\partial y} - \frac{\partial A_y}{\partial z}\right)\hat{\imath} + \left(\frac{\partial A_x}{\partial z} - \frac{\partial A_z}{\partial x}\right)\hat{\jmath} + \left(\frac{\partial A_y}{\partial x} - \frac{\partial A_x}{\partial y}\right)\hat{k}$$

$$\tag{1-30}$$

This operation, which yields another vector from a vector, can be written more conveniently as a determinant as in (1-19):

$$\text{curl } \mathbf{A} = \begin{vmatrix} \hat{\imath} & \hat{\jmath} & \hat{k} \\ \dfrac{\partial}{\partial x} & \dfrac{\partial}{\partial y} & \dfrac{\partial}{\partial z} \\ A_x & A_y & A_z \end{vmatrix} \tag{1-31}$$

The significance of the names "divergence" and "curl" will become clearer as we use them in the various contexts in which they naturally arise.

Another operator of great interest is the Laplacian:

$$\nabla^2 = \nabla \cdot \nabla = \text{div curl} = \frac{\partial^2}{\partial x^2} + \frac{\partial^2}{\partial y^2} + \frac{\partial^2}{\partial z^2} \qquad (1\text{-}32)$$

For example,

$$\nabla^2 u = \frac{\partial^2 u}{\partial x^2} + \frac{\partial^2 u}{\partial y^2} + \frac{\partial^2 u}{\partial z^2}$$

We now turn to two important integral theorems of vector analysis.

1-9   The divergence theorem

Consider the volume V enclosed by the surface S as illustrated in Fig. 1-16. At the location of an element of surface area da, the vector $\mathbf{A}$ makes the angle θ with the *outward* normal $\hat{\mathbf{n}}$. We want to prove that

$$\int_S A \cos \theta \, da = \int_S \mathbf{A} \cdot \hat{\mathbf{n}} \, da = \int_S \mathbf{A} \cdot d\mathbf{a} = \int_V \text{div } \mathbf{A} \, dv \qquad (1\text{-}33)$$

The integrals in (1-33) are taken over the total surface S and throughout the volume V whose volume element is dv. We also note that we have been able to introduce a vector representation of the element of area such that its magnitude is equal to the area and its direction is that of the unit normal vector, i.e.,

$$d\mathbf{a} = \hat{\mathbf{n}} \, da \qquad (1\text{-}34)$$

This is also illustrated in Fig. 1-16.

Using (1-29), we can write the volume integral as a sum:

$$\int_V \text{div } \mathbf{A} \, dv = \int_V \frac{\partial A_x}{\partial x} \, dx \, dy \, dz + \int_V \frac{\partial A_y}{\partial y} \, dx \, dy \, dz + \int_V \frac{\partial A_z}{\partial z} \, dx \, dy \, dz$$

$$(1\text{-}35)$$

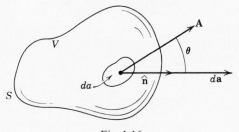

Fig. 1-16

Each of these integrals is, of course, a triple integral, just as the surface integrals are double integrals.

Consider the first integral. Our first step is to integrate over x while keeping y and z constant; after this is done, we can integrate over y and z. Thus we are integrating along the strip of cross section $dy\,dz$ shown shaded in Fig. 1-17. Since y and z are constant on the strip, we get

$$\iiint \frac{\partial A_x}{\partial x}\,dx\,dy\,dz = \iint [A_x(P_2) - A_x(P_1)]\,dy\,dz \qquad (1\text{-}36)$$

At P_2,

$$dy\,dz = da_2 \cos \beta = d\mathbf{a}_2 \cdot \hat{\mathbf{i}} = da_x,$$

while at P_1,

$$dy\,dz = -da_1 \cos \alpha = -d\mathbf{a}_1 \cdot \hat{\mathbf{i}} = -da_x \text{ since } \cos \alpha < 0.$$

As indicated by the dotted line in Fig. 1-17, the elements of area can be paired off into "P_2 like" and "P_1 like"; the P_2 like areas together constitute the area S_2, while S_1 is formed by the P_1 like areas. Thus we can write (1-36) as

$$\int_V \frac{\partial A_x}{\partial x}\,dx\,dy\,dz = \int_{S_2} A_x\,da_x + \int_{S_1} A_x\,da_x = \int_S A_x\,da_x \qquad (1\text{-}37)$$

The last two integrals in (1-35) will clearly be found equal to

$$\int_S A_y\,da_y \quad \text{and} \quad \int_S A_z\,da_z$$

respectively, so that, if we add these to (1-37), substitute into (1-35), and use (1-11), we find that

$$\int_V \operatorname{div} \mathbf{A}\,dv = \int_S (A_x\,da_x + A_y\,da_y + A_z\,da_z) = \int_S \mathbf{A} \cdot d\mathbf{a} \qquad (1\text{-}38)$$

which proves the theorem.

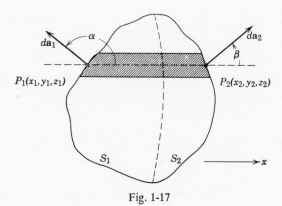

Fig. 1-17

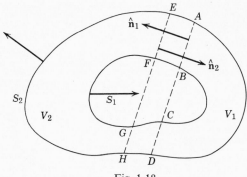

Fig. 1-18

We have proved this theorem only for a region bounded by a single surface, but we can easily extend the proof to a region bounded by several surfaces, such as a hollow ball. Figure 1-18 shows a volume V surrounded by the surfaces S_1 and S_2; the outward normals to the volume are shown in both cases. By introducing the coincident surfaces $ABCD$ and $EFGH$, we can divide V into the two volumes V_1 and V_2; each of these is now bounded by a single surface. Applying (1-38) to each of these and adding, we obtain

$$\int_{V_1+V_2} \operatorname{div} \mathbf{A}\, dv = \int_{S_1} \mathbf{A} \cdot d\mathbf{a} + \int_{S_2} \mathbf{A} \cdot d\mathbf{a} + \int_{ABCD} \mathbf{A} \cdot d\mathbf{a} + \int_{EFGH} \mathbf{A} \cdot d\mathbf{a}$$
(1-39)

However, the last integral in (1-39) is the negative of the next to the last, since the corresponding outward normals, $\hat{\mathbf{n}}_1$ and $\hat{\mathbf{n}}_2$ are oppositely directed. Then (1-39) becomes simply

$$\int_{V_1+V_2} \operatorname{div} \mathbf{A}\, dv = \int_{S_1+S_2} \mathbf{A} \cdot d\mathbf{a}$$

which is the same as (1-38), because the total volume is $V_1 + V_2$ and the total bounding surface is $S_1 + S_2$.

This proof can obviously be generalized to an arbitrary number of bounding surfaces by introducing as many other surfaces like $ABCD$ as would be necessary.

1-10 Stokes' theorem

Consider the surface S bounded by the perimeter L illustrated in Fig. 1-19a. We want to prove that

$$\oint_L \mathbf{A} \cdot d\mathbf{s} = \int_S \operatorname{curl} \mathbf{A} \cdot d\mathbf{a}$$
(1-40)

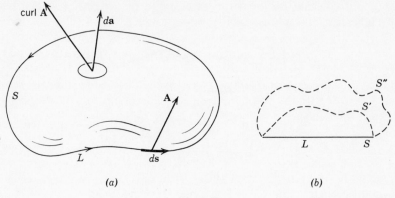

Fig. 1-19

In this equation, $d\mathbf{s}$ is a displacement along the perimeter and the integral sign used indicates that this line integral is taken over the complete closed curve L.

The sign convention shown should be carefully noted. The positive sense of traversal is indicated so that one goes around keeping the inside of the surface to the left. The direction of the normal to the surface (and hence of $d\mathbf{a}$) is then given by a right-hand rule: If the fingers of the right hand are curled in the sense of travel, then the thumb points in the direction of $d\mathbf{a}$.

Stokes' theorem (1-40) tells us that the surface integral of the curl depends only on the values of the vector along the perimeter; it also says that this integral has the same value over all surfaces with the same bounding curve, such as S, S', and S'' of Fig. 1-19b.

Using (1-30), we find that

$$\int_S \operatorname{curl} \mathbf{A} \cdot d\mathbf{a} = \int_S \left(\frac{\partial A_x}{\partial z}\, da_y - \frac{\partial A_x}{\partial y}\, da_z \right) + \int_S \left(\frac{\partial A_y}{\partial x}\, da_z - \frac{\partial A_y}{\partial z}\, da_x \right)$$
$$+ \int_S \left(\frac{\partial A_z}{\partial y}\, da_x - \frac{\partial A_z}{\partial x}\, da_y \right) \quad (1\text{-}41)$$

where we have grouped the terms by components of $\mathbf{A}$.

Let us integrate the first integral on the right side of (1-41) over the strip shown in Fig. 1-20. This strip is in the plane parallel to the yz plane and is at a distance x from the origin. The axes are chosen so that both y and z increase as we go from P_1 to P_2. We see then that $da_y = -dx\, dz$ and $da_z = dx\, dy$. Then we can write

$$I_x = \int_S \left(\frac{\partial A_x}{\partial z}\, da_y - \frac{\partial A_x}{\partial y}\, da_z \right) = -\int dx \int \left(\frac{\partial A_x}{\partial z}\, dz + \frac{\partial A_x}{\partial y}\, dy \right) \quad (1\text{-}42)$$

Since x is constant on this strip, $dx = 0$ and the expression in the last parentheses in (1-42) is dA_x, and (1-42) can now be written

$$I_x = -\int dx \int_{P_1}^{P_2} dA_x = -\int [A_x(P_2) - A_x(P_1)]\, dx \qquad (1\text{-}43)$$

But, at P_1, $dx = ds_x$; at P_2, $dx = -ds_x$; also, P_2 like points together form the L_2 portion of the perimeter, while P_1 like points together form L_1. Then (1-43) becomes

$$I_x = \int_{L_2} A_x(P_2)\, ds_x + \int_{L_1} A_x(P_1)\, ds_x = \oint_L A_x\, ds_x \qquad (1\text{-}44)$$

Similarly, the last two integrals of (1-41) can be shown to have the respective values

$$\oint A_y\, ds_y \quad \text{and} \quad \oint A_z\, ds_z$$

Substituting these values and (1-44) into (1-41), we find that

$$\int_S \text{curl } \mathbf{A} \cdot d\mathbf{a} = \oint_L (A_x\, ds_x + A_y\, ds_y + A_z\, ds_z) = \oint_L \mathbf{A} \cdot d\mathbf{s} \qquad (1\text{-}45)$$

which proves the theorem.

This theorem can also be extended to the case of a surface bounded by more than one curve by a method similar to that we used for the divergence theorem. We would divide it into surfaces bounded by a single curve by

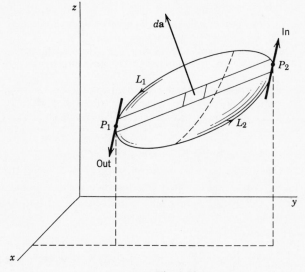

Fig. 1-20

introducing as many pairs of coincident lines as we would need. Then Stokes' theorem could be applied to each of these surfaces and the results added. The contributions to the line integrals along the cuts would cancel since they are traversed in opposite directions and the final result will again be (1-45).

Exercises

1-1. Verify equation (1-2) by graphical methods.

1-2. Given the two vectors $\mathbf{A} = 2\hat{\mathbf{i}} - 3\hat{\mathbf{j}} - 4\hat{\mathbf{k}}$ and $\mathbf{B} = 6\hat{\mathbf{i}} + 5\hat{\mathbf{j}} + \hat{\mathbf{k}}$, find the magnitudes and angles made with the x, y, and z axes for $\mathbf{A} + \mathbf{B}$ and $\mathbf{A} - \mathbf{B}$. [*Partial answer.* $|\mathbf{A} + \mathbf{B}| = 8.8$, $(\mathbf{A} + \mathbf{B}, x) = 24°$.]

1-3. Given the two vectors $\hat{\mathbf{i}} + 2\hat{\mathbf{j}} + 3\hat{\mathbf{k}}$ and $4\hat{\mathbf{i}} - 5\hat{\mathbf{j}} + 6\hat{\mathbf{k}}$, find the angle between them.

1-4. Verify (1-20) and (1-21). (This is most easily done by using rectangular coordinates. Is this enough to convince you that they are then true in general?)

1-5. Show that $\mathbf{A} \cdot (\mathbf{B} \times \mathbf{C})$ equals the volume of a parallelopiped if $\mathbf{A}$, $\mathbf{B}$, and $\mathbf{C}$ are the vectors representing the three edges with a common corner.

1-6. The equation of the surface of an ellipsoid is

$$\frac{x^2}{a^2} + \frac{y^2}{b^2} + \frac{z^2}{c^2} = 1$$

Show that the unit vector normal to each point on this surface is

$$\hat{\mathbf{n}} = f\left(\frac{x}{a^2}\hat{\mathbf{i}} + \frac{y}{b^2}\hat{\mathbf{j}} + \frac{z}{c^2}\hat{\mathbf{k}}\right)$$

where

$$f = \left(\frac{x^2}{a^4} + \frac{y^2}{b^4} + \frac{z^2}{c^4}\right)^{-\frac{1}{2}}$$

1-7. Calculate the surface integral of $\mathbf{r} = x\hat{\mathbf{i}} + y\hat{\mathbf{j}} + z\hat{\mathbf{k}}$ over the surface of a sphere of radius R and center at the origin and thus show directly that (1-33) is true in this case.

1-8. Calculate directly the line integral $\oint \mathbf{A} \cdot d\mathbf{s}$ of the vector $\mathbf{A} = -y\hat{\mathbf{i}} + x\hat{\mathbf{j}}$ around the closed path in the x-y plane given by: $(0, 0) \to (3, 0) \to (3, 4) \to (0, 4) \to (0, 0)$. Also calculate the surface integral of curl $\mathbf{A}$ and show that (1-40) is satisfied.

2 Kinematics

In mechanics, the purpose is to describe the motions of bodies—how their positions and configurations change in time when they are subject to various influences. In order to discuss these motions, we must consider

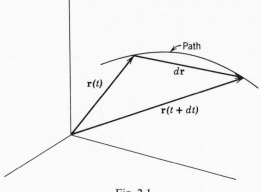

Fig. 2-1

first the way in which we describe their positions as well as some of the properties of motion in general, leaving the consideration of how motion is produced until later. This study of the geometric properties of motion is called *kinematics*.

At present, we shall restrict our attention to *mass points*, or *particles*, that is, bodies whose extension in space can be neglected.

The position is given by the vector **r** drawn from the origin of a suitably and conveniently chosen coordinate system as shown in Fig. 2-1. In general, the position vector changes with time t as the particle moves along its path so that $\mathbf{r} = \mathbf{r}(t)$. The basic purpose of mechanics is to determine this function of the time.

At a later time $t + dt$, we can write $\mathbf{r}(t + dt) = \mathbf{r}(t) + d\mathbf{r}$. We define

$$\text{Velocity} = \mathbf{v} = \frac{d\mathbf{r}}{dt} = \dot{\mathbf{r}} \qquad (2\text{-}1)$$

[The dot over **r** in (2-1) is the conventional way of writing a derivative with respect to the time.] From (1-22) and Fig. 2-1, we see that the velocity is tangent to the path.

In general, the velocity can also be a function of the time, so that $\mathbf{v} = \mathbf{v}(t)$. Accordingly, we can define

$$\text{Acceleration} = \mathbf{a} = \frac{d\mathbf{v}}{dt} = \dot{\mathbf{v}} = \frac{d^2\mathbf{r}}{dt^2} = \ddot{\mathbf{r}} \qquad (2\text{-}2)$$

Higher time derivatives of **r** can also be defined, but we shall not need them.

As an example, let us now look at the specific form of these quantities when they are written in terms of an important coordinate system.

2-1   Rectangular coordinates

Here the unit vectors $\hat{\imath}$, $\hat{\jmath}$, $\hat{k}$ of Fig. 1-8 are fixed in space so that

$$\mathbf{r} = x\hat{\imath} + y\hat{\jmath} + z\hat{k} \tag{2-3}$$

Therefore the components of $\mathbf{r}$ are the position coordinates of the particle: $x(t)$, $y(t)$, and $z(t)$. We then easily find from (2-1) and (2-2) that

$$\mathbf{v} = \dot{x}\hat{\imath} + \dot{y}\hat{\jmath} + \dot{z}\hat{k} \tag{2-4}$$

$$\mathbf{a} = \ddot{x}\hat{\imath} + \ddot{y}\hat{\jmath} + \ddot{z}\hat{k} \tag{2-5}$$

and the components are given by

$$v_x = \dot{x}, \quad v_y = \dot{y}, \quad v_z = \dot{z} \tag{2-6}$$

$$a_x = \dot{v}_x = \ddot{x}, \quad a_y = \dot{v}_y = \ddot{y}, \quad a_z = \dot{v}_z = \ddot{z} \tag{2-7}$$

2-2   The coordinate system of classical physics

Although we used a coordinate system in the discussion above, we did not specify it exactly for this was not necessary. But, when we come to our next problem, that of laws of motion and the discussion of *forces*, it is important that we have a clear idea of the reference frame in which these laws are valid, and to which ultimately all the results of classical physics must be referred.

This problem was first considered by Newton, and it has been found that these laws have their usual and simplest form when they are expressed with respect to a set of rigid coordinate axes which are fixed relative to the average position of the "fixed" stars.

This reference frame is called the *primary inertial system*. Any other set of axes which is moving without rotation and with a constant velocity with respect to the primary inertial system is called a *secondary inertial system*, for reasons which we shall discuss shortly.

Exercises

2-1. The position coordinates of a given particle are found to be these functions of the time: $x = 2at^3$, $y = \frac{1}{2}bt^2$, $z = 10ct$. Find all components of the velocity and acceleration.

2-2. A particle located at a point with plane polar coordinates (r, θ) has an acceleration $\mathbf{a}$ as shown in Fig. 2-2. Show that the components a_r and a_θ, in the

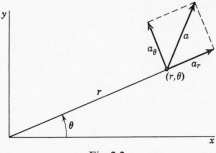

Fig. 2-2

directions of increasing r and θ, respectively, are given by $a_r = a_x \cos \theta + a_y \sin \theta$ and $a_\theta = -a_x \sin \theta + a_y \cos \theta$. By differentiating the transformation equations, $x = r \cos \theta$ and $y = r \sin \theta$, also show that $a_r = \ddot{r} - r\dot{\theta}^2$ and $a_\theta = r\ddot{\theta} + 2\dot{r}\dot{\theta}$.

3 Concepts of mass and force;
the laws of motion

The quantitative formulation of these ideas can be most easily discussed in terms of four *experimental* laws, which are actually generalizations from long and varied experience.

3-1 First experimental law

Let us consider two isolated particles which we label 0 and 1, and let them interact with each other *in any way whatsoever*. For example, we can let them collide with each other, or we can connect them with a spring and observe their motions when the spring is compressed or stretched and then released. (We also make the seemingly arbitrary requirement that all velocities involved be small compared to that of light; this is necessary in order that our results will not conflict later with those of the theory of relativity.)

If the particle motions are always referred to the primary inertial system, it is found experimentally that the acceleration of one particle is always opposite to the acceleration of the other, and the ratio of the magnitudes of the accelerations is a constant. If we let

$$\mathbf{a}_{01} = \text{acceleration of 0 in the presence of 1}$$
$$\mathbf{a}_{10} = \text{acceleration of 1 in the presence of 0}$$

then our experimental result stated above is that

$$\mathbf{a}_{01} = -C_{10}\mathbf{a}_{10} \tag{3-1}$$

where C_{10} is a positive constant characteristic of the two particles, but otherwise independent of the particular circumstances of their mutual interaction. This constant presumably reflects some inherent mechanical property of the particles.

3-2   Second experimental law

Suppose we remove particle 1, and let another particle 2 interact with 0 in any way. Since our previous discussion is equally applicable to this case, we see from (3-1) that we must also be able to write

$$\mathbf{a}_{02} = -C_{20}\mathbf{a}_{20} \tag{3-2}$$

where C_{20} is some positive constant. If we now let 1 and 2 interact with each other, we must also have

$$\mathbf{a}_{12} = -C_{21}\mathbf{a}_{21} \tag{3-3}$$

The universal result of experiment is that

$$C_{21} = \frac{C_{20}}{C_{10}} \tag{3-4}$$

and is our second experimental law. The form of this result, in which the left-hand side is independent of particle 0, suggests that the C's are *ratios* of quantities characteristic of the individual particles. Accordingly, we *define*

$$C_{10} = \frac{a_{01}}{a_{10}} = \frac{m_1}{m_0} = \text{ratio of the *masses* of the particles} \tag{3-5}$$

This definition is compatible with (3-4), which then takes on a correct algebraic form

$$\frac{m_2}{m_1} = \frac{(m_2/m_0)}{(m_1/m_0)}$$

The mass ratio defined in (3-5) is a constant, independent of the conditions under which it is determined, according to the result of the first law as given by (3-1). The mass defined in this way is called the "inertial" mass, and one often finds a statement to the effect that mass is a measure of the "inertia" of a particle. Although (3-5) gives only the experimental value of the mass ratio, absolute values of the mass can be obtained by choosing particle 0 to be a *standard* particle and assigning it a convenient but arbitrary *unit mass*. Then the mass of any other particle can be found in principle by letting it interact in any way with the standard particle, finding the ratio of the accelerations, and using (3-5).

Since we can write $C_{21} = m_2/m_1$, we also see that (3-3) can be written

$$m_1\mathbf{a}_{12} = -m_2\mathbf{a}_{21} \tag{3-6}$$

which no longer involves the standard particle directly. (However, we must bear in mind that m_1 and m_2 are ultimately determined by means of interactions with the standard particle.)

3-3 Third experimental law

We recall from its definition and (2-2) that $\mathbf{a}_{12} = d^2\mathbf{r}_1/dt^2$, etc. This emphasis on acceleration is a consequence of the third law, which we shall now state.

If we study the motion of particle 1 under all the different kinds of interactions which occur in nature between it and any other particle 2, we always find that $\mathbf{a}_{12}$ is the time derivative of $\mathbf{r}_1$ of *lowest* order which can be expressed as a function of the separation $\mathbf{r}_{12} = \mathbf{r}_1 - \mathbf{r}_2$ between the particles (and possibly the velocities $\mathbf{v}_1$ and $\mathbf{v}_2$) and *which contains no arbitrary constants depending on the initial conditions of the motion.*

In other words, the acceleration is the simplest function which can be taken to be characteristic *only of the interaction*, since it is independent of the precise details of the way in which the motion started and depends only on the instantaneous relation between the two particles. Instead of setting $\mathbf{a}_{12}$ directly equal to such a function, it is customary to write instead

$$m_1\mathbf{a}_{12} = \mathbf{F}_{12} \tag{3-7}$$

where $\mathbf{F}_{12}$ is a function of $\mathbf{r}_{12}$ (and possibly $\mathbf{v}_1$ and $\mathbf{v}_2$) which is characteristic *only* of the interaction.

The function $\mathbf{F}_{12}$ is defined as the *force* exerted by particle 2 on particle 1, and (3-7) is called the *equation of motion* for particle 1. The precise definition of force given in (3-7) is a generalization and sharpening of the anthropomorphic concept of "force" as a push or pull of some sort, generally associated with muscular effort.

Using (2-2), we can rewrite (3-7) as

$$m_1 \frac{d^2\mathbf{r}_1}{dt^2} = \mathbf{F}_{12} \tag{3-8}$$

Thus we see that, if we know the form of the function $\mathbf{F}_{12}$, we have a second order differential equation for $\mathbf{r}_1$. In principle, we can then integrate (3-8) and find r_1 as a function of time, $r_1(t)$. When this has been accomplished, the dynamical problem of the motion of the particle is considered to be solved.

We see, therefore, that the object of one's work in mechanics has two aspects. First, one must determine the form of F_{12} appropriate to a given case; if all other experience fails, one ultimately has to *guess* at F_{12}. Second, one then has to solve the resulting differential equation and compare the predicted motion, i.e., the dependence of r_1 on t, with the observed motion in order to determine how suitable a choice was made for F_{12}, or whether a new functional form should be tried for the force. As we proceed, we shall generally concentrate on one or the other of these aspects for a given mechanical situation.

We can write an equation similar to (3-7) for particle 2:

$$m_2 a_{21} = F_{21}(r_{12}) \tag{3-9}$$

Inserting (3-7) and (3-9) into (3-6), we obtain

$$F_{12} = -F_{21} \tag{3-10}$$

which is known as the law of action and reaction and which has been deduced from our experimental laws.

3-4 Fourth experimental law

This law tells us about the important *superposition* property of forces. Let: $a_{1,234...}$ = acceleration of particle 1 when particles 2, 3, 4, ... are simultaneously interacting with it; a_{12} = acceleration of 1 when *only* 2 is present; etc. Then it is found that

$$a_{1,234...} = a_{12} + a_{13} + a_{14} + \cdots = \sum_j a_{1j} \tag{3-11}$$

which says that the acceleration of a particle subject to the action of a number of other particles equals the vector sum of the accelerations which would be produced by the particles acting one at a time. In other words, the accelerations produced by the different interactions are *independent*.

If we multiply (3-11) through by m_1, we can state this result in terms of forces as

$$F_{1,234...} = F_{12} + F_{13} + F_{14} + \cdots = \sum_j F_{1j} \tag{3-12}$$

This is the law of superposition of forces, and it says that the individual forces are independent. This law will clearly simplify our work in mechanics, since if the interaction between a given pair depended on the presence or absence of another particle, our problem of describing the total force acting on a given particle would be considerably more involved.

These four experimental laws form the basis for our study of mechanics.

3-5 Inertial systems and classical relativity

Let us consider again the relation between a secondary inertial system and the primary inertial system which we first defined in Sec. 2-2. In Fig. 3-1, let XYZ be a set of axes fixed in the primary inertial system. Let $X'Y'Z'$ be a set of parallel axes fixed in a secondary inertial system which is moving relative to the fixed primary system with a constant velocity **v**.

If xyz are the coordinates of a particle with respect to the XYZ system, and $x'y'z'$ the coordinates with respect to $X'Y'Z'$, the connection between the two sets in classical physics is given by the common expressions

$$x' = x - v_x t - a, \quad y' = y - v_y t - b, \quad z' = z - v_z t - c \quad (3\text{-}13)$$

where a, b, c are constants. These formulas (3-13) relating the two sets of coordinates are called the *classical (or Galilean) transformation*.

Differentiating (3-13) with respect to the time, we find that

$$\dot{x}' = \dot{x} - v_x, \quad \dot{y}' = \dot{y} - v_y, \quad \dot{z}' = \dot{z} - v_z \quad (3\text{-}14)$$

$$\ddot{x}' = \ddot{x}, \quad \ddot{y}' = \ddot{y}, \quad \ddot{z}' = \ddot{z} \quad (3\text{-}15)$$

since **v** = const. We see from (3-15) that the *acceleration* of the particle is the same with respect to both systems. Therefore, from (3-7), the laws

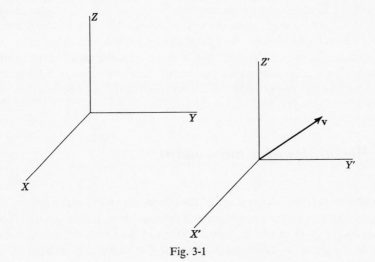

Fig. 3-1

of motion have the *same form* in all inertial systems. This result is called the *classical (or Galilean) principle of relativity*. It is also the reason for the name "secondary" inertial system, since we have just seen that a secondary inertial system is as good as the primary system as a reference system for describing the motion of our particle.

How does one get an inertial system in practice? It is sometimes convenient, and not too inaccurate, to treat as an inertial system a set of axes fixed relative to the surface of the earth. For certain problems, however, the effects of the rotation of the earth, which keeps it from being a true inertial system, are noticeable and important. We shall discuss some of these effects and their magnitudes later on, when we have learned how to describe rotations.

3-6   Systems of units

The two principal systems of units used in modern scientific work are the *meter-kilogram-second* and *centimeter-gram-second* systems, which are abbreviated *mks* and *cgs*, respectively. The terminology refers to the names given to the *arbitrary* choices of the standard units of length, mass, and time, respectively. Both systems use the second as standard time unit. The length units are simply related since 1 meter $= 10^2$ centimeters by definition; similarly, the mass units are related by 1 kilogram $= 10^3$ grams. The mks system is the more natural system to use in electromagnetic theory, and it is consequently becoming more and more universally used in other branches of physics as well.

From (2-1) and (2-2), we see that the unit of velocity is 1 meter/second or 1 centimeter/second, while the unit of acceleration is 1 meter/(second)^2 or 1 centimeter/(second)^2; no special names are given to these units.

From (3-7), we see that the unit of force is either 1 kilogram-meter/ (second)^2 or 1 gram-centimeter/ (second)^2; these units are given the names *newton* and *dyne*, respectively. It is easily seen that 1 newton $= 10^5$ dynes.

4 Mechanics of a mass point

In this chapter, we discuss some of the properties and consequences of the equation of motion for a single particle or mass point, that is, a body whose extension in space can be neglected. Many of the important concepts and results of mechanics can be easily illustrated with this simple case.

If we combine (3-7) and (3-12) and drop the unneeded subscripts, the equation of motion for our particle of mass m can be written simply

$$\mathbf{F} = m\mathbf{a} \tag{4-1}$$

where $\mathbf{F}$ is the total or resultant force acting on the particle. If we use (2-2), we can also write this fundamental result as

$$\mathbf{F} = m\frac{d\mathbf{v}}{dt} \tag{4-2}$$

and, if we assume m to be constant, as

$$\mathbf{F} = \frac{d}{dt}(m\mathbf{v}) \tag{4-3}$$

We see that it is convenient to define

$$\mathbf{p} = m\mathbf{v} = \text{momentum} \tag{4-4}$$

so that (4-3) can also be written

$$\mathbf{F} = \frac{d\mathbf{p}}{dt} \tag{4-5}$$

Thus we can also say that the force equals the time rate of change of momentum.

We see from (4-5) that, if $\mathbf{F} = 0$, then $\mathbf{p} = \text{const}$. This result is called the *conservation of momentum* for a single particle.

In the discussion above, we assumed that the particle mass was constant. There are cases, however, in which the mass is *not* a constant; examples are rockets and bodies moving with speeds comparable to that of light. In order to be able to discuss these and similar cases, we now extend our definition of force from the simple result (4-1), obtained from the experiments we discussed in the preceding chapter, to the more cautious and general form given in (4-3). Since this involves a generalization of results given by experiment to more complex cases, its final justification can be obtained only by seeing how well results deduced from (4-3) agree with experiment. As a matter of fact, it is found from experiment that (4-3) is the appropriate generalization of the definition of force; the problems we shall consider, however, will all involve constant mass so that (4-1) and (4-3) are equivalent.

Now we want to see what and how many general results we can obtain concerning motion under the influence of a force before it becomes necessary to consider a specific form for $\mathbf{F}$.

If $\mathbf{F}$ is given, for example, as $\mathbf{F}(\mathbf{r}, \dot{\mathbf{r}}, t)$, then (4-1) becomes $\mathbf{F}(\mathbf{r}, \dot{\mathbf{r}}, t) = m\ddot{\mathbf{r}}$ and this second order differential equation can, in principle, be integrated to give **r** as a function of t. We see, however, that since the equation is second order, the solution will involve essentially two integrations and hence the general solution will involve two arbitrary vector constants of integration (a total of six scalar constants of integration). However, the values of these two vector constants can, in principle, always be determined in terms of the *initial conditions* of the motion, namely, the position and velocity at some known time, often chosen as $t = 0$.

Example.   Motion under a Constant Force.   If **F** = **k** = const., then (4-1) becomes $m\ddot{\mathbf{r}} = \mathbf{k}$. If we integrate this once, we obtain

$$m\dot{\mathbf{r}} = m\mathbf{v} = \mathbf{k}t + \mathbf{c}_1 \tag{4-6}$$

where $\mathbf{c}_1$ is a constant. If $\mathbf{v} = \mathbf{v}_0$ when $t = 0$, then we see from (4-6) that $\mathbf{c}_1 = m\mathbf{v}_0$ and the differential equation is now $m\dot{\mathbf{r}} = \mathbf{k}t + m\mathbf{v}_0$. Integrating again, we get

$$m\mathbf{r} = \tfrac{1}{2}\mathbf{k}t^2 + m\mathbf{v}_0 t + \mathbf{c}_2 \tag{4-7}$$

where $\mathbf{c}_2$ is a constant. If $\mathbf{r} = \mathbf{r}_0$ when $t = 0$, then we see from (4-7) that $\mathbf{c}_2 = m\mathbf{r}_0$, and (4-7) can now be written

$$\mathbf{r} = \frac{1}{2}\left(\frac{\mathbf{k}}{m}\right)t^2 + \mathbf{v}_0 t + \mathbf{r}_0 = \mathbf{r}(t) \tag{4-8}$$

and, for example,

$$x = \frac{1}{2}\left(\frac{k_x}{m}\right)t^2 + v_{0x}t + x_0 = x(t)$$

The result (4-8) is the complete solution to our problem, and we see that the two integration constants could be evaluated in terms of the initial position and velocity.

4-1 Integrals of the force

The time integral of the force, $\displaystyle\int_{t_1}^{t_2} \mathbf{F}\,dt$, is called the *impulse*. Using this definition and (4-5), we see that

$$\int_{t_1}^{t_2} \mathbf{F}\,dt = \int_{t_1}^{t_2} d\mathbf{p} = \mathbf{p}(t_2) - \mathbf{p}(t_1) \tag{4-9}$$

so that the impulse equals the change in momentum.

If a force **F** acts on a body, the work done *on* the body in the displacement $d\mathbf{r}$ is defined as

$$dW = \mathbf{F} \cdot d\mathbf{r} \tag{4-10}$$

If we recall (1-7), we see that the element of work done equals the component of the force in the direction of the displacement times the displacement. The units of work are 1 newton-meter = 1 joule and 1 dyne-centimeter = 1 erg, so that 1 joule = 10^7 ergs.

Thus the line integral of the force is equal to

$$\text{Total work done} = W = \int_{\mathbf{r}_1}^{\mathbf{r}_2} \mathbf{F} \cdot d\mathbf{r} \tag{4-11}$$

Using (4-2) and (2-1), we can also write (4-11) as

$$W = \int_{t_1}^{t_2} \mathbf{F} \cdot \frac{d\mathbf{r}}{dt} \, dt = m \int_{t_1}^{t_2} \mathbf{v} \cdot \frac{d\mathbf{v}}{dt} \, dt \tag{4-12}$$

But, if we note that

$$\frac{d}{dt}(\mathbf{v}^2) = \frac{d}{dt}(\mathbf{v} \cdot \mathbf{v}) = 2\mathbf{v} \cdot \frac{d\mathbf{v}}{dt} = \frac{d}{dt}(v^2) \tag{4-13}$$

we see that we can also write (4-12) as

$$W = \frac{m}{2} \int_{t_1}^{t_2} \frac{d}{dt}(v^2) \, dt = \frac{m}{2} \int_{1}^{2} d(v^2) = (\tfrac{1}{2}mv_2^2) - (\tfrac{1}{2}mv_1^2) \tag{4-14}$$

If we now define:

$$\text{Kinetic energy} = T = \tfrac{1}{2}mv^2 \tag{4-15}$$

we can write (4-14) as

$$W = T_2 - T_1 \tag{4-16}$$

which says that the total work done on the particle equals the change in its kinetic energy. The unit of kinetic energy is evidently a joule or an erg.

We should note here that, if $\mathbf{F} = \mathbf{F}(\mathbf{r}, \mathbf{v}, t)$, for example, then we cannot evaluate the total work done, (4-11), unless we know the complete details of the motion, because without this information we shall not be able to evaluate $\mathbf{F}$ at each point of the path, as is required by (4-11).

4-2 Potential energy

We suppose now that $\mathbf{F}$ depends only on the coordinates, i.e., $\mathbf{F} = \mathbf{F}(\mathbf{r}) = \mathbf{F}(x, y, z)$. Such a situation is called a *field of force*.

Let us consider the two points P_1 and P_2 in Fig. 4-1. The work done on the particle if it is moved from P_1 to P_2 along some arbitrary path C is

$$W_C = \int_C \mathbf{F} \cdot d\mathbf{r}$$

Similarly, the work done if the particle is moved along some other arbitrary path C' is

$$W_{C'} = \int_{C'} \mathbf{F} \cdot d\mathbf{r}$$

There are now two possibilities: (1) if $W_C = W_{C'}$, then the work done is *independent of the path* and depends only on the end points P_1 and P_2—in this case, the force is called a *conservative force*, as is, for example, the gravitational force field of the earth; (2) if $W_C \neq W_{C'}$, then the work done depends on the path and the force is called *non-conservative*.

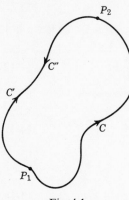

Fig. 4-1

Let us now restrict our considerations to conservative forces. If we trace the path C' in the opposite direction so as to get the path C'', then, at each point, $(d\mathbf{r})'' = -(d\mathbf{r})'$ while $\mathbf{F}'' = \mathbf{F}'$ and therefore $W_{C''} = -W_{C'} = -W_C$; the last equality holds because the force is conservative. Then we see that, for the *closed* path $C + C''$, the total work done $= W = W_C + W_{C''} = 0$, or

$$\int_C \mathbf{F} \cdot d\mathbf{r} + \int_{C''} \mathbf{F} \cdot d\mathbf{r} = 0$$

or

$$\oint \mathbf{F} \cdot d\mathbf{r} = 0 \tag{4-17}$$

Thus, for a conservative force, the total work done in following any closed path is zero. If we combine (4-17) with Stokes' theorem (1-40), we also see that, if $\mathbf{F}$ is conservative, then

$$\operatorname{curl} \mathbf{F} = 0 \tag{4-18}$$

In a conservative field, the negative of the work done between two points is defined as the *difference of potential energy V* between the points, i.e.,

$$V(\mathbf{r}_2) - V(\mathbf{r}_1) = V_2 - V_1 = -\int_{\mathbf{r}_1}^{\mathbf{r}_2} \mathbf{F} \cdot d\mathbf{r} \tag{4-19}$$

Combining (4-19) with (4-11) and (4-16), we see that

$$V_2 - V_1 = -(T_2 - T_1)$$

so that

$$T_2 + V_2 = T_1 + V_1 = \text{const.} \tag{4-20}$$

Therefore, in a conservative field of force, the sum of the kinetic and potential energy is a constant. This constant is called the *total (mechanical) energy E*, and

$$E = T + V \qquad (4\text{-}21)$$

Then the result (4-20) is precisely the statement of the *conservation of energy* for mechanics. In other words, if the force is conservative, then no matter how complicated the actual motion may be, we can be certain that the total energy, at least, is some constant characteristic of the whole situation.

We can also write (4-19) as

$$V_2 - V_1 = -\int_{\mathbf{r}_1}^{\mathbf{r}_2} \mathbf{F} \cdot d\mathbf{r} = \int_{V_1}^{V_2} dV = \int_{\mathbf{r}_1}^{\mathbf{r}_2} \text{grad } V \cdot d\mathbf{r} \qquad (4\text{-}22)$$

with the help of (1-26). Since the points $\mathbf{r}_1$ and $\mathbf{r}_2$ are arbitrary, we can equate the integrands, so that for a conservative force

$$\mathbf{F} = -\text{grad } V \qquad (4\text{-}23)$$

That is,

$$F_x = -\frac{\partial V}{\partial x}, \quad F_y = -\frac{\partial V}{\partial y}, \quad F_z = -\frac{\partial V}{\partial z} \qquad (4\text{-}23')$$

The two results (4-18) and (4-23) are, of course, compatible because of the general theorem curl grad $V = 0$; or, if one prefers, since they must be compatible because of the way they were derived, we can combine them to prove the theorem.

We note that, if we add any constant to the potential energy V, then the force given by (4-23) is unchanged, and the net effect is only to add this constant to the total energy E given by (4-21). Thus the potential energy of the system always includes an arbitrary additive constant, and we can assign this constant any convenient value without changing any essential features of a given problem.

A particle is said to be in *equilibrium* when the force on it is zero, or, from (4-23'), when

$$\frac{\partial V}{\partial x} = \frac{\partial V}{\partial y} = \frac{\partial V}{\partial z} = 0 \qquad (4\text{-}24)$$

so that a point at which the potential energy is a maximum or a minimum is a position of equilibrium. If the potential energy is a maximum, the equilibrium is called *unstable*, since, if the particle is displaced from the equilibrium position, the direction of the force is such as to displace the particle even further. Similarly, if the potential energy is a minimum, the equilibrium is called *stable*. These types are illustrated schematically in

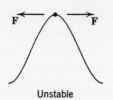
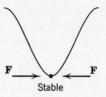

Fig. 4-2

Fig. 4-2 where the potential energy is plotted as a function of some co-ordinate. If the point corresponding to (4-24) happens to be a point of inflection, the equilibrium is called neutral.

Exercises

4-1. A mass of 0.4 kilogram is acted on by the following forces: 2 newtons to the north, 4 newtons to the east, and 7 newtons to the west. Find the direction and magnitude of the resultant acceleration.

4-2. A force acting on a particle has the following components: $F_x = ay$, $F_y = -ax$, $F_z = 0$ where a = const. Is this a conservative force? Verify your conclusion in two ways.

4-3. The potential energy of a particle is given by $V = k/r$ where k = const., and r is the distance of the particle from the origin. Find the rectangular components of the force acting on the particle, and, from these, verify directly that the force is actually conservative.

4-4. The potential energy of a particle which is restricted to move along the x axis is given by $V(x) = (-a/x) + (b/x^2)$, where a and b are positive constants. Find the equilibrium position and determine whether the equilibrium is stable or unstable. Find the general expression for the total energy and thereby find the velocity of the particle as a function of position. Under what conditions could the motion be periodic, i.e., repeat itself indefinitely? Find the extreme limits of the motion for periodic motion, i.e., the possible range of x.

5 The linear oscillator

The force on the single particle of this important system depends on position in a particularly simple manner. If a particle is displaced from its equilibrium position and is found to have a force on it which is pro-portional to and oppositely directed to the displacement, it is called a harmonic oscillator. Therefore the force is given by

$$F = -k(r - r_0) \tag{5-1}$$

where k = const., and r_0 = equilibrium position = const. We easily find that curl $\mathbf{F} = -k$ curl $\mathbf{r} = 0$ with the aid of (1-30). Therefore the force field described by (5-1) is conservative, and, by (4-23), $\mathbf{F}$ should be derivable from a potential energy V.

We shall not continue our discussion of the three-dimensional harmonic oscillator, but, for simplicity, shall restrict ourselves to a study of the corresponding one-dimensional motion. Because the concept of the harmonic oscillator constantly recurs throughout many diverse portions of theoretical physics, it is essential to have a thorough understanding of its properties.

5-1 Undamped linear harmonic oscillator

If we choose our direction of motion to be the x axis, choose the equilibrium point as the origin, and assume that (5-1) gives the only force, we obtain

$$F = -kx = -\frac{dV}{dx} \tag{5-2}$$

with the use of (4-23′). We can easily integrate (5-2) to get

$$V(x) = \tfrac{1}{2}kx^2 \tag{5-3}$$

where, for convenience, we have chosen the constant of integration to be zero. This parabolic dependence of the potential energy on displacement is shown in Fig. 5-1.

According to (4-21), the energy is

$$E = \tfrac{1}{2}mv^2 + \tfrac{1}{2}kx^2 = \text{const.} \tag{5-4}$$

from which v can be found:

$$v = \pm\left(\frac{2E - kx^2}{m}\right)^{1/2} \tag{5-5}$$

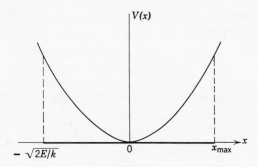

Fig. 5-1

Since v must be real, the magnitude of x has a maximum value given by

$$|x|_{max} = \sqrt{2E/k} \tag{5-6}$$

so that the motion is restricted to the region of the x axis shown in Fig. 5-1, that is, for those values of x for which $V(x) \leqslant E$. At the limits of the displacement, the velocity is zero; however, the force, and the acceleration as well, is directed back toward the origin and thus the particle motion is reversed. In other words, we see that the motion is *periodic*, a fact which we have discovered solely from a consideration of the potential energy curve of Fig. 5-1.

Substituting (5-2) into (4-1), we find the equation of motion to be

$$m\ddot{x} = -kx \tag{5-7}$$

or

$$\ddot{x} + \omega_0^2 x = 0 \tag{5-8}$$

where

$$\omega_0 = \sqrt{k/m} \tag{5-9}$$

We can easily solve (5-8) by noting that $a_c \cos \omega_0 t$ and $a_s \sin \omega_0 t$ separately are solutions of this differential equation, where a_c and a_s are constants. Therefore the general solution of (5-8), which contains the required two constants of integration, is the sum

$$x = a_c \cos \omega_0 t + a_s \sin \omega_0 t \tag{5-10}$$

If x_0 and v_0 are the position and velocity at $t = 0$, one can easily evaluate the constants in (5-10) in terms of them; the result is that we can write

$$x = x_0 \cos \omega_0 t + \left(\frac{v_0}{\omega_0}\right) \sin \omega_0 t \tag{5-11}$$

We see at once that this is indeed a periodic solution, as we had already learned. The *period* τ is the time interval in which the argument of the sine and cosine increases by 2π, for then the motion will begin to repeat itself. Therefore $\omega_0 \tau = 2\pi$, or

$$\tau = \frac{2\pi}{\omega_0} = 2\pi \sqrt{\frac{m}{k}} \tag{5-12}$$

The *frequency* v_0 is the number of times a particular aspect of the motion occurs in one second:

$$v_0 = \frac{1}{\tau} = \frac{\omega_0}{2\pi} = \frac{1}{2\pi} \sqrt{\frac{k}{m}} \tag{5-13}$$

Circular or angular frequency is a name often given to $\omega_0 = 2\pi v_0$.

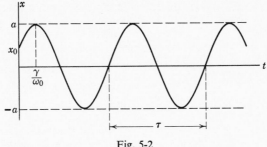

Fig. 5-2

It is sometimes convenient to put the solution (5-11) in a somewhat different form. If we introduce two new constants, a and γ, by means of the relations

$$x_0 = a \cos \gamma \quad \text{and} \quad v_0/\omega_0 = a \sin \gamma \tag{5-14}$$

so that

$$a = \left(x_0^2 + \frac{v_0^2}{\omega_0^2}\right)^{1/2} \quad \text{and} \quad \tan \gamma = \frac{v_0}{x_0\omega_0} \tag{5-15}$$

then, when (5-14) is substituted into (5-11), we get $x = a(\cos \omega_0 t \cos \gamma + \sin \omega_0 t \sin \gamma)$, or

$$x = a \cos (\omega_0 t - \gamma) \tag{5-16}$$

This form of the solution shows the periodic nature somewhat more clearly than does (5-11); Fig. 5-2 also illustrates it. In (5-16), a is called the *amplitude* and γ the *phase angle*.

5-2 Damped linear oscillator

In reality, all our mechanical systems are subject to frictional or damping forces, such as the friction of the air. The question then arises: How can we describe this frictional force so that we can introduce it into the equation of motion? A simple assumption, which was first made by Newton and which is often quite accurate, is that the frictional force is proportional to the velocity; that is,

$$F_{\text{friction}} = -\beta \dot{x} \tag{5-17}$$

where β is a positive constant characteristic of the particular situation involved. Combining this equation with (5-2), we find that the total force on the particle now is

$$F = -kx - \beta \dot{x} \tag{5-18}$$

We see that the total force is non-conservative, since it no longer depends only on position.

If we insert (5-18) into the equation of motion, $F = m\ddot{x}$, we find that the result can be written

$$\ddot{x} + \alpha\dot{x} + \omega_0^2 x = 0 \tag{5-19}$$

where ω_0 is again given by (5-9), and

$$\alpha = \frac{\beta}{m} \tag{5-20}$$

In (5-19), we have an example of a linear, homogeneous differential equation with constant coefficients. A standard general method of solution of an equation of this type is to try to find a solution in exponential form; that is, we try to write

$$x = ae^{\lambda t} \tag{5-21}$$

where a and λ are constants to be determined so that (5-21) will be a solution of (5-19). We easily find that $\dot{x} = \lambda a e^{\lambda t}$ and $\ddot{x} = \lambda^2 a e^{\lambda t}$, and (5-19) becomes

$$(\lambda^2 + \alpha\lambda + \omega_0^2)ae^{\lambda t} = 0 \tag{5-22}$$

In order to get a meaningful solution, we must have $a \neq 0$; therefore λ must satisfy the equation

$$\lambda^2 + \alpha\lambda + \omega_0^2 = 0 \tag{5-23}$$

Hence, in general, there are *two* possible values of λ given by

$$\lambda_+ = -\tfrac{1}{2}\alpha + (\tfrac{1}{4}\alpha^2 - \omega_0^2)^{\frac{1}{2}} \quad \text{and} \quad \lambda_- = -\tfrac{1}{2}\alpha - (\tfrac{1}{4}\alpha^2 - \omega_0^2)^{\frac{1}{2}} \tag{5-24}$$

Correspondingly, there will be two forms of x like that in (5-21) and they are solutions of (5-19); these forms will be

$$x_+ = a_+ e^{\lambda_+ t} \quad \text{and} \quad x_- = a_- e^{\lambda_- t},$$

where a_+ and a_- are arbitrary constants, and λ_+ and λ_- are given by (5-24). We see that in order to get the two necessary constants of integration in our general solution for x, we must write this general solution as a sum of the two special solutions x_+ and x_-. Therefore we finally obtain

$$x = a_+ e^{\lambda_+ t} + a_- e^{\lambda_- t} \tag{5-25}$$

or

$$x = e^{-\frac{1}{2}\alpha t}(a_+ e^{[(\alpha^2/4) - \omega_0^2]^{\frac{1}{2}}t} + a_- e^{-[(\alpha^2/4) - \omega_0^2]^{\frac{1}{2}}t}) \tag{5-26}$$

It turns out that the motion of the particle has quite a different character, depending on the relative values of the constants involved.

CASE I. $\tfrac{1}{4}\alpha^2 > \omega_0^2$. This is the case of *large damping*. We see from (5-24) that λ_+ and λ_- are both negative. Therefore, the solution (5-25) consists of a sum of two exponential terms, both of which decrease with time. As time goes on, then, the magnitude of x steadily decreases and becomes zero at $t = \infty$, so that the particle is back at its equilibrium position without ever having passed through it, since the exponential terms are always positive.

CASE II. $\frac{1}{4}\alpha^2 = \omega_0^2$. This is called *critical damping*. Now $\lambda_+ = \lambda_-$, so that (5-26) becomes $x = (a_+ + a_-)\,e^{-\frac{1}{2}\alpha t} = a_c e^{-\frac{1}{2}\alpha t}$. Again this represents an exponential decay of the displacement back to the equilibrium position, but, since it has only one arbitrary constant, it cannot be the general solution, and we must look for another independent solution for this special situation. It turns out, as can be easily verified by direct substitution, that $x = bte^{-\frac{1}{2}\alpha t}$ satisfies (5-19) for this case, where $b = $ const. Therefore the general solution for critical damping has the form

$$x = e^{-\frac{1}{2}\alpha t}(a_c + bt) \tag{5-27}$$

CASE III. $\frac{1}{4}\alpha^2 < \omega_0^2$. In this case, it is more convenient to write

$$(\tfrac{1}{4}\alpha^2 - \omega_0^2)^{\frac{1}{2}} = [-(\omega_0^2 - \tfrac{1}{4}\alpha^2)]^{\frac{1}{2}} = i\omega_1 \tag{5-28}$$

where $i = \sqrt{-1}$ and ω_1 is the real quantity given by

$$\omega_1 = (\omega_0^2 - \tfrac{1}{4}\alpha^2)^{\frac{1}{2}} \tag{5-29}$$

Inserting (5-28) into (5-26), we get our solution in the form

$$x = e^{-\frac{1}{2}\alpha t}(a_+ e^{i\omega_1 t} + a_- e^{-i\omega_1 t}) \tag{5-30}$$

This is apparently a complex solution, but, since x is a physical displacement, we must get a real value for it from (5-30); therefore a_+ and a_- must also be complex. We can put (5-30) into a more familiar form in the following way. By definition,

$$e^z = 1 + \frac{z}{1!} + \frac{z^2}{2!} + \frac{z^3}{3!} + \cdots \tag{5-31}$$

so that

$$e^{iu} = 1 + iu + \frac{i^2 u^2}{2!} + \frac{i^3 u^3}{3!} + \cdots$$

$$= \left(1 - \frac{u^2}{2!} + \frac{u^4}{4!} - \cdots\right) + i\left(u - \frac{u^3}{3!} + \frac{u^5}{5!} - \cdots\right) \tag{5-32}$$

If we recall the series expansions for $\cos u$ and $\sin u$, (5-32) becomes

$$e^{iu} = \cos u + i \sin u \tag{5-33}$$

and, also,

$$e^{-iu} = \cos u - i \sin u \tag{5-34}$$

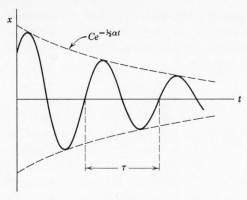

Fig. 5-3

Using these last results, we obtain

$$a_{+}e^{i\omega_1 t} + a_{-}e^{-i\omega_1 t} = (a_{+} + a_{-})\cos \omega_1 t + i(a_{+} - a_{-})\sin \omega_1 t$$
$$= A \cos \omega_1 t + B \sin \omega_1 t$$

where A and B must be real; then (5-30) becomes

$$x = e^{-\frac{1}{2}\alpha t}(A \cos \omega_1 t + B \sin \omega_1 t) \qquad (5\text{-}35)$$

which is the form of the general solution appropriate for this case—A and B can be evaluated in terms of the initial conditions of the motion.

It is sometimes convenient to write (5-35) in another form by introducing two new constants, C and θ, by the relations

$$A = C \cos \theta \quad \text{and} \quad B = C \sin \theta$$

Then

$$C = (A^2 + B^2)^{\frac{1}{2}} \quad \text{and} \quad \tan \theta = B/A$$

and (5-35) becomes

$$x = Ce^{-\frac{1}{2}\alpha t} \cos (\omega_1 t - \theta) \qquad (5\text{-}36)$$

θ is called the phase angle, and the name amplitude is given to C, or sometimes to $Ce^{-\frac{1}{2}\alpha t}$. Either (5-35) or (5-36) is correct, of course, but one is sometimes more convenient than the other.

We see from (5-36) that the displacement is given by the product of a periodic function and a term which makes the displacement decay back to the equilibrium position $x = 0$, as we would expect the frictional forces to do. The displacement as a function of time is shown in Fig. 5-3, and we see that the motion is not periodic in a strict sense because the system does not completely retrace its path. However, it is periodic in the sense that the displacement vanishes after equal time intervals because the cosine term in (5-36) goes through zero each time its argument changes by π; the cosine passes through zero in the same direction each time its argument changes by 2π. The latter result enables us to define a period τ and a frequency ν_1 for this motion; that is, $\omega_1 \tau = 2\pi$, so that $\tau = 2\pi/\omega_1$, and therefore

$$\nu_1 = \frac{1}{\tau} = \frac{\omega_1}{2\pi} = \frac{1}{2\pi}\,(\omega_0{}^2 - \tfrac{1}{4}\alpha^2)^{\frac{1}{2}} < \nu_0 \qquad (5\text{-}37)$$

where ν_0 is the undamped frequency given by (5-13).

In general terms, we see that the damping has two effects: It causes the displacement to decrease exponentially to zero, and the frequency of the oscillation to decrease from its value for the corresponding undamped oscillator.

As a check on our results, we should get the previous case back as the damping is decreased, and, in fact, we see that, as $\alpha \to 0$, $\omega_1 \to \omega_0$, so that (5-35) gives $x \to A \cos \omega_0 t + B \sin \omega_0 t$, which is just what we found for the undamped oscillator in (5-11).

5-3 Forced oscillations

Let us now assume that there is applied to our system an additional periodic force $F_a = F_0 \cos \omega t$, where $F_0 = $ const. and ω is the circular frequency of this time-dependent force. Adding this to (5-18), we find that our equation of motion is $m\ddot{x} = -kx - \beta\dot{x} + F_0 \cos \omega t$, or

$$\ddot{x} + \alpha\dot{x} + \omega_0{}^2 x = (F_0/m) \cos \omega t = f_0 \cos \omega t \qquad (5\text{-}38)$$

In order to find the solution of this equation, we can make use of the following theorem: Suppose that $x_h(t, A, B)$ is the general solution of the homogeneous equation $\ddot{x}_h + \alpha\dot{x}_h + \omega_0{}^2 x_h = 0$, which contains the two arbitrary constants A and B; suppose that $x_i(t)$ is *any* solution of the inhomogeneous equation $\ddot{x}_i + \alpha\dot{x}_i + \omega_0{}^2 x_i = F(t)$; then the complete *general* solution of the inhomogeneous equation is the sum, $x = x_h(t, A, B) + x_i(t)$. This is very easy to show. First of all, x satisfies the given differential equation; that is

$$\ddot{x} + \alpha\dot{x} + \omega_0{}^2 x = (\ddot{x}_h + \alpha\dot{x}_h + \omega_0{}^2 x_h) + (\ddot{x}_i + \alpha\dot{x}_i + \omega_0{}^2 x_i)$$
$$= (0) + [F(t)] = F(t)$$

as it should. Secondly, this sum form of x contains the two arbitrary constants of integration needed to satisfy any given initial conditions. The advantage of all of this for us is that the homogeneous form of (5-38) is precisely (5-19), whose general solution we have just finished discussing.

Therefore our problem is now reduced to that of finding *some* solution of (5-38).

Since the applied force is periodic, it seems plausible that the corresponding displacement obtained from (5-38) should also be periodic and with the same period. Because of the friction, however, it is not at all evident that the displacement will be zero when the force is zero, or will be a maximum when the force is a maximum; that is, the displacement need not be *in phase* with the applied force. Therefore let us be rather cautious and try to find a solution of (5-38) in the form

$$x = p \cos \omega t + q \sin \omega t \qquad (5\text{-}39)$$

where p and q are constants to be determined. If we substitute (5-39) into (5-38) and rearrange the terms, we find that

$$\cos \omega t[-\omega^2 p + \alpha \omega q + \omega_0^2 p - f_0] + \sin \omega t[-\omega^2 q - \alpha \omega p + \omega_0^2 q] = 0$$

Because this expression cannot be zero for *all* values of t unless the coefficients of $\cos \omega t$ and $\sin \omega t$ vanish separately,

$$p(\omega_0^2 - \omega^2) + q\alpha\omega = f_0$$

$$-p\alpha\omega + q(\omega_0^2 - \omega^2) = 0$$

and therefore

$$p = \frac{f_0(\omega_0^2 - \omega^2)}{(\omega_0^2 - \omega^2)^2 + (\alpha\omega)^2} \qquad (5\text{-}40)$$

$$q = \frac{f_0\alpha\omega}{(\omega_0^2 - \omega^2)^2 + (\alpha\omega)^2} \qquad (5\text{-}41)$$

and x can be obtained by inserting these results into (5-39).

It is often convenient to have this in another form. If we let

$$p = r \cos \phi, \quad q = r \sin \phi \qquad (5\text{-}42)$$

so that

$$r = (p^2 + q^2)^{\frac{1}{2}}, \quad \tan \phi = q/p \qquad (5\text{-}43)$$

and

$$x = r \cos (\omega t - \phi) \qquad (5\text{-}44)$$

we find that

$$r = \frac{(F_0/m)}{[(\omega_0^2 - \omega^2)^2 + \alpha^2\omega^2]^{\frac{1}{2}}} \qquad (5\text{-}45)$$

$$\tan \phi = \frac{\alpha\omega}{\omega_0^2 - \omega^2} \qquad (5\text{-}46)$$

where we have used $f_0 = F_0/m$.

In order to have a specific situation to consider, let us assume that we have small damping; then the solution of the homogeneous equation is given by (5-36), and, if we add this to (5-44), we find the general solution of (5-38) to be

$$x = Ce^{-\frac{1}{2}\alpha t} \cos\left(\omega_1 t - \theta\right) + \frac{(F_0/m) \cos\left(\omega t - \phi\right)}{[(\omega_0^2 - \omega^2)^2 + \alpha^2 \omega^2]^{\frac{1}{2}}} \qquad (5\text{-}47)$$

Thus the general solution is the sum of two parts with different frequencies: the damped free oscillation whose frequency v_1 is slightly less than the frequency v_0 of the undamped system; and the forced oscillation whose frequency is the same as that of the driving force. After a time, the exponentially damped part of the motion will have vanished—hence it is called the *transient* part of the displacement. Then all that will remain will be the *steady state* displacement given by the last term of (5-47), which is proportional to the amplitude of the driving force. We also see that, if the damping becomes very large, the transient part of the solution becomes the aperiodic or strongly damped term discussed as Case I of the previous section. This term, of course, also will vanish in time, whereas the form of the steady state motion in (5-47) is unaffected by the value of the damping constant α.

We now want to discuss some of the properties of the steady state motion, beginning with the amplitude r given by (5-45). We see that, in general, r is a function of ω; the frequency ω_r for which r is a maximum is called the *resonance frequency*. We can find ω_r by calculating the value of ω that makes $dr/d\omega = 0$; the result is easily found, from (5-45), to be given by

$$\omega_r = (\omega_0^2 - \tfrac{1}{2}\alpha^2)^{\frac{1}{2}} \qquad (5\text{-}48)$$

and is equal to neither the frequency of free oscillation nor that of the damped oscillation. In fact, we see from (5-48) and (5-29) that

$$\omega_r < \omega_1 < \omega_0 \qquad (5\text{-}49)$$

For small damping, however, the resonance frequency is close to the natural frequency of the undamped system; that is, $\omega_r \simeq \omega_0$ for α "small."

The maximum amplitude is obtained by substituting (5-48) into (5-45), with the result that

$$r_{\max} = r(\omega_r) = \frac{F_0}{\alpha \omega_1 m} \qquad (5\text{-}50)$$

and we see that, as $\alpha \to 0$, $r_{\max} \to \infty$.

The amplitude of the steady state motion is shown as a function of applied frequency ω in Fig. 5-4, for which it has been assumed that there is a large amount of damping and consequently the resonance frequency is appreciably different from either of the natural frequencies of the system.

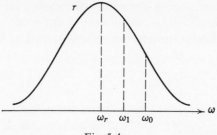

Fig. 5-4

An interesting effect occurs when $\omega = \omega_0$, for then we see from (5-39), (5-40), and (5-41) that $p = 0$, $q = F_0/\alpha m\omega_0$, so that the steady state displacement is $x = (F_0/\alpha m\omega_0) \sin \omega_0 t$ while the driving force is $F_0 \cos \omega_0 t$. In this situation, the displacement is said to be completely *out of phase* with the driving force.

The general dependence of the phase angle ϕ on applied frequency ω can be easily found from (5-46); the results are shown in Fig. 5-5, and we see that the displacement does not get completely out of phase until after the resonance frequency at which the amplitude is a maximum.

We now want to consider the effect of the damping parameter α on the shape of the resonance curve, which is the amplitude of the steady state displacement as a function of frequency. For simplicity, let us assume that the damping is small so that the maximum in the amplitude occurs approximately for $\omega = \omega_0$. In order to avoid complications with the square root in (5-45), it will be sufficient for our purposes to consider r^2, and to consider only frequencies near resonance. From (5-45), we obtain

$$r^2 = \frac{(F_0/m)^2}{(\omega_0{}^2 - \omega^2)^2 + \alpha^2\omega^2} = \left(\frac{F_0}{\alpha m\omega}\right)^2 \frac{1}{1 + [(\omega_0{}^2 - \omega^2)/\alpha\omega]^2}$$

$$\simeq r_{\max}^2 \frac{1}{1 + [(\omega_0{}^2 - \omega^2)/\alpha\omega]^2} \tag{5-51}$$

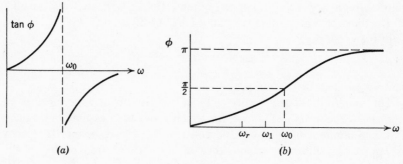

(a)   (b)

Fig. 5-5

the last step following from (5-50) and our condition that ω is never much different from ω_0.

If we let η represent the deviation from resonance so that

$$\omega - \omega_0 = \eta \qquad (5\text{-}52)$$

and recognize that $\omega + \omega_0 \simeq 2\omega$ in the region of our interest, we can write

$$\omega^2 - \omega_0{}^2 = (\omega + \omega_0)(\omega - \omega_0) \simeq 2\omega\eta$$

so that (5-51) becomes

$$\frac{r^2}{r_{\max}^2} = \frac{1}{1 + (2\eta/\alpha)^2} \qquad (5\text{-}53)$$

which is plotted in Fig. 5-6. A convenient measure of the half-width of this curve is the value $\bar{\eta}$ for which the curve has dropped to half its maximum value, as shown. Therefore, from (5-53), we see that $(2\bar{\eta}/\alpha)^2 = 1$, or

$$\bar{\eta} = \omega_{1/2} - \omega_0 = \tfrac{1}{2}\alpha \qquad (5\text{-}54)$$

so that the half-width is proportional to the strength of the damping. Thus, the greater the damping, the broader (and lower) is the resonance curve. This is a general feature of the effect of frictional forces which we shall have occasion to observe in several different contexts as we proceed.

We can see directly the way in which α can be interpreted as describing a frictional effect, if we calculate:

Work done by the external force per cycle of the external force
$$= \int_{\text{cycle}} F_a \, dx = \int_0^{\tau=2\pi/\omega} F_0 \cos \omega t \cdot \dot{x} \, dt$$

$$= F_0 \int_0^{2\pi/\omega} \cos \omega t[-p \sin \omega t + q \cos \omega t](\omega \, dt)$$

$$= F_0 \int_0^{2\pi} (-p \cos s \sin s + q \cos^2 s) \, ds$$

$$= \pi F_0 q \sim \alpha F_0{}^2 \qquad (5\text{-}55)$$

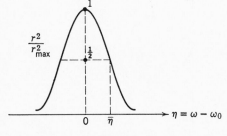

Fig. 5-6

with the aid of (5-39) and (5-41). Therefore the work done per cycle *on* the oscillating system is proportional to the out-of-phase component of the displacement, and thereby proportional to the damping constant α, in addition to being proportional to the square of the amplitude of the driving force.

5-4   Harmonic oscillations in general systems

We can get some idea of the reason the harmonic oscillator is so important to us if we consider the type of approximation we might make in a typical problem involving one-dimensional motion. Suppose $V(x)$ has the general appearance shown in Fig. 5-7; the exact shape of this curve is not important so long as it has a minimum, located at a point whose coordinate we call x_0.

Now suppose that we are interested only in motions such that the displacements from equilibrium are always small. Then we shall not need to consider (or even need to know) the complete behavior of V as a function of x, but only its form for small values of $x - x_0$ will be of importance; the remainder of the curve will be irrelevant for this particular class of motions. Thus we should be able to get an approximation to $V(x)$ which will be suitable for our purposes by expanding $V(x)$ in a Taylor series about $x = x_0$:

$$V(x) = V(x_0) + \left(\frac{\partial V}{\partial x}\right)_{x_0} (x - x_0) + \frac{1}{2!}\left(\frac{\partial^2 V}{\partial x^2}\right)_{x_0} (x - x_0)^2$$

$$+ \frac{1}{3!}\left(\frac{\partial^3 V}{\partial x^3}\right)_{x_0} (x - x_0)^3 + \cdots \quad (5\text{-}56)$$

Since x_0 is a position of stable equilibrium, $(\partial V/\partial x)_{x_0} = 0$. If we are

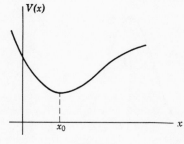

Fig. 5-7

interested only in "small" displacements, we need keep only the lowest power of $x - x_0$ in the expansion (5-56), so that we can take

$$V(x) \simeq V(x_0) + \frac{1}{2}\left(\frac{\partial^2 V}{\partial x^2}\right)_{x_0} (x - x_0)^2 \tag{5-57}$$

which gives a force

$$F = -\frac{dV}{dx} = -\left(\frac{\partial^2 V}{\partial x^2}\right)_{x_0} (x - x_0) \tag{5-58}$$

If we compare this with the one-dimensional form of (5-1), we see that the potential (5-57) for small displacements is just that of a linear harmonic oscillator with

$$k = \left(\frac{\partial^2 V}{\partial x^2}\right)_{x_0} \tag{5-59}$$

and with a corresponding natural frequency, as obtained from (5-9), given by

$$\omega_0 = \left[\frac{1}{m}\left(\frac{\partial^2 V}{\partial x^2}\right)_{x_0}\right]^{\frac{1}{2}} \tag{5-60}$$

Thus we see that we are going to meet harmonic oscillations in any sort of system as soon as we consider sufficiently small displacements from any position of stable equilibrium, and that we can calculate the frequency from (5-60) without having to inquire into the details of the motion each time.

We can also see in general that, as the displacement increases, we shall have to include more and more terms in the Taylor expansion (5-56) in order to keep a sufficiently good approximation to the potential energy. As a result, the motion will no longer be simple harmonic but will have a more complicated nature and will generally require more complicated methods of solution. For very large displacements, the whole method based on the Taylor expansion may become too cumbersome to be useful. In the next section, we shall briefly illustrate the effect of an increase in the displacement.

5-5 Anharmonic linear oscillator

For simplicity, let us choose the origin at the equilibrium position so that $x_0 = 0$, and let us include one more term in the expansion of the potential energy so that instead of (5-57) we have

$$V(x) = V(0) + \tfrac{1}{2}kx^2 + \tfrac{1}{3}\epsilon x^3 \tag{5-61}$$

where we have used (5-59), and let $\epsilon = \frac{1}{2}(\partial^3 V/\partial x^3)_0$. As the force is

$$F = -dV/dx = -kx - \epsilon x^2 \qquad (5\text{-}62)$$

the equation of motion, $F = m\ddot{x}$, becomes

$$m\ddot{x} + kx + \epsilon x^2 = 0 \qquad (5\text{-}63)$$

Rather than trying to solve (5-63) exactly, we shall try to obtain an approximate solution of it in order to illustrate the extremely useful method of *successive approximations*. We assume that ϵ is small, and we look for a solution in the form of a power series in this small parameter; that is, we write

$$x(t) = x_0(t) + \epsilon x_1(t) + \epsilon^2 x_2(t) + \cdots \qquad (5\text{-}64)$$

where $x_0, x_1, x_2, \ldots$ are functions of t to be determined. We shall need

$$x^2 = x_0{}^2 + \epsilon(2x_0 x_1) + \epsilon^2(x_1{}^2 + 2x_0 x_2) + \cdots \qquad (5\text{-}65)$$

Substituting (5-64) and (5-65) into the differential equation (5-63), we obtain

$$m(\ddot{x}_0 + \epsilon\ddot{x}_1 + \epsilon^2\ddot{x}_2 + \cdots) + k(x_0 + \epsilon x_1 + \epsilon^2 x_2 + \cdots)$$
$$+ \epsilon(x_0{}^2 + \epsilon 2x_0 x_1 + \cdots) = 0$$

or

$$(m\ddot{x}_0 + kx_0) + \epsilon(m\ddot{x}_1 + kx_1 + x_0{}^2)$$
$$+ \epsilon^2(m\ddot{x}_2 + kx_2 + 2x_0 x_1) + \cdots = 0 \qquad (5\text{-}66)$$

where the terms omitted in (5-66) are proportional to $\epsilon^3, \epsilon^4, \ldots$; that is, (5-66) includes all terms of order ϵ^2.

The expression in (5-66) cannot, in general, be always equal to zero for all possible values of t unless the coefficients of the various powers of ϵ vanish separately; equating these to zero, we get the series of equations,

$$m\ddot{x}_0 + kx_0 = 0 \qquad (5\text{-}67)$$

$$m\ddot{x}_1 + kx_1 + x_0{}^2 = 0 \qquad (5\text{-}68)$$

$$m\ddot{x}_2 + kx_2 + 2x_0 x_1 = 0, \quad \text{etc.} \qquad (5\text{-}69)$$

We can now solve these equations in succession in order to get the various functions needed in our series (5-64). We see that this procedure is possible in principle because each successive differential equation for a given function involves only functions of a lower order, which can be obtained from the previous solutions. We shall illustrate this procedure only for the first two equations, (5-67) and (5-68).

The first approximation to x is obtained as the solution of (5-67). Since this is identical with (5-7), the solution is given by (5-16) as

$$x_0 = a \cos (\omega_0 t - \gamma) \tag{5-70}$$

In order to find the second approximation, we substitute (5-70) into (5-68) and find that

$$m\ddot{x}_1 + kx_1 = -x_0{}^2 = -a^2 \cos^2 (\omega_0 t - \gamma) = -\tfrac{1}{2}a^2[1 + \cos (2\omega_0 t - 2\gamma)] \tag{5-71}$$

We try the form

$$x_1 = b \cos (2\omega_0 t - 2\gamma) + c \tag{5-72}$$

where b and c are constants. Substituting (5-72) into (5-71), we find that we must have

$$-4m\omega_0{}^2 b \cos (2\omega_0 t - 2\gamma) + kb \cos (2\omega_0 t - 2\gamma) + kc$$
$$= -\tfrac{1}{2}a^2 - \tfrac{1}{2}a^2 \cos (2\omega_0 t - 2\gamma)$$

which is satisfied if $kc = -\tfrac{1}{2}a^2$, or

$$c = -\frac{a^2}{2k} \tag{5-73}$$

and if

$$b(k - 4m\omega_0{}^2) = -\tfrac{1}{2}a^2 = b(k - 4k) = -3kb$$

or

$$b = \frac{a^2}{6k} \tag{5-74}$$

where we have used (5-9). Therefore (5-72) becomes

$$x_1 = \left(\frac{a^2}{6k}\right) \cos (2\omega_0 t - 2\gamma) - \frac{a^2}{2k} \tag{5-75}$$

so that, to this approximation, the solution to our problem is found from (5-64), (5-70), and (5-75) to be

$$x = x_0 + \epsilon x_1 = a \cos (\omega_0 t - \gamma) + \frac{\epsilon}{k}\left(\frac{a^2}{6}\right) \cos (2\omega_0 t - 2\gamma) - \frac{\epsilon}{k}\left(\frac{a^2}{2}\right) \tag{5-76}$$

This solution contains the two necessary constants of integration, a and γ, which can be evaluated in terms of the initial conditions, if desired.

We note the appearance in (5-76) of the term involving twice the frequency of the harmonic oscillation, and it is clear that higher harmonics (i.e., larger multiples of ω_0) will become involved as we go to the higher approximations to x. This appearance of multiples of the simple harmonic oscillator frequency is characteristic of non-linear systems such as this, non-linear meaning that the force depends on powers of the displacement other than the first.

We also see that this approximation (5-76) is better, the smaller the ratio ϵ/k. One could now continue this process and find x_2, x_3, ... by a series of integrations of this type. However, if the values of x involved get too large, or the value of ϵ is too great, this whole method of solution may not result in a usable approximation to x, and one would have to turn to other methods in order to find the displacement as a function of the time.

Exercises

5-1. Solve equation (5-5), which gives $v = dx/dt$ as a function of position, for the time interval dt spent in the region dx. Integrate the resulting expression over a complete cycle of the motion in order to find the period, and thus show in this way that the period is given by (5-12). [You must be careful in your choices of the plus or minus sign in (5-5). Explain.]

5-2. Show that for the undamped linear oscillator the time averages of the kinetic and potential energies, taken over one complete period, are equal.

5-3. If the initial position and velocity of an oscillator are x_0 and v_0, respectively, find the constants C and θ in (5-47).

5-4. A particle which is confined to move only along the x axis is acted on by the forces $-kx$ and $(t/T)f$, where k, T, and f are constants. Solve the equation of motion and discuss the motion, finding the frequency and point of "equilibrium."

5-5. Find the frequency of small oscillations about equilibrium for a particle subject to the potential energy of Exercise 4-4.

6 Systems of particles

If we desire to discuss mechanical systems more complicated than those consisting of a single particle, the question immediately arises: How can we describe them? We shall make a natural extension of our line of thought up to this point and assume that they are composed of a number of individual mass points or particles. Hence we shall be interested in the properties of systems of particles, and first of all we shall want to see what sort of general statements we can make about such systems.

The forces acting on the constituents of the system can be divided into two classes: *external* forces which result from influences apart from the system, and *internal* forces which originate within the system and describe the interactions among the particles. Suppose there is a total of N particles in the system; let us try to find the total force acting on one of these particles, the ith, for example. There may be a number of external forces acting on the *i*th particle which we can replace by their resultant, $\mathbf{F}_i$. If we let $\mathbf{F}_{ij}$ be the internal force on the *i*th particle due to the *j*th particle, then the total force on the *i*th particle is

$$\mathbf{F}_{it} = \mathbf{F}_i + \sum_{j=1}^{N} \mathbf{F}_{ij} \tag{6-1}$$

In the sum we must actually have $j \neq i$, since $\mathbf{F}_{ii} = 0$. The equation of motion of the *i*th particle of mass m_i then is

$$m_i \ddot{\mathbf{r}}_i = \mathbf{F}_i + \sum_{j} \mathbf{F}_{ij} \tag{6-2}$$

Since $i = 1, 2, \ldots, N$, there is a total of N equations like (6-2).

Let us add all these N equations together, that is, sum (6-2) over the index *i*. The result is that

$$\sum_{i} m_i \ddot{\mathbf{r}}_i = \sum_{i} \mathbf{F}_i + \sum_{i} \sum_{j} \mathbf{F}_{ij} \tag{6-3}$$

Let us consider the double sum in (6-3); it will contain a term like $\mathbf{F}_{34} + \mathbf{F}_{43}$ due to the interaction of the third and fourth particles. But we know from (3-10) that $\mathbf{F}_{34} = -\mathbf{F}_{43}$ so that $\mathbf{F}_{34} + \mathbf{F}_{43} = 0$. The same result will hold for each pair of particles; thus we can say that the internal forces will cancel out in pairs in the double sum, so that

$$\sum_{i} \sum_{j} \mathbf{F}_{ij} = 0 \tag{6-4}$$

and (6-3) becomes

$$\sum_{i} m_i \ddot{\mathbf{r}}_i = \sum_{i} \mathbf{F}_i = \mathbf{F}_e \tag{6-5}$$

where $\mathbf{F}_e$ is the resultant of all of the external forces acting on the whole system.

The last equation can be put into an interesting form if we first define the position vector of the center of mass of the system, $\mathbf{R}$, by the equation

$$\mathbf{R} = \frac{\sum\limits_{i} m_i \mathbf{r}_i}{\sum\limits_{i} m_i} = \frac{\sum\limits_{i} m_i \mathbf{r}_i}{M} \tag{6-6}$$

where M is the total mass of the system. Since M is a constant, if we differentiate (6-6) twice with respect to the time, we find that $M \ddot{\mathbf{R}} = \sum_i m_i \ddot{\mathbf{r}}_i$, so that (6-5) can be written

$$M \ddot{\mathbf{R}} = \mathbf{F}_e \tag{6-7}$$

This result says that the center of mass of the system moves as if the total mass of the system were concentrated at the center of mass and the total external force acting on the whole system were acting at that point. Here we have found the justification for the common procedure in elementary treatments of replacing extended bodies by point particles and letting the total external force act at these points. We also see that, if $\mathbf{F}_e = 0$, the center of mass moves with constant velocity or remains at rest.

We can restate (6-7) in still other terms. If we use (4-4) and define the total linear momentum of the system by

$$\mathbf{P} = \sum_i \mathbf{p}_i = \sum_i m_i \dot{\mathbf{r}}_i \tag{6-8}$$

then we see from (6-6) that

$$\mathbf{P} = M\dot{\mathbf{R}} \tag{6-9}$$

and that (6-7) can be written

$$\dot{\mathbf{P}} = \mathbf{F}_e \tag{6-10}$$

Thus the total linear momentum equals the momentum of a single particle whose mass equals the total mass of the system and which is moving with the center of mass, and the total linear momentum changes only as a result of the action of external forces.

If $\mathbf{F}_e = 0$, then $\mathbf{P} = $ const. This is a statement of the *conservation of momentum* for a system of particles. We note that, if only a given component of $\mathbf{F}_e$ vanishes, the corresponding component of the total momentum will be conserved, although other components might not be.

The *angular momentum of a particle* l, is defined by

$$\mathbf{l} = \mathbf{r} \times \mathbf{p} = \mathbf{r} \times m\mathbf{v} = m(\mathbf{r} \times \dot{\mathbf{r}}) \tag{6-11}$$

From (1-13), we see that the magnitude of l is given by the component of p which is perpendicular to r times the magnitude of r.

The *total angular momentum* of the system of particles, L, is defined by

$$\mathbf{L} = \sum_i \mathbf{l}_i = \sum_i \mathbf{r}_i \times \mathbf{p}_i = \sum_i m_i(\mathbf{r}_i \times \dot{\mathbf{r}}_i) \tag{6-12}$$

Suppose we now take the cross product of each position vector $\mathbf{r}_i$ with its corresponding equation of motion (6-2), and sum the resulting equations; the result is

$$\sum_i m_i(\mathbf{r}_i \times \ddot{\mathbf{r}}_i) = \sum_i \mathbf{r}_i \times \mathbf{F}_i + \sum_i \sum_j \mathbf{r}_i \times \mathbf{F}_{ij} \tag{6-13}$$

The *torque* (or moment) of the force $\mathbf{F}_i$ is written $\mathbf{n}_i$ and is defined by

$$\mathbf{n}_i = \mathbf{r}_i \times \mathbf{F}_i \tag{6-14}$$

If we use (1-15), we find that

$$\frac{d}{dt}(\mathbf{r}_i \times \dot{\mathbf{r}}_i) = \dot{\mathbf{r}}_i \times \dot{\mathbf{r}}_i + \mathbf{r}_i \times \ddot{\mathbf{r}}_i = \mathbf{r}_i \times \ddot{\mathbf{r}}_i$$

so that (6-13) can also be written

$$\frac{d}{dt}\left[\sum_i m_i(\mathbf{r}_i \times \dot{\mathbf{r}}_i) \right] = \frac{d\mathbf{L}}{dt} = \mathbf{N}_e + \sum_i \sum_j \mathbf{r}_i \times \mathbf{F}_{ij} \tag{6-15}$$

with the help of (6-12); $\mathbf{N}_e = \sum_i \mathbf{n}_i$ is the resultant torque produced by external forces.

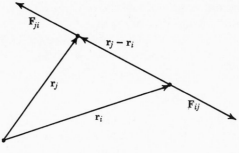

Fig. 6-1

In order to obtain a result analogous to (6-10), we shall make the plausible assumption that the internal forces act along the lines connecting the particles; this is illustrated in Fig. 6-1. The pair of particles formed from the ith and jth will contribute to the double sum in (6-15) the total term

$$\mathbf{r}_i \times \mathbf{F}_{ij} + \mathbf{r}_j \times \mathbf{F}_{ji} = (\mathbf{r}_j - \mathbf{r}_i) \times \mathbf{F}_{ji} = 0$$

since $\mathbf{F}_{ij} = -\mathbf{F}_{ji}$ by (3-10), and since the cross product of the two parallel vectors $\mathbf{F}_{ji}$ and $\mathbf{r}_j - \mathbf{r}_i$ vanishes. The same result will be obtained for each pair of particles, so that

$$\sum_i \sum_j \mathbf{r}_i \times \mathbf{F}_{ij} = 0 \qquad (6\text{-}16)$$

and (6-15) becomes

$$\frac{d\mathbf{L}}{dt} = \mathbf{N}_e \qquad (6\text{-}17)$$

Thus we have shown that, if the force between any two particles of the system always acts along the line joining them, the rate of change of the total angular momentum of the system equals the resultant of the torques due to the external forces.

We now see that, if $\mathbf{N}_e = 0$, then $\mathbf{L} = $ const. This is a statement of the *conservation of angular momentum* for a system of particles. As we remarked for (6-10), we can see from (6-17) that, if a given component of the external torque vanishes, the corresponding component of the total angular momentum remains constant, although the other components may not be constants.

We found previously in (6-9) that the value of the total linear momentum of the system is the same as it would be if the entire mass were concentrated at the center of mass and moving with this point. Let us make a similar investigation for the total angular momentum; we shall get a more complicated result.

If $\mathbf{r}_i$ is the position vector of the ith particle with respect to some arbitrary origin, and if we let $\mathbf{r}_i'$ be the position vector of the ith particle with respect to the center of mass, then

$$\mathbf{r}_i = \mathbf{R} + \mathbf{r}_i' \tag{6-18}$$

as we can see from Fig. 6-2. If follows directly from (6-18) that

$$\mathbf{v}_i = \mathbf{V} + \mathbf{v}_i' \tag{6-19}$$

where $\mathbf{V} = \dot{\mathbf{R}}$ is the velocity of the center of mass, and $\mathbf{v}_i' = \dot{\mathbf{r}}_i'$ is the velocity of the ith particle with respect to the center of mass. Substituting (6-18) and (6-19) into (6-12), we find that

$$
\begin{aligned}
\mathbf{L} &= \sum_i m_i(\mathbf{r}_i \times \mathbf{v}_i) = \sum_i m_i[(\mathbf{R} + \mathbf{r}_i') \times (\mathbf{V} + \mathbf{v}_i')] \\
&= \sum_i \mathbf{R} \times m_i\mathbf{V} + \sum_i \mathbf{r}_i' \times m_i\mathbf{v}_i' + \left(\sum_i m_i\mathbf{r}_i'\right) \times \mathbf{V} \\
&\quad + \mathbf{R} \times \frac{d}{dt}\left(\sum_i m_i\mathbf{r}_i'\right)
\end{aligned}
\tag{6-20}
$$

Now, by substituting (6-18) into (6-6), we see that $\sum_i m_i\mathbf{r}_i' = 0$, and (6-20) becomes

$$\mathbf{L} = \mathbf{R} \times M\mathbf{V} + \sum_i \mathbf{r}_i' \times m_i\mathbf{v}_i' \tag{6-21}$$

Thus we see that the total angular momentum of the system with respect to the origin O equals the angular momentum of a particle of mass equal to the total mass, the particle being located at the center of mass and moving with it, *plus* the angular momentum of the system about the center of mass. The total angular momentum therefore depends on the coordinate origin one is using; however, the total torque also does, so that we always have (6-17) as a valid equation, regardless of what coordinate system we use, provided that we calculate $\mathbf{L}$ and $\mathbf{N}_e$ with respect to the same origin.

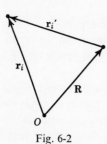

Fig. 6-2

We now turn to the related concepts of work and energy as they apply to a system of particles. Suppose we let W_{12} be the total work done by *all* forces when the system is changed from an initial configuration labeled 1 to a final configuration 2. This total work will be the sum of the work done on each particle; thus, if we use (4-11) and (6-1), we obtain

$$W_{12} = \sum_i \int_1^2 \mathbf{F}_{it} \cdot d\mathbf{r}_i = \sum_i \int_1^2 \mathbf{F}_i \cdot d\mathbf{r}_i + \sum_i \sum_j \int_1^2 \mathbf{F}_{ij} \cdot d\mathbf{r}_i \tag{6-22}$$

We can proceed as we did before in (4-12) and (4-14) to obtain

$$\sum_i \int_1^2 \mathbf{F}_{it} \cdot d\mathbf{r}_i = \sum_i m_i \int_1^2 \dot{\mathbf{v}}_i \cdot \mathbf{v}_i \, dt = \sum_i \int_1^2 d(\tfrac{1}{2} m_i v_i^2)$$

$$= \left(\sum_i \tfrac{1}{2} m_i v_i^2 \right)_2 - \left(\sum_i \tfrac{1}{2} m_i v_i^2 \right)_1 \tag{6-23}$$

If we define the *total kinetic energy* of the system as

$$T = \sum_i \tfrac{1}{2} m_i v_i^2 \tag{6-24}$$

and combine (6-24) with (6-22) and (6-23), we obtain

$$W_{12} = T_2 - T_1 \tag{6-25}$$

so that the total work done equals the change in the total kinetic energy; this result is similar to that we found earlier for a single particle in (4-16).

Before proceeding with the discussion of (6-22), let us investigate the total kinetic energy a little more closely. If we use (6-19) and (6-24), we get

$$T = \tfrac{1}{2} \sum_i m_i (\mathbf{V} + \mathbf{v}_i') \cdot (\mathbf{V} + \mathbf{v}_i')$$

$$= \tfrac{1}{2} \sum_i m_i \mathbf{V}^2 + \tfrac{1}{2} \sum_i m_i \mathbf{v}_i'^2 + \mathbf{V} \cdot \frac{d}{dt} \left(\sum_i m_i \mathbf{r}_i' \right)$$

$$= \tfrac{1}{2} M \mathbf{V}^2 + \sum_i \tfrac{1}{2} m_i \mathbf{v}_i'^2 \tag{6-26}$$

since $\sum_i m_i \mathbf{r}_i' = 0$, as before. Thus the total kinetic energy of the system equals the kinetic energy of the total mass of the system concentrated at the center of mass and moving with it *plus* the kinetic energy of the motion of the particles with respect to the center of mass.

Suppose that the external forces can be derived from a potential energy, that is, according to (4-23),

$$\mathbf{F}_i = - \frac{\partial V_i}{\partial x_i} \hat{\mathbf{i}} - \frac{\partial V_i}{\partial y_i} \hat{\mathbf{j}} - \frac{\partial V_i}{\partial z_i} \hat{\mathbf{k}} = -\text{grad}_i \, V_i \tag{6-27}$$

If we use (6-27) and (1-26), the first summation on the right side of (6-22) can be written

$$\sum_i \int_1^2 \mathbf{F}_i \cdot d\mathbf{r}_i = -\sum_i \int_1^2 \text{grad}_i \, V_i \cdot d\mathbf{r}_i = -\sum_i \int_1^2 dV_i$$

$$= -\sum_i (V_{i2} - V_{i1}) \tag{6-28}$$

That is, the work done on the system by the external forces equals the total decrease in the external potential energy.

Now let us suppose that the internal forces are also conservative and hence $\mathbf{F}_{ij}$ and $\mathbf{F}_{ji}$ can be derived from a potential energy V_{ij}. In order to satisfy (3-10), V_{ij} can be a function only of the magnitude of the distance between the particles; that is,

$$V_{ij} = V_{ij}(|\mathbf{r}_i - \mathbf{r}_j|) = V_{ij}(x_i - x_j, y_i - y_j, z_i - z_j) \qquad (6\text{-}29)$$

We can show that this is true by calculating the force components from (4-23) and (6-29); for example,

$$F_{ij,x} = -\frac{\partial V_{ij}}{\partial x_i} = -\frac{\partial V_{ij}}{\partial(x_i - x_j)}\frac{\partial(x_i - x_j)}{\partial x_i} = -\frac{\partial V_{ij}}{\partial(x_i - x_j)} \qquad (6\text{-}30)$$

$$F_{ji,x} = -\frac{\partial V_{ij}}{\partial x_j} = -\frac{\partial V_{ij}}{\partial(x_i - x_j)}\frac{\partial(x_i - x_j)}{\partial x_j} = +\frac{\partial V_{ij}}{\partial(x_i - x_j)} \qquad (6\text{-}31)$$

so that $F_{ij,x} = -F_{ji,x}$ and therefore $\mathbf{F}_{ij} = -\mathbf{F}_{ji}$ as required by (3-10).

The double sum on the right side of (6-22) can now be written as a sum over all the pairs of the particles:

$$\sum_i \sum_j \int_1^2 \mathbf{F}_{ij} \cdot d\mathbf{r}_i = \sum_{\text{pairs}} \int_1^2 (\mathbf{F}_{ij} \cdot d\mathbf{r}_i + \mathbf{F}_{ji} \cdot d\mathbf{r}_j)$$

$$= \sum_{\text{pairs}} \int_1^2 \mathbf{F}_{ij} \cdot d(\mathbf{r}_i - \mathbf{r}_j)$$

$$= \sum_{\text{pairs}} \int_1^2 \mathbf{F}_{ij} \cdot d\mathbf{r}_{ij} \qquad (6\text{-}32)$$

where $\mathbf{r}_{ij} = \mathbf{r}_i - \mathbf{r}_j$. Now, from (6-20), $F_{ij,x} = -\partial V_{ij}/\partial x_{ij}$, etc., so that

$$\mathbf{F}_{ij} \cdot d\mathbf{r}_{ij} = -\left(\frac{\partial V_{ij}}{\partial x_{ij}}dx_{ij} + \frac{\partial V_{ij}}{\partial y_{ij}}dy_{ij} + \frac{\partial V_{ij}}{\partial z_{ij}}dz_{ij}\right) = -dV_{ij}$$

and (6-32) then becomes equal to

$$-\sum_{\text{pairs}} \int_1^2 dV_{ij} = -\sum_{\text{pairs}}[(V_{ij})_2 - (V_{ij})_1] = -\tfrac{1}{2}\sum_i \sum_j [(V_{ij})_2 - (V_{ij})_1] \qquad (6\text{-}33)$$

The factor $\frac{1}{2}$ arises because, as one goes through all the possible values of i and j for each sum, each pair of particles is counted twice.

If we combine (6-22), (6-28), (6-32), and (6-33), we see that if both the external and internal forces are conservative we can write

$$W_{12} = -(V_2 - V_1) \qquad (6\text{-}34)$$

since we are able to define a *total potential energy* as

$$V = \sum_i V_i + \tfrac{1}{2}\sum_i \sum_j V_{ij} \qquad (6\text{-}35)$$

If (6-25) and (6-34) are now equated, we obtain $T_2 - T_1 = -(V_2 - V_1)$, or

$$T_2 + V_2 = T_1 + V_1 = \text{const.} \tag{6-36}$$

Hence we can also define a *total energy*

$$E = T + V \tag{6-37}$$

which is conserved quite analogously to what we obtained in (4-21) for a single particle.

The double sum in (6-35) is generally called the total internal potential energy of the system of particles. It is ordinarily different from zero, and in general it changes in time as the distances between the particles change in time as a result of their motion. However, the internal potential energy is always constant for those systems known as *rigid bodies*. By definition, a rigid body is one for which the distances between the particles are constant and cannot change with time; that is, $r_{ij}^2 = \mathbf{r}_{ij} \cdot \mathbf{r}_{ij} = \text{const.}$ If we differentiate this expression, we get $2\mathbf{r}_{ij} \cdot d\mathbf{r}_{ij} = 0$, which shows that $d\mathbf{r}_{ij}$ must be perpendicular to $\mathbf{r}_{ij}$ for any possible motion of a rigid body. Since the internal forces are parallel to the line connecting the particles, we can write $\mathbf{F}_{ij} = f\mathbf{r}_{ij}$, where f is some scalar. Therefore $\mathbf{F}_{ij}$ and $d\mathbf{r}_{ij}$ are perpendicular, and $\mathbf{F}_{ij} \cdot d\mathbf{r}_{ij} = 0$, showing that the internal forces do no work. But, in that case, the internal potential energy is constant; since the total potential energy is always uncertain with respect to an additive constant, the internal potential energy can therefore always be neglected in the discussion of the motion of *rigid* bodies.

Exercises

6-1. Two canoes, each of mass M, are at rest in the water and pointing in the same direction. A man of mass m jumps from the first to the second, and then immediately back into the first. If the friction with the water is neglected, and if the man does not fall into the water, show that the ratio of the final velocities of the canoes is $(M + m)/M$.

6-2. On a certain day 3 centimeters of rain fell in 10 hours, the drops falling with a speed of 6 meters per second. Find the average force produced by the impact of the raindrops on a square meter of the horizontal canvas roof of a tent. (The density of water is 1 gram per cubic centimeter.)

7 Generalized coordinates and

Lagrange's equations

Problems in mechanics generally involve more than simply writing down all the equations of motion like (6-2) and proceeding to solve them. In our discussion to this point, we have had rectangular coordinates implicitly in mind whenever any specific references to coordinate systems have been made; it may well turn out that rectangular coordinates might not be the natural or simplest ones to use for a given problem, and it would be convenient if we could write our basic equations in some form that would once and for all be equally suitable for all coordinate systems.

However, it is generally much more pressing a matter to take into account whatever possible *constraints* may limit the motion of the system. Constraints usually reflect some geometric condition imposed on the motion; for example, a bead may be constrained to move on a wire, a particle may be constrained to move on some surface, and the bob of a pendulum, being constrained to move at a fixed distance from its support, may possibly be constrained to move in some plane as well.

The usual system of classifying constraints is as follows.

Holonomic

The conditions of constraint can be expressed as *equations* connecting the *coordinates* of the particles and the time, that is, of the general form

$$f(x_1, y_1, z_1, x_2, \ldots, y_N, z_N, t) = 0 \tag{7-1}$$

Of course, every coordinate need not be involved in each equation describing a constraint.

Example. Rigid Body. The constraints are that

$r_{ij}^2 = (\mathbf{r}_i - \mathbf{r}_j)^2 = \text{const.} = a_{ij}^2$, or

$$(\mathbf{r}_i - \mathbf{r}_j)^2 - a_{ij}^2 = 0 \tag{7-2}$$

which has the form (7-1). There will be one equation like (7-2) for each pair of particles in the rigid body.

Example. Bead Sliding on a Circular Wire of radius a. If the plane of the circle is chosen as the xy plane and the origin put at the center, the equation of constraint is $x^2 + y^2 - a^2 = 0$, which has the form (7-1).

Non-holonomic

The constraints are not expressible as equations involving the coordinates.

Example. A Particle Which Cannot Penetrate a Sphere of Radius a. If the origin is chosen at the center of the sphere, then the condition of constraint is that $x^2 + y^2 + z^2 \geqslant a^2$. But this has the form of an inequality, not an *equation*, and therefore the constraint is non-holonomic.

Scleronomous

The constraints are independent of the time. The rigid body constraints (7-2) are examples of time-independent constraints.

Rheonomous

The constraints explicitly depend on the time. For example, in the example of the particle which could not penetrate the sphere, if the sphere were expanding, contracting, or pulsating in some way so that $a(t)$, then the constraint would be time dependent.

The existence of constraints gives rise to two types of difficulties. First, the coordinates of the particles are not all independent since they are connected by the equations of constraint. As a result, the equations of motion (6-2) are not all independent, and we must somehow take this into account during our solution of the problem. Second, we are not given the forces of constraint, that is, the forces which keep the bead on the wire, keep the rigid body rigid, prevent the particle from penetrating the sphere, etc. In fact, the forces of constraint are actually some of the unknowns, and they must be found, or perhaps somehow be bypassed, during the course of solution; all of this obviously adds to the difficulties of solving the problem.

7-1 Generalized coordinates

For holonomic constraints, the first difficulty can readily be taken care of by the use of *generalized coordinates*. In general, any convenient set of parameters which can be used to specify the configuration of the system can be taken as the generalized coordinates.

Suppose our system contains N particles. Since each particle needs three coordinates to specify its position, we require a total of $3N$ coordinates to describe the configuration completely, if there are no constraints on the system. We say that the system has $3N$ *degrees of freedom*. However, the number of degrees of freedom will be reduced if there are constraints. In particular, let us suppose there are k equations like (7-1) which express holonomic constraints. These k equations can be used to eliminate k of the $3N$ coordinates from the equations of motion by solving the k equations for the k eliminated coordinates in terms of the others. Then we shall be left with a total of $(3N - k)$ *independent* coordinates, and the system is said to have $(3N - k)$ *degrees of freedom*.

Rather than using the $(3N - k)$ rectangular coordinates as the independent variables, it is often convenient to introduce instead $(3N - k)$ *new independent* variables, $q_1, q_2, \ldots, q_{3N-k}$. The original coordinates can be expressed in terms of this set of generalized coordinates, and we shall have $3N$ relations of the form

$$x_1 = x_1(q_1, q_2, \ldots, q_{3N-k}, t)$$
$$y_1 = y_1(q_1, q_2, \ldots, q_{3N-k}, t)$$
$$\cdots\cdots\cdots\cdots\cdots\cdots\cdots\cdots \tag{7-3}$$
$$z_N = z_N(q_1, q_2, \ldots, q_{3N-k}, t)$$

which are known as transformation equations.

Example.   Simple Pendulum in a Plane.   This system consists of a particle of mass m which is connected to a point of support by a rigid, massless rod of length l. The support is such that the particle is confined to move in a given plane; this is illustrated in Fig. 7-1.

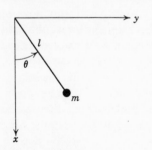

The two physical constraints are that the particle moves only in the xy plane, and that it is always a constant distance l from the origin. These constraints can be expressed by the *two* equations

$$z = 0, \quad x^2 + y^2 = l^2 \tag{7-4}$$

Fig. 7-1

and are therefore holonomic. Hence there is only *one* degree of freedom, which could be chosen as either x or y. However, it is clear from the figure that the configuration is completely specified by the single variable θ, which is actually a more natural one to choose for this system. The transformation equations for this case then are

$$x = l \cos \theta, \quad y = l \sin \theta \tag{7-5}$$

with the last one, $z = 0$, being actually one of the equations of constraint. Therefore, for this system our single generalized coordinate can be taken to be the *angle* θ.

The preceding example shows that generalized coordinates need not be coordinates in the usual sense. They can be angles, angular momentum components, energies, amplitudes of Fourier series expansions—in short, any variables which are independent and are sufficient to determine the configuration of the system if their values are known.

We have seen that, for holonomic constraints, where we have equations involving the coordinates, we can bypass the first difficulty of non-independent coordinates by introducing independent generalized coordinates. For non-holonomic constraints, where equations connecting the coordinates are not available, there is no general way of eliminating the extra dependent coordinates, and each problem must usually be considered separately. The net result is that non-holonomic systems are generally much more difficult to deal with than are holonomic ones. Fortunately, however, virtually all the aspects of mechanics which are important in the study of atomic and molecular properties can be safely assumed to involve only holonomic systems, and, in fact, the whole concept of constraint is somewhat artificial for these problems and generally enters only as a result of some mathematical idealization of the actual situation. Accordingly, we shall assume from now on that we are dealing only with holonomic and scleronomous systems, so that we can always assume equations of constraint which do not explicitly contain the time.

The second difficulty, which arises because the forces of constraint are not known, is still with us even though we are using generalized coordinates. One of our previous results, however, gives us a hint about what we can do next. We know that rigid bodies are systems which are described by holonomic constraints and, in addition, the forces of constraint which keep the particles at fixed separations are simply the internal forces. At the end of Chapter 6, we saw that the internal constraining forces do no work and, therefore, do not even enter into the problem. In other words, for this particular holonomic system, the constraint forces have been eliminated, in effect. As a result, we are led to think that it would really be very nice if we could somehow formulate mechanics so that *the unknown forces of constraint would not even appear* and only the known external forces would need to concern us. This is what we shall now proceed to do.

7-2   D'Alembert's principle

We begin by defining a *virtual infinitesimal displacement* of a system as any change in the configuration of the system which would be the result of any arbitrary infinitesimal changes in the coordinates which we can imagine, consistent, however, with the forces and constraints of the system at a given instant t.

We represent the changes in the positions of the particles in a virtual displacement by $\delta\mathbf{r}_i$. As this displacement of the system is one we are visualizing, these particle displacements will not necessarily correspond to any actual displacements which occur during the natural motion of the system; we shall reserve the symbol $d\mathbf{r}_i$ to represent these actual displacements of the particles.

Suppose the system is in equilibrium so that $\mathbf{F}_i = 0$ for all i. Then, clearly,

$$\mathbf{F}_i \cdot \delta\mathbf{r}_i = 0 \qquad (7\text{-}6)$$

or, the virtual work (that is, the work done in a virtual displacement) done on the ith particle is zero. Summing (7-6) over all the particles, we find the total virtual work to be

$$\delta W = \sum_i \mathbf{F}_i \cdot \delta\mathbf{r}_i = 0 \qquad (7\text{-}7)$$

As yet, absolutely nothing new is represented by (7-7). Now, however, we want to divide the force on the ith particle into the applied force $\mathbf{F}_{ia}$ and the force of constraint $\mathbf{f}_i$; hence

$$\mathbf{F}_i = \mathbf{F}_{ia} + \mathbf{f}_i \qquad (7\text{-}8)$$

Then (7-7) becomes

$$\sum_i \mathbf{F}_{ia} \cdot \delta\mathbf{r}_i + \sum_i \mathbf{f}_i \cdot \delta\mathbf{r}_i = 0 \qquad (7\text{-}9)$$

We now assume that the virtual work of the forces of constraint is zero, so that

$$\sum_i \mathbf{f}_i \cdot \delta\mathbf{r}_i = 0 \qquad (7\text{-}10)$$

Actually, this is practically the only possible situation we can imagine, namely, that the forces of constraint must be perpendicular to any possible displacement so that $\mathbf{f}_i \cdot \delta\mathbf{r}_i = 0$; if the constraint forces were not perpendicular, the system could be spontaneously accelerated by the forces of constraint alone, and we know that this does not occur. The only other possible conditions for which (7-10) would not hold would be for frictional forces which act along the direction opposite to the displacement; we shall, however, exclude frictional forces from our considerations.

Substituting (7-10) into (7-9), we get the *principle of virtual work*,

$$\sum_i \mathbf{F}_{ia} \cdot \delta\mathbf{r}_i = 0 \qquad (7\text{-}11)$$

which holds for the equilibrium case and which does not involve the forces of constraint. We cannot say, however, that (7-11) implies that each $\mathbf{F}_{ia} = 0$ even though the displacements are arbitrary, since they are not all independent but are connected by the equations of constraint. In order to be able to equate coefficients to zero, we would have to transform (7-11) to a form involving only the virtual displacements of the independent generalized coordinates q_j; we shall not do this for (7-11), however, as (7-11) holds only for the static case and we are primarily interested in the dynamic case.

Let us now consider the equation of motion $\mathbf{F}_i = \dot{\mathbf{p}}_i$ or

$$\mathbf{F}_i - \dot{\mathbf{p}}_i = 0 \tag{7-12}$$

This form (7-12) can be taken to say that the particle will be in equilibrium for a force equal to the actual force acting on the particle plus a "reversed effective force," $-\dot{\mathbf{p}}_i$; thus dynamics can, in a sense, be thought of as being reduced to statics.

Proceeding exactly as above, we can start with (7-12) and obtain

$$\sum_i (\mathbf{F}_i - \dot{\mathbf{p}}_i) \cdot \delta\mathbf{r}_i = 0$$

and then

$$\sum_i (\mathbf{F}_{ia} - \dot{\mathbf{p}}_i) \cdot \delta\mathbf{r}_i + \sum_i \mathbf{f}_i \cdot \delta\mathbf{r}_i = 0 \tag{7-13}$$

Again we require that the forces of constraint do no work so that (7-10) is satisfied and (7-13) becomes

$$\sum_i (\mathbf{F}_{ia} - \dot{\mathbf{p}}_i) \cdot \delta\mathbf{r}_i = 0 \tag{7-14}$$

which is known as *D'Alembert's principle*. We see that in (7-14) we have attained our goal of eliminating the unknown forces of constraint; we can now drop the identifying subscript a, as only applied forces will be encountered and (7-14) can be written

$$\sum_i (\mathbf{F}_i - \dot{\mathbf{p}}_i) \cdot \delta\mathbf{r}_i = 0 \tag{7-15}$$

7-3 Lagrange's equations

In order to obtain useful separate equations from (7-15), we must transform it and express it in terms of the independent generalized co-ordinates q_j. Let the system have n degrees of freedom; the generalized coordinates are $q_1, q_2, \ldots, q_j, \ldots, q_n$. Now, because of (7-3), we have

$$\delta x_i = \sum_j \frac{\partial x_i}{\partial q_j} \delta q_j, \quad \dot{x}_i = \sum_j \frac{\partial x_i}{\partial q_j} \dot{q}_j \tag{7-16}$$

and so on, so that

$$\delta\mathbf{r}_i = \sum_j \frac{\partial \mathbf{r}_i}{\partial q_j} \delta q_j \tag{7-17}$$

$$\dot{\mathbf{r}}_i = \sum_j \frac{\partial \mathbf{r}_i}{\partial q_j} \dot{q}_j \tag{7-18}$$

(In all these equations, $i = 1, 2, \ldots, N$ and $j = 1, 2, \ldots, n$).

Let us consider the virtual work term of (7-15); with the use of (7-17), this becomes

$$\delta W = \sum_i \mathbf{F}_i \cdot \delta\mathbf{r}_i = \sum_j \left(\sum_i \mathbf{F}_i \cdot \frac{\partial \mathbf{r}_i}{\partial q_j} \right) \delta q_j = \sum_j Q_j \, \delta q_j \tag{7-19}$$

where

$$Q_j = \sum_i \mathbf{F}_i \cdot \frac{\partial \mathbf{r}_i}{\partial q_j} = \sum_i \left(F_{ix} \frac{\partial x_i}{\partial q_j} + F_{iy} \frac{\partial y_i}{\partial q_j} + F_{iz} \frac{\partial z_i}{\partial q_j} \right) \tag{7-20}$$

and is called the jth component of the *generalized force*.

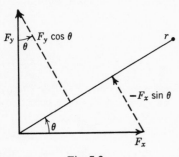

Fig. 7-2

Example.   Use of Polar Coordinates.
Suppose we had decided to use the plane polar coordinates (r, θ) shown in Fig. 7-2 rather than the rectangular coordinates (x, y). For any particle, the equations connecting the two sets are

$$x = r \cos \theta, \quad y = r \sin \theta \tag{7-21}$$

If we take $q_1 = r$ and $q_2 = \theta$, then we find from (7-20) and (7-21) that

$$Q_1 = Q_r = F_x \frac{\partial x}{\partial r} + F_y \frac{\partial y}{\partial r} = F_x \cos \theta + F_y \sin \theta = F_r \tag{7-22}$$

where F_r is the component of the force along r. Similarly,

$$Q_2 = Q_\theta = F_x \frac{\partial x}{\partial \theta} + F_y \frac{\partial y}{\partial \theta} = -F_x r \sin \theta + F_y r \cos \theta = N \tag{7-23}$$

where N is the magnitude of the torque which tends to increase the angle θ, as we can see from Fig. 7-2 and (6-14). We also see that (7-19) becomes

$$\delta W = F_x \, dx + F_y \, dy = Q_r \, dr + Q_\theta \, d\theta \tag{7-24}$$

Thus we have seen in this example how we can identify the generalized force components; we have also found that they need not be actual forces, as such, but may be torques, for example.

Now let us return to the consideration of the remaining term of (7-15). Using (4-4) and (7-17), we find that

$$\sum_i \dot{\mathbf{p}}_i \cdot \delta\mathbf{r}_i = \sum_i m_i\ddot{\mathbf{r}}_i \cdot \delta\mathbf{r}_i = \sum_j \left(\sum_i m_i\ddot{\mathbf{r}}_i \cdot \frac{\partial\mathbf{r}_i}{\partial q_j} \right) \delta q_j \qquad (7\text{-}25)$$

Now we can write

$$\sum_i m_i\ddot{\mathbf{r}}_i \cdot \frac{\partial\mathbf{r}_i}{\partial q_j} = \sum_i \left[\frac{d}{dt}\left(m_i\dot{\mathbf{r}}_i \cdot \frac{\partial\mathbf{r}_i}{\partial q_j} \right) - m_i\dot{\mathbf{r}}_i \cdot \frac{d}{dt}\left(\frac{\partial\mathbf{r}_i}{\partial q_j} \right) \right] \qquad (7\text{-}26)$$

and, if we apply (7-18) to $\partial\mathbf{r}_i/\partial q_j$ rather than to $\mathbf{r}_i$, we get

$$\frac{d}{dt}\left(\frac{\partial\mathbf{r}_i}{\partial q_j} \right) = \sum_k \frac{\partial}{\partial q_k}\left(\frac{\partial\mathbf{r}_i}{\partial q_j} \right)\dot{q}_k = \frac{\partial}{\partial q_j}\left(\sum_k \frac{\partial\mathbf{r}_i}{\partial q_k}\dot{q}_k \right)$$

$$= \frac{\partial\dot{\mathbf{r}}_i}{\partial q_j} = \frac{\partial}{\partial q_j}\left(\frac{d\mathbf{r}_i}{dt} \right) \qquad (7\text{-}27)$$

We also see that, if we differentiate (7-18), we obtain

$$\frac{\partial\dot{\mathbf{r}}_i}{\partial\dot{q}_j} = \frac{\partial\mathbf{r}_i}{\partial\dot{q}_j} \qquad (7\text{-}28)$$

Substituting (7-27) and (7-28) into (7-26), we get

$$\sum_i m_i\ddot{\mathbf{r}}_i \cdot \frac{\partial\mathbf{r}_i}{\partial q_j} = \sum_i \left[\frac{d}{dt}\left(m_i\dot{\mathbf{r}}_i \cdot \frac{\partial\dot{\mathbf{r}}_i}{\partial\dot{q}_j} \right) - m_i\dot{\mathbf{r}}_i \cdot \frac{\partial\dot{\mathbf{r}}_i}{\partial q_j} \right]$$

$$= \frac{d}{dt}\left[\frac{\partial}{\partial\dot{q}_j}\left(\sum_i \tfrac{1}{2}m_i\dot{r}_i^2 \right) \right] - \frac{\partial}{\partial q_j}\left(\sum_i \tfrac{1}{2}m_i\dot{r}_i^2 \right)$$

$$= \frac{d}{dt}\left(\frac{\partial T}{\partial\dot{q}_j} \right) - \frac{\partial T}{\partial q_j} \qquad (7\text{-}29)$$

after using (6-24) in order to introduce the kinetic energy T. As a result, (7-25) can be written

$$\sum_i \dot{\mathbf{p}}_i \cdot \delta\mathbf{r}_i = \sum_j \left[\frac{d}{dt}\left(\frac{\partial T}{\partial\dot{q}_j} \right) - \frac{\partial T}{\partial q_j} \right] \delta q_j \qquad (7\text{-}30)$$

so that, when (7-19) and (7-30) are substituted into (7-15), we obtain

$$\sum_{j=1}^n \left[\frac{d}{dt}\left(\frac{\partial T}{\partial\dot{q}_j} \right) - \frac{\partial T}{\partial q_j} - Q_j \right] \delta q_j = 0 \qquad (7\text{-}31)$$

For a holonomic system, the δq_j are all independent; this means that (7-31) cannot be generally always zero unless the coefficient of each δq_j is independently zero. Thus we get the n equations

$$\frac{d}{dt}\left(\frac{\partial T}{\partial\dot{q}_j} \right) - \frac{\partial T}{\partial q_j} = Q_j \qquad (7\text{-}32)$$

These equations are valid whether the applied forces are conservative or non-conservative.

Now suppose the forces are conservative and thus derivable from the potential energy V so that

$$F_{ix} = -\frac{\partial V}{\partial x_i}, \quad F_{iy} = -\frac{\partial V}{\partial y_i}, \quad F_{iz} = -\frac{\partial V}{\partial z_i} \qquad (7\text{-}33)$$

If we substitute (7-33) into (7-20), we obtain

$$Q_j = -\sum_i \left(\frac{\partial V}{\partial x_i}\frac{\partial x_i}{\partial q_j} + \frac{\partial V}{\partial y_i}\frac{\partial y_i}{\partial q_j} + \frac{\partial V}{\partial z_i}\frac{\partial z_i}{\partial q_j} \right) = -\frac{\partial V}{\partial q_j} \qquad (7\text{-}34)$$

and (7-33) can be written

$$\frac{d}{dt}\left(\frac{\partial T}{\partial \dot{q}_j} \right) - \frac{\partial (T - V)}{\partial q_j} = 0 \qquad (7\text{-}35)$$

Since V can be a function of position only, and thus is independent of the generalized velocities $\dot{q}_j$, we must have

$$\frac{\partial V}{\partial \dot{q}_j} = 0 \qquad (7\text{-}36)$$

The time derivative of (7-36) will also be zero, and we can add this to (7-35) to get

$$\frac{d}{dt}\left[\frac{\partial (T - V)}{\partial \dot{q}_j} \right] - \frac{\partial (T - V)}{\partial q_j} = 0 \qquad (7\text{-}37)$$

If we define the *Lagrangian function* L by

$$L = L(q_1, \ldots, q_n, \dot{q}_1, \ldots, \dot{q}_n) = T - V \qquad (7\text{-}38)$$

then we can write the n equations (7-37) as

$$\frac{d}{dt}\left(\frac{\partial L}{\partial \dot{q}_j} \right) - \frac{\partial L}{\partial q_j} = 0 \qquad (7\text{-}39)$$

which are known as *Lagrange's equations of motion* for conservative, holonomic systems.

We should remember that Lagrange's equations are simply Newton's laws of motion ($\mathbf{F}_i = m_i\mathbf{a}_i$) expressed in terms of generalized coordinates; consequently, we have added nothing new to mechanics, but we have expressed the basic results in a more convenient form. One of the principal advantages of (7-39) is that we deal only with the *scalar* quantities T and V, rather than with vector forces and accelerations.

Lagrange's equations (7-39) can be used when the forces can be derived from a potential energy V. If they cannot, one can always go back to the equations (7-32). We now want to illustrate the procedures followed in the use of Lagrange's equations by considering a few specific examples.

7-4 Examples of Lagrangian methods

Linear harmonic oscillator

From (4-15) and (5-3), we have

$$T = \tfrac{1}{2}m\dot{x}^2, \quad V = \tfrac{1}{2}kx^2 \tag{7-40}$$

so that (7-38) becomes

$$L = L(x, \dot{x}) = \tfrac{1}{2}m\dot{x}^2 - \tfrac{1}{2}kx^2 \tag{7-41}$$

Since there is only one degree of freedom, the single Lagrangian equation of motion (7-39) becomes

$$\frac{d}{dt}\left(\frac{\partial L}{\partial \dot{x}}\right) - \frac{\partial L}{\partial x} = 0 = \frac{d}{dt}(m\dot{x}) - (-kx) = m\ddot{x} + kx \tag{7-42}$$

which is, of course, exactly the equation of motion (5-7) which we have already studied.

Particle moving near the surface of the earth

We use rectangular coordinates and let the z axis be along the upward vertical direction. From (4-15), the kinetic energy is

$$T = \tfrac{1}{2}m(\dot{x}^2 + \dot{y}^2 + \dot{z}^2) \tag{7-43}$$

The only applied force we consider is the weight of the body, w, which is in the negative z direction so that $F_x = F_y = 0$, $F_z = -w$. It is found that all bodies have the same acceleration g when falling freely near the surface of the earth where, to a good approximation, the value of g is 9.8 meters/second^2 = 980 centimeters/second^2 and is approximately constant. Thus, for this special case, (4-1) becomes

$$\text{Weight} = w = mg \tag{7-44}$$

in terms of magnitudes. Since $F_z = -mg = -dV/dz$, we see that the gravitational potential energy for a particle near the surface of the earth is

$$V = mgz \tag{7-45}$$

where we have set the additive constant equal to zero.

When (7-43) and (7-45) are substituted into (7-38), we obtain

$$L = \tfrac{1}{2}m(\dot{x}^2 + \dot{y}^2 + \dot{z}^2) - mgz \qquad (7\text{-}46)$$

and the equations of motion

$$\frac{d}{dt}\left(\frac{\partial L}{\partial \dot{x}}\right) - \frac{\partial L}{\partial x} = 0, \quad \frac{d}{dt}\left(\frac{\partial L}{\partial \dot{y}}\right) - \frac{\partial L}{\partial y} = 0, \quad \frac{d}{dt}\left(\frac{\partial L}{\partial \dot{z}}\right) - \frac{\partial L}{\partial z} = 0$$

become

$$\ddot{x} = 0, \quad \ddot{y} = 0, \quad \ddot{z} = -g \qquad (7\text{-}47)$$

Atwood's machine

This system consists of two masses, m_1 and m_2, suspended over a massless pulley of radius a and connected by a flexible string of constant length as shown in Fig. 7-3. The configuration clearly can be specified by the two coordinates z_1 and z_2. There is an equation of constraint for this system; it is given by

$$z_1 + z_2 + \pi a = l \qquad (7\text{-}48)$$

where l is the constant length of the string. Therefore this is a holonomic system of one degree of freedom. As a generalized coordinate, we take z_1; we can always find z_2 from (7-48) to be

$$z_2 = l - \pi a - z_1$$

so that

$$\dot{z}_2 = -\dot{z}_1, \quad \ddot{z}_2 = -\ddot{z}_1 \qquad (7\text{-}49)$$

The kinetic energy is given by

$$T = \tfrac{1}{2}m_1\dot{z}_1^2 + \tfrac{1}{2}m_2\dot{z}_2^2 = \tfrac{1}{2}(m_1 + m_2)\dot{z}_1^2 \qquad (7\text{-}50)$$

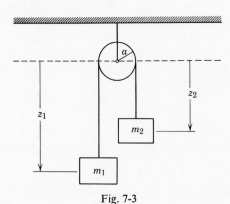

Fig. 7-3

with the use of (7-49). The only external forces are the weights of the two masses, and if we use (7-45) and remember that our z coordinates are measured *downward* here, we find, with the aid of (7-48), that

$$V = -m_1 g z_1 - m_2 g z_2 = -(m_1 - m_2)g z_1 + V_0 \qquad (7\text{-}51)$$

where

$$V_0 = -g m_2(l - \pi a) = \text{const.}$$

The Lagrangian then becomes

$$L = L(z_1, \dot{z}_1) = T - V = \tfrac{1}{2}(m_1 + m_2)\dot{z}_1{}^2 + (m_1 - m_2)g z_1 - V_0 \quad (7\text{-}52)$$

Since

$$\frac{\partial L}{\partial \dot{z}_1} = (m_1 + m_2)\dot{z}_1, \quad \frac{\partial L}{\partial z_1} = (m_1 - m_2)g$$

the equation of motion (7-39) becomes

$$\frac{d}{dt}\left[(m_1 + m_2)\dot{z}_1\right] - (m_1 - m_2)g = 0$$

or

$$\ddot{z}_1 = \frac{(m_1 - m_2)}{(m_1 + m_2)}\, g = -\ddot{z}_2 \qquad (7\text{-}53)$$

which is the standard result. We see from (7-53) that we will have equilibrium ($\ddot{z}_1 = 0$) when $m_1 = m_2$; this is certainly clear from the construction of the system.

Simple pendulum

This system is illustrated in Fig. 7-1. From the transformation equations (7-5), we find that

$$\dot{x} = -l\dot{\theta}\sin\theta, \quad \dot{y} = l\dot{\theta}\cos\theta$$

so that

$$T = \tfrac{1}{2}m(\dot{x}^2 + \dot{y}^2) = \tfrac{1}{2}m l^2 \dot{\theta}^2 \qquad (7\text{-}54)$$

The potential energy is

$$V = -mgx = -mgl\cos\theta \qquad (7\text{-}55)$$

[We can easily see that (7-55) is correct because it gives the correct force, $F_x = -dV/dx = mg$, for the vertical axis pointing down.] Therefore the Lagrangian function becomes

$$L = L(\theta, \dot{\theta}) = T - V = \tfrac{1}{2}m l^2 \dot{\theta}^2 + mgl\cos\theta \qquad (7\text{-}56)$$

and since

$$\frac{\partial L}{\partial \dot\theta} = ml^2\dot\theta, \quad \frac{\partial L}{\partial \theta} = -mgl \sin \theta$$

the equation of motion (7-39) becomes

$$\frac{d}{dt}(ml^2\dot\theta) - (-mgl \sin \theta) = 0$$

or

$$\ddot\theta + \left(\frac{g}{l}\right) \sin \theta = 0 \tag{7-57}$$

If the amplitude of the motion is small enough that $\sin \theta \simeq \theta$, then (7-57) becomes $\ddot\theta + (g/l)\theta = 0$, which is the harmonic oscillator equation of motion (5-8) with $\omega_0^2 = g/l$. Hence the pendulum angle will vary sinusoidally with the time, and, from (5-12), the period will be

$$\tau = \frac{2\pi}{\omega_0} = 2\pi \sqrt{\frac{l}{g}} \tag{7-58}$$

The general solution of (7-57) involves elliptic functions; we do not discuss this here but simply point out that, in general, the period depends on the amplitude and increases as the amplitude increases, although the effect is not large.

General analytical form of the kinetic energy when expressed in generalized coordinates

Basically, we have defined the kinetic energy only in rectangular coordinates, and we must use the transformation equations in order to express it in generalized coordinates. Using (6-24) and (7-18), we obtain

$$T = \sum_i \tfrac{1}{2}m_i \dot{\mathbf{r}}_i^2 = \sum_i \tfrac{1}{2}m_i \left(\sum_j \frac{\partial \mathbf{r}_i}{\partial q_j}\dot{q}_j\right) \cdot \left(\sum_k \frac{\partial \mathbf{r}_i}{\partial q_k}\dot{q}_k\right)$$

$$= \sum_j \sum_k \left(\sum_i \tfrac{1}{2}m_i \frac{\partial \mathbf{r}_i}{\partial q_j}\cdot\frac{\partial \mathbf{r}_i}{\partial q_k}\right)\dot{q}_j\dot{q}_k = \tfrac{1}{2}\sum_j \sum_k a_{jk}\dot{q}_j\dot{q}_k \tag{7-59}$$

where

$$a_{jk} = a_{jk}(q_1, \ldots, q_n) = \sum_i m_i \frac{\partial \mathbf{r}_i}{\partial q_j}\cdot\frac{\partial \mathbf{r}_i}{\partial q_k}$$

$$= \sum_i m_i \left(\frac{\partial x_i}{\partial q_j}\frac{\partial x_i}{\partial q_k} + \frac{\partial y_i}{\partial q_j}\frac{\partial y_i}{\partial q_k} + \frac{\partial z_i}{\partial q_j}\frac{\partial z_i}{\partial q_k}\right) \tag{7-60}$$

For the holonomous scleronomous systems we are considering, we see by (7-59) that the kinetic energy is always a homogeneous quadratic form in the generalized velocities, that is, in the $\dot{q}_j$. We shall make extensive use of this result later on.

Although the use of Lagrange's equations almost gives one a purely routine and mechanical way of deriving the equations of motion, it is still possible to make mistakes. The most common mistake made by beginning students is to get the wrong expression for the kinetic energy in terms of the generalized coordinates. The main reason for this is that they try to guess at the form, and their experience is too limited for this to be generally successful. The only *foolproof* method is to start with the undoubtedly correct expression for T in rectangular coordinates (6-24), and then to substitute the expressions for $\dot{x}_i$, $\dot{y}_i$, etc., obtained from the transformation equations; this is what we did for the simple pendulum to obtain (7-54). Sometimes this method is tedious, but it is guaranteed; an alternative method, of course, is to evaluate the a_{jk} from (7-60) and use (7-59).

As an example of the latter procedure, we can apply (7-60) to the simple pendulum. There is only one particle, and one generalized coordinate $q_1 = \theta$; the equations of transformation are given by (7-5). Therefore (7-60) reduces to

$$a_{\theta\theta} = m\left[\left(\frac{\partial x}{\partial \theta}\right)^2 + \left(\frac{\partial y}{\partial \theta}\right)^2\right] = m[(-l \sin \theta)^2 + (l \cos \theta)^2]$$

$$= ml^2 \tag{7-61}$$

and then (7-59) becomes $T = \frac{1}{2}a_{\theta\theta}\dot{\theta}^2 = \frac{1}{2}ml^2\dot{\theta}^2$, which is the same as (7-54).

7-5 Generalized momenta and conservation theorems

Up to this point, we have concerned ourselves mainly with obtaining the equations of motion, rather than with solving them once we have them. Many of the general remarks we previously made are applicable here, too. A system of n degrees of freedom will have n differential equations of motion, each of which is second order in the time. Because the solution of each equation will require two integrations, one will end up with a total of $2n$ constants of integration, which can be determined from the initial conditions, that is, the initial values of the $n\,q_j$ and the $n\,\dot{q}_j$. Most problems cannot be completely solved in terms of known functions, but often certain incomplete information about the mechanical properties of the system can be obtained fairly easily and is often of greater interest and importance, particularly in the study of atomic and molecular properties, than a complete knowledge of all the q_j as functions of t.

In many cases, one can quickly obtain a number of *first integrals* of the equations of motion. These are relations of the general type $f(q_1, q_2, \ldots, q_n, \dot{q}_1, \ldots, \dot{q}_n, t) = $ const., and they are first order differential equations. In fact, the conservation theorems for linear momentum, angular momentum, and energy which we obtained in Chapters 4 and 6 are exactly of this type, since they involve only first derivatives of the coordinates with respect to time. We now want to see how these conservation theorems, as well as first integrals in general, can be handled in our Lagrangian formulation.

Let us consider first a system of particles subject to conservative forces. If we use (7-36), we obtain, for example,

$$\frac{\partial L}{\partial \dot{x}_l} = \frac{\partial (T - V)}{\partial \dot{x}_l} = \frac{\partial T}{\partial \dot{x}_l} = \frac{\partial}{\partial \dot{x}_l} \sum_i \tfrac{1}{2} m_i (\dot{x}_i^2 + \dot{y}_i^2 + \dot{z}_i^2)$$

$$= m_l \dot{x}_l = p_{lx}$$

where p_{lx} is the x component of the linear momentum of the lth particle. This result immediately suggests a generalization of the concept of momentum.

The *generalized momentum* associated with the generalized coordinate q_j is written p_j and defined by

$$p_j = \frac{\partial L}{\partial \dot{q}_j} \tag{7-62}$$

Often p_j is called the canonical momentum or conjugate momentum. We also see that, if q_j is not a rectangular coordinate, then p_j need not even have the dimensions of a linear momentum.

Example. Simple Pendulum. We find from (7-56) and (7-62) that

$$p_\theta = \frac{\partial L}{\partial \dot{\theta}} = m l^2 \dot{\theta} \tag{7-63}$$

For this example, p_θ is the angular momentum of the particle since $\dot{\theta}$ is the angular velocity and, therefore, $p_\theta = ml(l\dot{\theta}) = mlv = |\mathbf{r} \times m\mathbf{v}| = |\mathbf{l}|$, according to (6-11).

If the Lagrangian does not contain a given coordinate q_j (although it may contain $\dot{q}_j$), then q_j is said to be *cyclic* or *ignorable*. As an immediate consequence, we see that, if q_j is cyclic, then $\partial L/\partial q_j = 0$ and (7-39) becomes

$$\frac{d}{dt}\left(\frac{\partial L}{\partial \dot{q}_j}\right) = \frac{dp_j}{dt} = 0$$

so that

$$p_j = \text{const.} \qquad (7\text{-}64)$$

In (7-64), we have a general conservation theorem: *The generalized momentum conjugate to a cyclic coordinate is conserved.* Or, in other words, for each cyclic coordinate, the corresponding generalized momentum is one of the first integrals of the motion.

It is not completely evident at this point that there is any connection at all between (7-64) and our previous discussion of special conservation theorems, and the additional question naturally arises about what general properties of a system lead to some coordinate being cyclic. It would take us somewhat far afield to discuss this point in great detail, but, in general terms, the existence of cyclic coordinates is closely related to the *symmetry properties* of the system. As an example to show how this comes about, let us suppose that our system is completely invariant to a translation along the x axis of a rectangular coordinate system; by this we mean that the whole problem is independent of the particular value of x and is completely unaffected by a change in x. This can only mean that x cannot appear in the mechanical description of the system, for, if it did, the particular numerical value of x would make a difference, contrary to our assumption. Thus x is a cyclic coordinate, $-\partial V/\partial x = 0 = F_x$, and the total x component of the linear momentum is constant as stated after (6-10). In short, if a *translation* of a system along a given coordinate leaves the whole problem unaltered, that coordinate is cyclic, and the component of the total linear momentum along that direction is conserved. Similarly, it can be shown that, if the change in a given generalized coordinate corresponds to a rotation about some axis, and if the system is unchanged by such a rotation, the corresponding coordinate is cyclic and the component of the total angular momentum along the axis of rotation is conserved.

The conservation theorem which we have not yet considered is that of conservation of energy for conservative systems. Since L is a function of the q_j and $\dot{q}_j$ and is otherwise independent of the time, we obtain

$$\frac{dL}{dt} = \sum_j \frac{\partial L}{\partial q_j}\frac{dq_j}{dt} + \sum_j \frac{\partial L}{\partial \dot{q}_j}\frac{d\dot{q}_j}{dt} \qquad (7\text{-}65)$$

If we substitute $\partial L/\partial q_j$, as obtained from (7-39), into (7-65), we get

$$\frac{dL}{dt} = \sum_j \left[\frac{d}{dt}\left(\frac{\partial L}{\partial \dot{q}_j}\right)\dot{q}_j + \frac{\partial L}{\partial \dot{q}_j}\frac{d\dot{q}_j}{dt} \right] = \sum_j \frac{d}{dt}\left(\dot{q}_j \frac{\partial L}{\partial \dot{q}_j}\right)$$

so that

$$\frac{d}{dt}\left(\sum_j \dot{q}_j \frac{\partial L}{\partial \dot{q}_j} - L\right) = \frac{d}{dt}\left(\sum_j \dot{q}_j p_j - L\right) = 0$$

and therefore

$$h = \sum_j \dot{q}_j p_j - L = \text{const.} \tag{7-66}$$

Thus the quantity h is one of the first integrals of the motion, and we now want to show that it is numerically equal to the total energy.

For conservative systems,

$$p_j = \frac{\partial L}{\partial \dot{q}_j} = \frac{\partial T}{\partial \dot{q}_j}$$

so that (7-66) can also be written

$$h = \sum_j \dot{q}_j \frac{\partial T}{\partial \dot{q}_j} - L \tag{7-67}$$

We have also seen in (7-59) that T is a homogeneous quadratic function of the generalized velocities, and therefore

$$\frac{\partial T}{\partial \dot{q}_j} = \tfrac{1}{2} \sum_k a_{jk} \dot{q}_k + \tfrac{1}{2} \sum_k a_{kj} \dot{q}_k = \sum_k a_{jk} \dot{q}_k \tag{7-68}$$

since $a_{jk} = a_{kj}$, according to (7-60) and (1-8). Therefore

$$\sum_j \dot{q}_j \frac{\partial T}{\partial \dot{q}_j} = \sum_j \sum_k a_{jk} \dot{q}_j \dot{q}_k = 2T$$

so that (7-67) becomes

$$h = 2T - L = 2T - (T - V) = T + V \tag{7-69}$$

and therefore h equals the total energy (6-37) and is conserved, according to (7-67).

In a sense, we can also see that the conservation of total energy, from the point of view of our general momentum conservation theorem (7-64), indicates that the energy is essentially the generalized momentum conjugate to the time, since the time did not explicitly appear in L and hence could be thought of as being cyclic. This idea plays an important role in more advanced formulations of mechanics and is also of great importance in the development and application of quantum mechanics and atomic theory.

Exercises

7-1. A more elaborate Atwood's machine is constructed by passing a string of length l_1 over a massless pulley and hanging a mass m_1 on one end of the string and a pulley of mass m_2 (but negligible moment of inertia) on the other end. Then a string of length l_2 is passed over the second pulley, and masses m_3 and m_4 are fastened to its ends. Show that this system has two degrees of freedom, and find the Lagrangian and Lagrange's equation of motion. Under what conditions will m_1 be in equilibrium?

7-2. A bead of mass m is constrained to slide on a smooth wire which has the shape of a parabola in the xy plane and has its axis in the vertical direction. What is (are) the equation(s) of constraint? How many degrees of freedom does this system have? Find the Lagrangian and the Lagrange equation(s) of motion.

7-3. Find the Lagrangian and Lagrange equations of motion of the double pendulum shown in Fig. 7-4. Assume that the masses of the rods can be neglected, that the motion of both pendulums is confined to the same vertic plane, and that the only external forces acting are the weights of m_1 and m_2.

7-4. A particle of mass m moves in three dimensions. Show that, if the position is described by the spherical coordinate system of Fig. 18-4b, the kinetic energy is given by $T = \frac{1}{2}m(\dot{r}^2 + r^2\dot{\theta}^2 + r^2\sin^2\theta\dot{\varphi}^2)$. Find the Lagrange equations of motion if $V = V(t, \theta, \varphi)$.

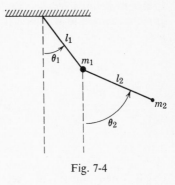

Fig. 7-4

8 Two bodies with central forces

As an example of the use of Lagrange's equations, we shall consider the important general problem in which our system consists of two particles of masses m_1 and m_2, which form a conservative system with potential energy V. We shall assume to begin with that V depends only on the separation between the particles; that is, $V = V(\mathbf{r}_1 - \mathbf{r}_2) = V(\mathbf{r})$. We shall show first that this can always be reduced to a simpler problem.

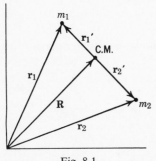

Fig. 8-1

8-1 The equivalent one-body problem

Our system of two particles has six degrees of freedom. Let us choose them to be the three components of $\mathbf{R}$, the position vector of the center of mass, and the three components of $\mathbf{r}$. The relations among the various coordinates are illustrated in Fig. 8-1, where $\mathbf{r}$ is the vector which would go from m_2 to m_1 if it were drawn in.

From the figure, we see that

$$\mathbf{r}_1 = \mathbf{R} + \mathbf{r}_1', \quad \mathbf{r}_2 = \mathbf{R} + \mathbf{r}_2' \tag{8-1}$$

where the primed vectors are the position vectors with respect to the center of mass and are also shown in Fig. 8-1. Therefore

$$\mathbf{r} = \mathbf{r}_1 - \mathbf{r}_2 = \mathbf{r}_1' - \mathbf{r}_2' \tag{8-2}$$

Also from the definition of the center of mass [compare the remark after (6-20)], we have

$$m_1\mathbf{r}_1' + m_2\mathbf{r}_2' = 0 \tag{8-3}$$

so that

$$\mathbf{r}_1' = -\left(\frac{m_2}{m_1}\right)\mathbf{r}_2' \tag{8-4}$$

which, when substituted into (8-2), gives

$$\mathbf{r} = \mathbf{r}_1' + \left(\frac{m_1}{m_2}\right)\mathbf{r}_1' = \frac{m_1 + m_2}{m_2}\mathbf{r}_1'$$

If we solve this for $\mathbf{r}_1'$ and use (8-4), we finally obtain

$$\mathbf{r}_1' = \left(\frac{m_2}{m_1 + m_2}\right)\mathbf{r} \quad \text{and} \quad \mathbf{r}_2' = -\left(\frac{m_1}{m_1 + m_2}\right)\mathbf{r} \tag{8-5}$$

Thus we can locate the particles if we know $\mathbf{R}$ and $\mathbf{r}$, for, when (8-5) and (8-1) are combined, we get

$$\mathbf{r}_1 = \mathbf{R} + \left(\frac{m_2}{m_1 + m_2}\right)\mathbf{r}, \quad \mathbf{r}_2 = \mathbf{R} - \left(\frac{m_1}{m_1 + m_2}\right)\mathbf{r} \tag{8-6}$$

The kinetic energy is obtained from (6-26) and is

$$T = \tfrac{1}{2}(m_1 + m_2)\dot{\mathbf{R}}^2 + \tfrac{1}{2}m_1\dot{\mathbf{r}}_1'^2 + \tfrac{1}{2}m_2\dot{\mathbf{r}}_2'^2 \tag{8-7}$$

We can express T in terms of our chosen variables by differentiating (8-5) and substituting into (8-7); the result is

$$T = \tfrac{1}{2}M\dot{\mathbf{R}}^2 + \tfrac{1}{2}m\dot{\mathbf{r}}^2 \tag{8-8}$$

where $M = m_1 + m_2$ is the total mass and where m is given by

$$m = \frac{m_1 m_2}{m_1 + m_2} \quad \text{or} \quad \frac{1}{m} = \frac{1}{m_1} + \frac{1}{m_2} \tag{8-9}$$

and is called the *reduced mass*.

The Lagrangian is therefore found from (7-38) and (8-8) to be

$$L = \tfrac{1}{2}M\dot{\mathbf{R}}^2 + \tfrac{1}{2}m\dot{\mathbf{r}}^2 - V(\mathbf{r}) \tag{8-10}$$

We see that the three components of **R** do not appear in L and are therefore cyclic. Hence the components of momentum conjugate to **R** are constant, and thus the center of mass of the system has a constant velocity $\mathbf{V_0} = \dot{\mathbf{R}}$ and therefore

$$\mathbf{R} = \mathbf{V_0}t + \mathbf{R_0} \tag{8-11}$$

where the constant $\mathbf{R_0}$ is the location of the center of mass at $t = 0$.

We see from (7-39) and (8-10) that the Lagrangian equations of motion for the components of **r** will not contain **R** or $\dot{\mathbf{R}}$. Since we already know the solution (8-11) for **R**, we can therefore drop (ignore) from (8-10) the term involving $\dot{\mathbf{R}}$ so that our effective Lagrangian is simply

$$L = L(\mathbf{r}, \dot{\mathbf{r}}) = \tfrac{1}{2}m\dot{\mathbf{r}}^2 - V(\mathbf{r}) \tag{8-12}$$

Thus the whole problem is exactly the same as that of a single particle of mass m moving at a distance **r** from a fixed center of force which gives rise to the potential energy $V(\mathbf{r})$. In other words, we can always reduce this type of two-body problem to the equivalent one of the motion of a single particle about a fixed force center.

8-2 Central forces

We now assume that V depends only on the magnitude of **r**, i.e., $V = V(|\mathbf{r}|) = V(r)$. Then the only force component is along the direction of **r** and has the magnitude

$$f(r) = -\frac{dV}{dr} \tag{8-13}$$

Therefore we can also write

$$\mathbf{F} = f(r)\hat{\mathbf{r}} = f(r)\left(\frac{\mathbf{r}}{r}\right) = m\ddot{\mathbf{r}} \tag{8-14}$$

Taking the cross product of **r** with (8-14), using (1-15) and (6-11), we obtain

$$m(\mathbf{r} \times \ddot{\mathbf{r}}) = 0 = \frac{d}{dt}(\mathbf{r} \times m\dot{\mathbf{r}}) = \frac{d\mathbf{l}}{dt} \tag{8-15}$$

so that the angular momentum **l** is constant. Thus **l** is a vector fixed in space, and **r** is always perpendicular to it. In other words, for central forces, the *orbit always lies in a plane* which is perpendicular to the fixed direction of the angular momentum.

It will be convenient to use the polar coordinates r and θ to describe the particle's position in this plane. We shall then have

$$x = r \cos \theta, \quad y = r \sin \theta \tag{8-16}$$

$$\dot{x} = r \cos \theta - r\dot{\theta} \sin \theta, \quad \dot{y} = \dot{r} \sin \theta + r\dot{\theta} \cos \theta \tag{8-17}$$

so that $\frac{1}{2}m(\dot{x}^2 + \dot{y}^2) = \frac{1}{2}m(\dot{r}^2 + r^2\dot{\theta}^2)$ and (8-12) becomes

$$L = \frac{1}{2}m(\dot{r}^2 + r^2\dot{\theta}^2) - V(r) \tag{8-18}$$

We see that θ is a cyclic coordinate and therefore, by (7-64), its conjugate momentum is constant:

$$p_\theta = \frac{\partial L}{\partial \dot{\theta}} = mr^2\dot{\theta} = l \tag{8-19}$$

In fact, the equations of motion obtained from (7-39) are

$$\frac{d}{dt}(m\dot{r}) - \left(mr\dot{\theta}^2 - \frac{dV}{dr}\right) = 0 \tag{8-20}$$

$$\frac{d}{dt}(mr^2\dot{\theta}) = 0 \tag{8-21}$$

The second of these equations, (8-21), immediately gives (8-19).

Equation (8-21) can also be written

$$\frac{d}{dt}(\tfrac{1}{2}r^2\dot{\theta}) = 0 \tag{8-22}$$

to which we can give an interesting geometrical interpretation. From Fig. 8-2, we see that, if dA is the area swept out by the radius vector in a time dt, $dA = \frac{1}{2}r(r\,d\theta)$; then the rate at which the radius vector sweeps out area is

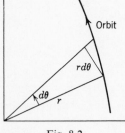

Fig. 8-2

$$\frac{dA}{dt} = \frac{1}{2}r^2\dot{\theta} = \frac{l}{2m} = \text{const.} \tag{8-23}$$

Therefore conservation of angular momentum is equivalent to a constant areal velocity dA/dt. This result (8-23) is also known as *Kepler's second law of planetary motion*; we see, however, that it holds for any central force, and not only for the inverse square law characteristic of planetary motion.

If we use (8-13), we can write (8-20) as

$$m\ddot{r} - mr\dot{\theta}^2 = f(r) \tag{8-24}$$

We can eliminate $\dot{\theta}$ from (8-24) by using (8-19); the result is

$$m\ddot{r} - \frac{l^2}{mr^3} = f(r) = -\frac{dV}{dr} \tag{8-25}$$

which is a second order differential equation for $r(t)$. We can also write (8-25) as

$$m\ddot{r} = -\frac{d}{dr}\left(V + \frac{l^2}{2mr^2}\right) \tag{8-26}$$

Multiplying both sides of (8-26) by $\dot{r}$, we obtain

$$m\dot{r}\ddot{r} = \frac{d}{dt}(\tfrac{1}{2}m\dot{r}^2) = -\frac{d}{dr}\left(V + \frac{l^2}{2mr^2}\right)\frac{dr}{dt} = -\frac{d}{dt}\left(V + \frac{l^2}{2mr^2}\right)$$

so that

$$\frac{d}{dt}\left(\tfrac{1}{2}m\dot{r}^2 + \frac{l^2}{2mr^2} + V\right) = 0$$

or

$$\tfrac{1}{2}m\dot{r}^2 + \frac{l^2}{2mr^2} + V = \text{const.} = E \tag{8-27}$$

We can show that E is actually the total energy by using (8-19) to rewrite the middle term of (8-27) as $\tfrac{1}{2}mr^2\dot{\theta}^2$ so that $E = T + V$. Thus, in (8-27), we have again proved the conservation of energy directly from the equations of motion.

At this point, we are able to write the complete formal solution to the problem. We can solve (8-27) for

$$\dot{r} = \frac{dr}{dt} = \left[\frac{2}{m}\left(E - V - \frac{l^2}{2mr^2}\right)\right]^{\frac{1}{2}}$$

and therefore we have

$$dt = \frac{dr}{\left[\dfrac{2}{m}\left(E - V - \dfrac{l^2}{2mr^2}\right)\right]^{\frac{1}{2}}}$$

so that, upon integration, we get

$$t = \int_{r_0}^{r} \frac{dr}{\left[\dfrac{2}{m}\left(E - V - \dfrac{l^2}{2mr^2}\right)\right]^{\frac{1}{2}}} \tag{8-28}$$

where $r = r_0$ when $t = 0$. After performing the integration in (8-28), we can then in principle solve for r as a function of time, i.e., $r = r(t)$.

Once $r(t)$ has been determined, we can find $\theta(t)$ from (8-19) because we can integrate $d\theta = (l/mr^2)\,dt$ to obtain

$$\theta = \frac{l}{m}\int_0^t \frac{dt}{r^2(t)} + \theta_0 \tag{8-29}$$

where θ_0 is the value of θ at $t = 0$.

Thus the solution of our problem has been reduced to the integrations shown in (8-28) and (8-29), which can be done in principle once the law of force, i.e., the form of $V(r)$, has been given. These results are stated in terms of the four constants of integration, l, E, r_0, and θ_0, which have entered into the description of the problem in quite a natural way and hence are more appropriate than those we might have originally expected to appear, namely, r_0, θ_0, $\dot{r}_0$, and $\dot{\theta}_0$.

8-3   Equivalent one-dimensional problem

Although (8-28) and (8-29) do represent the complete solution, it is not always convenient to use them in particular practical problems, and it will be useful to discuss the whole problem from a somewhat different point of view. Before we do this, and before we also discuss a particular law of force, let us see what we can learn about some of the general features of the motion; the qualitative graphical method briefly used in Sec. 5-1 will be useful for this purpose.

We can write (8-25) and (8-26) as

$$m\ddot{r} = -\frac{d}{dr}\left(V + \frac{l^2}{2mr^2}\right) = f + \frac{l^2}{mr^3} \tag{8-30}$$

which is exactly the form we would have for the *one-dimensional* motion of m if it were subject to the "force"

$$f' = f + \frac{l^2}{mr^3} \tag{8-31}$$

since then (8-30) would be written $m\ddot{r} = f'$. The term added to f in (8-31) to get f' can be easily interpreted: If we use (8-19), we can write this term as $mr\dot{\theta}^2 = mr\omega^2$, where ω is the magnitude of the angular velocity of the particle about the origin. The last form can be recognized as a common way of writing the "centrifugal force," which enters into the one-dimensional equation of motion (8-30) as a result of our going over into this moving coordinate system whose rotation prevents it from being an inertial system. We shall give a more systematic discussion of these fictitious forces later.

We see also that the effective force f' can be written in terms of an effective potential energy $V'(r)$:

$$f' = -\frac{dV'}{dr} \ ; \quad V'(r) = V(r) + \frac{l^2}{2mr^2} \tag{8-32}$$

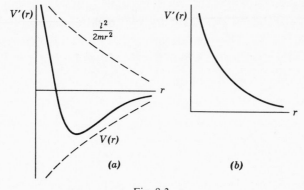

Fig. 8-3

Thus, in this coordinate system, the potential energy has an additional term added to it as a result of the angular motion. We can also write the total energy E as given in (8-27) as

$$E = \tfrac{1}{2}m\dot{r}^2 + V'(r) \tag{8-33}$$

This equation has the form appropriate to a one-dimensional motion under the influence of the effective potential energy $V'(r)$.

Depending on $V(r)$, the shape of the curve $V'(r)$ vs. r can have various forms; two of the more important types are shown in Fig. 8-3. If $V'(r)$ has the form shown in (a), i.e., if it has a minimum, there are various possibilities for the type of motion, depending on the value of E. If E is negative, then we shall have bound, periodic motion since the values of r will be restricted to those regions for which $V'(r) \leqslant E$; this does not necessarily mean that the particle will move in a closed orbit, only that the motion will have r periodic. If $E \geqslant 0$, and if the particle is originally coming in toward the origin, it will come in until it reaches the point where $V'(r) = E$, reverse its motion, and go back out to infinity; this is clearly a non-periodic motion.

If $V'(r)$ has no minimum, as is illustrated in Fig. 8-3b, then $E \geqslant 0$ always, and one can never obtain periodic motion in r. This graphical method in general provides a valuable way of learning qualitative features of the motion; we recall that we used it previously to discover that the motion of the linear oscillator was periodic.

8-4 Equation of the orbit

Rather than being interested in knowing the values of $r(t)$ and $\theta(t)$ as obtained from (8-28) and (8-29), we more often want to know the equation of the orbit, i.e., the relation between r and θ from which the time has been eliminated and which gives us the spatial path followed by the particle. Our purpose is now to find a way of obtaining $r = r(\theta)$ directly; we shall do this by going back to the equations of motion.

It is convenient to introduce the new variable

$$u = \frac{1}{r} \tag{8-34}$$

When (8-34) is substituted into (8-19), we obtain

$$\dot{\theta} = u^2 l/m \tag{8-35}$$

which can be used to eliminate the time from (8-25). We see first of all that, if we use (8-35), we can get

$$\frac{dr}{dt} = \frac{d}{dt}\frac{1}{u} = -\frac{1}{u^2}\frac{du}{dt} = -\frac{1}{u^2}\frac{du}{d\theta}\frac{d\theta}{dt} = -\frac{l}{m}\frac{du}{d\theta} \tag{8-36}$$

If we differentiate (8-36) and use (8-35) once more, we have

$$\frac{d^2r}{dt^2} = -\frac{l}{m}\frac{d^2u}{d\theta^2}\frac{d\theta}{dt} = -\left(\frac{lu}{m}\right)^2\frac{d^2u}{d\theta^2} \tag{8-37}$$

If we now substitute (8-34) and (8-37) into (8-25), we obtain

$$\frac{d^2u}{d\theta^2} + u = -\frac{m}{l^2u^2}f\left(\frac{1}{u}\right) \tag{8-38}$$

where $f(1/u)$ means that r has been replaced by $1/u$ wherever it occurs in the expression for f.

This result (8-38) is known as the *differential equation of the orbit*. We see that, in principle, once we know the law of force $f(1/u)$, we can integrate (8-38) to find $u = u(\theta)$, and thus $r = r(\theta)$, i.e., the equation of the orbit. The converse problem, that of finding the law of force by differentiating the equation of the orbit and using (8-38) to find f, is also quite important.

At this point, we have gone about as far as we conveniently can with making only general statements about motion under central forces, and now we want to discuss a particular case in some detail.

8-5 Inverse square law

The most important central force is the inverse square force; that is,

$$f(r) = -\frac{k}{r^2} \tag{8-39}$$

where $k = $ const. The corresponding potential energy can be written

$$V(r) = -\frac{k}{r} \tag{8-40}$$

For example, Newton first proposed that one can describe the interaction between two point masses m_1 and m_2 by saying that there is a gravitational force of attraction between them given by (8-39), in which the positive constant k is written

$$k = Gm_1m_2 \tag{8-41}$$

in terms of the universal gravitational constant $G = 6.67 \times 10^{-11}$ newton-(meter)^2/(kilogram)^2. Therefore (8-39) and (8-41) combined give the force law which we can use to describe planetary motion. Another important example of an inverse square force law is the static force between point electric charges; this will be discussed in detail in Chapter 19, but for now it suffices to say that this force is attractive (k positive) when charges of opposite sign are involved, and repulsive (k negative) when the charges have the same sign.

We find at once from (8-39) that $f(1/u) = -ku^2$; then (8-38) becomes

$$\frac{d^2u}{d\theta^2} + u = \frac{mk}{l^2} \tag{8-42}$$

and is just the type of inhomogeneous differential equation we studied in connection with the harmonic oscillator. A special solution of (8-42) is $u = mk/l^2$; therefore we can immediately write the general solution of (8-42):

$$u = \frac{1}{r} = \frac{mk}{l^2} + u' \cos(\theta - \theta') \tag{8-43}$$

where u' and θ' are constants. For simplicity, let us orient our coordinate system so that $\theta' = 0$. We see in fact that $\theta = \theta'$ or $\theta' + \pi$ results in a maximum or minimum value for r; thus θ' is one of the angles at which the orbit turns and is called a turning point. Therefore we can write (8-43)

$$\frac{1}{r} = \frac{mk}{l^2} + u' \cos\theta$$

or

$$r = \frac{(l^2/mk)}{1 + (u'l^2/mk)\cos\theta} \tag{8-44}$$

In order to identify our result (8-44), we can try to see if it coincides with the empirical result known as *Kepler's first law of planetary motion*: The orbits are conic sections (ellipses for the planets) with the center of

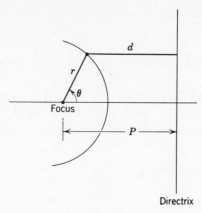

Directrix

Fig. 8-4

force at one of the foci. In order to do this, we shall have to digress a little in order to discuss conic sections and their equations in polar coordinates.

A conic section is defined as a curve such that the ratio of its distance from a fixed point to that from a fixed line is a constant. In terms of the distances shown in Fig. 8-4 from the fixed point (focus) and the fixed line (directrix), our definition becomes

$$\frac{r}{d} = \text{const.} = \epsilon = \text{eccentricity} \tag{8-45}$$

From the figure and (8-45) we see that

$$P = d + r \cos \theta = (r/\epsilon) + r \cos \theta$$

which, if we solve for r and let $p = \epsilon P$, becomes

$$r = \frac{p}{1 + \epsilon \cos \theta} \tag{8-46}$$

We see at once that our result (8-44) is of this form (8-46); therefore the orbit under an inverse square force is always a conic section.

We now want to consider some of the geometric properties of the conic sections and, in particular, their relation to the value of ϵ. In order to do this, it will be convenient to transform to rectangular coordinates with the origin at the focus, i.e., we set

$$x = r \cos \theta, \quad y = r \sin \theta \tag{8-47}$$

Substituting (8-47) into (8-46), we obtain $r + \epsilon x = p$, or $r = \sqrt{x^2 + y^2} = p - \epsilon x$, and, when we square both sides of this, we finally obtain

$$(1 - \epsilon^2)x^2 + 2p\epsilon x + y^2 = p^2 \tag{8-48}$$

If $\epsilon = 1$, (8-48) becomes

$$y^2 = -2px + p^2 \qquad (8\text{-}49)$$

which is the equation of a *parabola*.

By completing the square, one can also show that (8-48) can be put into the form

$$\frac{\left(x + \dfrac{p\epsilon}{1 - \epsilon^2}\right)^2}{\left(\dfrac{p}{1 - \epsilon^2}\right)^2} + \frac{y^2}{\dfrac{p^2}{1 - \epsilon^2}} = 1 \qquad (8\text{-}50)$$

If $\epsilon < 1$, (8-50) has the form

$$\frac{(x + x_0)^2}{a^2} + \frac{y^2}{b^2} = 1 \qquad (8\text{-}51)$$

with

$$a = \frac{p}{1 - \epsilon^2}, \quad b = \frac{p}{\sqrt{1 - \epsilon^2}}, \quad b = a\sqrt{1 - \epsilon^2} \qquad (8\text{-}52)$$

which is the equation of an *ellipse*. A special case of this occurs when $\epsilon = 0$ and the curve is then a *circle*.

If $\epsilon > 1$, (8-50) has the form

$$\frac{(x + x_0')^2}{a'^2} - \frac{y^2}{b'^2} = 1 \qquad (8\text{-}53)$$

with

$$a' = \frac{p}{\epsilon^2 - 1}, \quad b' = \frac{p}{\sqrt{\epsilon^2 - 1}}, \quad b' = a'\sqrt{\epsilon^2 - 1} \qquad (8\text{-}54)$$

which is the equation of a *hyperbola*.

We now want to use these results to learn what types of orbits are actually possible for inverse square forces. The equation of the orbit is given by (8-44) and (8-46), where

$$p = \frac{l^2}{mk}, \quad \epsilon = \frac{u'l^2}{mk} \qquad (8\text{-}55)$$

From the definition of ϵ given by (8-45), we must also have $\epsilon \geqslant 0$. We shall base our discussion on the fact that r *must be positive*, according to the way in which we derived (8-46).

Attractive force

Under this condition, $k > 0$ and therefore $p > 0$. It is then evident from (8-46) that the conditions $\epsilon < 1$ and $\epsilon = 1$ are possible since

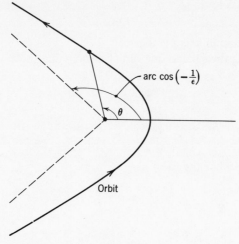

Fig. 8-5

$|\cos \theta| \leqslant 1$, so that r will be positive. Thus we can have both parabolic and elliptic orbits.

If $\epsilon > 1$, we must have $1 + \epsilon \cos \theta > 0$, or

$$-\frac{1}{\epsilon} < \cos \theta < 1$$

Here θ is restricted to the range

$$-\text{arc cos} \left(-\frac{1}{\epsilon}\right) < \theta < \text{arc cos} \left(-\frac{1}{\epsilon}\right) \tag{8-56}$$

and the orbit has the shape shown in Fig. 8-5. Thus we see that the hyperbolic orbit for attractive forces has the center of force at the interior focus.

Therefore, for attractive inverse square forces, all three types of orbits are possible.

Repulsive force

Under this condition, $k < 0$ and $p < 0$. Therefore $1 + \epsilon \cos \theta$ must always be negative. We see at once that this cannot be done for $\epsilon \leqslant 1$, because then $\epsilon \cos \theta \geqslant -1$ or $1 + \epsilon \cos \theta \geqslant 0$; therefore parabolic and elliptic orbits are not possible.

If $\epsilon > 1$, as it is for the hyperbola, we must have

$$-1 < \cos \theta < -\frac{1}{\epsilon}$$

in order to have $1 + \epsilon \cos \theta < 0$. Thus θ is restricted to the values in the range

$$\text{arc cos} \left(-\frac{1}{\epsilon} \right) < \theta < 2\pi - \text{arc cos} \left(-\frac{1}{\epsilon} \right) \qquad (8\text{-}57)$$

and the orbit has the shape shown in Fig. 8-6. Therefore, for repulsive inverse square forces, only hyperbolic orbits are possible, and the center of force lies at the exterior focus.

In order to tell which orbits arise in a given case, we must relate the geometric constants of the orbit to the dynamical constants of the motion. First, we shall find a relation between the energy and the eccentricity. If we substitute (8-40) into (8-27), we find that

$$E = \tfrac{1}{2} m \dot{r}^2 + \frac{l^2}{2mr^2} - \frac{k}{r} \qquad (8\text{-}58)$$

Since E is constant, we can evaluate it at any convenient point on the orbit; when r has its minimum value, $r_{\min}$, then the particle is turning around so that $\dot{r} = 0$. We also see from (8-46) and (8-55) that

$$r_{\min} = \frac{l^2}{mk(1 + \epsilon)}$$

so that

$$E = \frac{l^2}{2mr_{\min}^2} - \frac{k}{r_{\min}} = \frac{mk^2}{2l^2}(\epsilon^2 - 1) \qquad (8\text{-}59)$$

If we solve (8-59) for ϵ and substitute into (8-46), we obtain

$$\epsilon = \left(1 + \frac{2l^2 E}{mk^2} \right)^{1/2} \qquad (8\text{-}60)$$

$$r = \frac{l^2/mk}{1 + \left(1 + \dfrac{2l^2 E}{mk^2} \right)^{1/2} \cos \theta} \qquad (8\text{-}61)$$

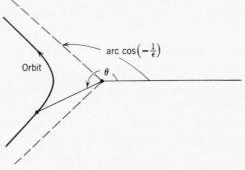

Fig. 8-6

Using (8-60) and the results obtained above, we can construct the following interesting table which relates the orbit type to the energy of the particle and thus to one of the initial features of the motion.

$$
\begin{aligned}
E > 0 \quad & \epsilon > 1 \quad & \text{hyperbola} \\
E = 0 \quad & \epsilon = 1 \quad & \text{parabola}
\end{aligned} \Bigg\} \text{ non-periodic}
$$

$$
E < 0 \quad \epsilon < 1 \quad \text{ellipse} \quad \} \text{ periodic}
$$

(The special case of the periodic circular orbit occurs when $E = -mk^2/2l^2$ and $\epsilon = 0$.) These results, of course, agree qualitatively with what we were able to say about the general features of the motion after a study of the curves of V' vs. r like those of Fig. 8-3.

Now let us restrict ourselves to the elliptic orbits; these are the ones which are of importance in the study of planetary motion, and in the Bohr theory of atomic structure. The semimajor axis of the ellipse is found from (8-52) and (8-55) to be

$$
a = \frac{l^2}{mk(1 - \epsilon^2)} \tag{8-62}
$$

If we solve (8-62) for $(1 - \epsilon^2)$ and substitute the result into (8-59), we find that

$$
E = -\frac{k}{2a} \tag{8-63}
$$

which is a simple relation between the energy and the geometric property of the orbit; (8-63) shows that all ellipses with the same major axis have the same energy.

If we use (8-23), we can easily calculate the period τ of the elliptic motion as the ratio of the total area of the ellipse to the rate of sweeping out area:

$$
\tau = \frac{\text{area}}{dA/dt} = \frac{\pi ab}{l/2m} = \frac{2\pi ma^2\sqrt{1 - \epsilon^2}}{l}
$$

and, if we square this equation and use (8-62), we find that

$$
\tau^2 = \frac{4\pi^2 m^2 a^4(1 - \epsilon^2)}{l^2} = \left(\frac{4\pi^2 m}{k}\right) a^3 \tag{8-64}
$$

This is known as *Kepler's third law*: The square of the period is proportional to the cube of the major axis and is independent of the minor axis. (Hyperbolic and parabolic orbits, of course, have infinite periods; we can also obtain this result from (8-64) in a crude way by letting $a \to \infty$.)

Exercises

8-1. Find the laws of force for which the following orbits are possible: $r = ae^{\alpha\theta}$, $r = a \cos \theta$, where a and α are constants.

8-2. Suppose a planet were suddenly stopped in its orbit, which we assume to be circular. Find how long it would take it to fall into the sun, and express the result in terms of the original period of the motion.

8-3. A comet travels in a parabolic orbit whose plane is the same as the plane of the earth's orbit, which we assume to be circular. The point of closest approach of the comet to the sun is at a distance from the sun equal to one third the radius of the earth's orbit. Show that the comet remains within the earth's orbit 74.5 days. (This problem can be worked in two ways.)

9 Rigid bodies

We have already defined a rigid body as a system of particles which are always separated from each other by constant distances. Thus we are neglecting the deformations which occur in all actual solids. In order to discuss the mechanics of a rigid body, we must have some means of describing its position and orientation. It is clear that, because of the large number of equations of constraint (7-2), the number of degrees of freedom of the rigid body will be much less than $3N$.

If we consider the situation illustrated in Fig. 9-1, it is evident that the position and orientation of the body can be completely specified by giving the coordinates of any *three* points which do not lie on the same straight line, that is, by giving the nine numbers x_1, y_1, z_1, x_2, y_2, z_2, x_3, y_3, z_3. In addition, the fact that the body is rigid provides us with three equations of constraint involving these quantities:

$$(x_1 - x_2)^2 + (y_1 - y_2)^2 + (z_1 - z_2)^2 = \text{const.}$$
$$(x_2 - x_3)^2 + (y_2 - y_3)^2 + (z_2 - z_3)^2 = \text{const.}$$
$$(x_3 - x_1)^2 + (y_3 - y_1)^2 + (z_3 - z_1)^2 = \text{const.}$$

Since three of the nine coordinates can always be calculated from these equations, once the rest are known, only six of them are independent; hence a rigid body has *six degrees of freedom*. This can be seen in another way. It would take three coordinates to locate a given point in the body (e.g., point 1 of Fig. 9-1); then it would require two direction cosines to specify the orientation of a line which is fixed in the body and passes through the given point (e.g., the line connecting 1 and 2); then it would require one more coordinate to give the angle of rotation of the body about this line (e.g., the angle of rotation of the plane formed by 1, 2, 3 about

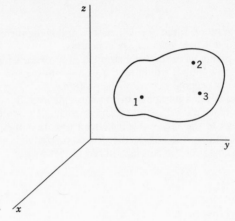

Fig. 9-1

the line from 1 to 2). The configuration of the rigid body would be completely specified by these six quantities, again showing that there are six degrees of freedom.

9-1 Euler's theorem

This theorem provides the basis for the description of the motion of a rigid body and says that the general displacement of a rigid body with one point fixed is a rotation about some line passing through the fixed point. We can prove this theorem with the aid of Fig. 9-2.

Let A and B be the initial positions of two points located in the rigid body, and let A' and B' be their final positions after the arbitrary displacement. The line $A'B'$ is the final position of the line AB; this line is also fixed in the body. We let O be the fixed point. Therefore OA and OB are the initial positions of two more lines which are fixed in the body, and OA' and OB' are their final positions. If we connect A with A', and B with B', the triangles OAA' and OBB' determine two planes. We construct the two planes N_1 and N_2 so that they are perpendicular to the planes OAA' and OBB' and, at the same time, N_1 bisects the angle AOA' while N_2 bisects the angle BOB'. The two planes N_1 and N_2 will intersect along some line OC.

Now we can say that, by construction, each point on N_1 is equidistant from A and A', and each point on N_2 is equidistant from B and B'. The line OC has the properties of both planes, and therefore each point on OC is equidistant from A and A' and from B and B'. Also, angle AOC = angle $A'OC$, and angle BOC = angle $B'OC$. Therefore the line OC stands in

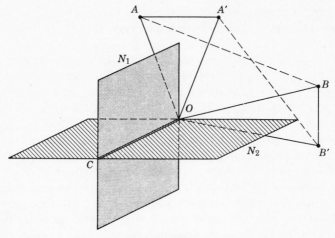

Fig. 9-2

exactly the same spatial relation to the system $OA'B'$ as it does to OAB; that is, the system $OABC$ itself has the properties of a rigid body. Therefore, when the initial system OAB is brought into the final system $OA'B'$, the line OC must remain unchanged, so that the displacement of the system is equivalent to a rotation about the fixed line OC drawn through the fixed point O. This proves the theorem.

When a rigid body is moving continuously about one of its points, which is fixed in space, the displacement from its position at a time t to its position at $t + \Delta t$ can, therefore, be obtained by rotating the body about some definite line through the fixed point. The limiting position of this line as $\Delta t \to 0$ is called the *instantaneous axis of rotation* of the body at the time t.

It is now a simple matter to prove *Chasles' theorem*: The most general displacement of a rigid body is a translation plus a rotation about some line. With the aid of Fig. 9-3, we can easily see that we can get from the

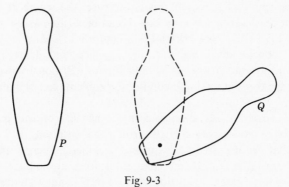

Fig. 9-3

configuration P to the configuration Q by first moving the body so that all the points move in parallel lines, and then rotating it about some appropriate line.

The form of Chasles' theorem makes one think that it might be possible to divide the problem of rigid body motion into two parts—one part dealing only with the translational motion, the other part being concerned solely with the rotational motion. If one point of the body is fixed, the division is automatic because there is only the rotational motion about the fixed point. However, a separation of the problem into translational and rotational parts is *often* possible even for the general case. We can see from some of our results how this can come about.

The six coordinates needed to describe the motion have already been discussed in a way which naturally suggests such a division, for it was pointed out that they can be so chosen that three of them are used to locate a point fixed in the body, while the other three can be angles used to describe the rotation about this point. If we choose the fixed point to be the center of mass, then we have seen that some of the dynamical properties are naturally divided. For example, we saw in (6-21) that the angular momentum is a sum of a contribution from the translational motion of the center of mass and one from the motion about the center of mass, so that the first term will involve only the center of mass coordinates and the second term only the rotation angles. Similarly, we found in (6-26) that the kinetic energy can be written as a sum of terms, one associated with the motion of the center of mass and the other with the motion about the center of mass.

The potential energy can often be divided into terms each of which involves only one of the sets of coordinates, the translational or the rotational; and, in fact, almost all the problems which can actually be solved will involve such a separation for the potential energy. For example, the gravitational potential energy will involve only the vertical coordinate locating the center of mass. If this is the case, the whole problem does divide, since the Lagrangian $L = T - V$ can be written as the sum of two parts, one involving only translational coordinates and one only the rotational coordinates, i.e., $L = L_{\text{trans}} + L_{\text{rot}}$. The Lagrangian equations of motion for one set of coordinates will not involve the other set; hence the translational and rotational problems can be independently considered.

Since we have already discussed many aspects of the translational problem, we can concentrate on the rotational motion; it is important therefore that we be able to express the kinetic energy and angular momentum for the motion about some point fixed in the body in terms of the variables describing the rotation, and we shall begin with the discussion of a concept which is very important for this purpose.

9-2   Angular velocity

At a given instant we can regard all the particles as rotating in circles about the instantaneous axis of rotation passing through the fixed point with the centers of the circles on this axis. Let ϕ be the angle giving the rotation about this axis, and let the rate at which it is changing be $\dot{\phi}$. We define a quantity $\boldsymbol{\omega}$ as having the magnitude $\omega = \dot{\phi}$ and the direction of the instantaneous axis of rotation; this direction is determined by the right-hand rule by which, if we curl the fingers of the right hand in the direction of the particle motion, the thumb points in the direction of $\boldsymbol{\omega}$, as illustrated in Fig. 9-4. This quantity $\boldsymbol{\omega}$ is called the *angular velocity*; it has a magnitude and a direction, and we now want to show that it is also a vector.

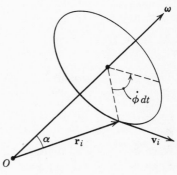

Fig. 9-4

If we choose the origin O at the fixed point, then the position vectors of the particles, $\mathbf{r}_i$, are constants with respect to the body. We see from Fig. 9-4 that the magnitude of the velocity of the ith particle is $|\mathbf{v}_i| = (r_i \sin \alpha)\dot{\phi} = \omega r_i \sin \alpha$, or

$$|\mathbf{v}_i| = |\boldsymbol{\omega} \times \mathbf{r}_i| \tag{9-1}$$

In other words, *if* we treat $\boldsymbol{\omega}$ as a vector in calculating its cross product with the vector $\mathbf{r}_i$, we see from Fig. 9-4 and (9-1) that we get the correct magnitude and direction of the vector $\mathbf{v}_i$ from

$$\mathbf{v}_i = \dot{\mathbf{r}}_i = \boldsymbol{\omega} \times \mathbf{r}_i \tag{9-2}$$

Now suppose we consider two angular velocities, $\boldsymbol{\omega}_1$ and $\boldsymbol{\omega}_2$. The velocity of the ith particle due to the first is $\mathbf{v}_1 = \boldsymbol{\omega}_1 \times \mathbf{r}_i$, and that due to the second is $\mathbf{v}_2 = \boldsymbol{\omega}_2 \times \mathbf{r}_i$. Since $\mathbf{v}_1$ and $\mathbf{v}_2$ are both vectors, the resultant velocity is given by the rules of vector addition as

$$\mathbf{v} = \mathbf{v}_1 + \mathbf{v}_2 = \boldsymbol{\omega}_1 \times \mathbf{r}_i + \boldsymbol{\omega}_2 \times \mathbf{r}_i = (\boldsymbol{\omega}_1 + \boldsymbol{\omega}_2) \times \mathbf{r}_i = \boldsymbol{\omega} \times \mathbf{r}_i \tag{9-3}$$

where we have replaced $\boldsymbol{\omega}_1 + \boldsymbol{\omega}_2$ by a resultant $\boldsymbol{\omega}$. Since the resultant vector $\mathbf{v}$ is obtained from the same cross-product form as in (9-2) but the resultant $\boldsymbol{\omega}$ is used, the angular velocities as we defined them obey the same law of addition as vectors and must be vectors themselves.

Since $\boldsymbol{\omega} = \boldsymbol{\omega}_1 + \boldsymbol{\omega}_2$, we also have

$$\boldsymbol{\omega}\, dt = \boldsymbol{\omega}_1\, dt + \boldsymbol{\omega}_2\, dt \tag{9-4}$$

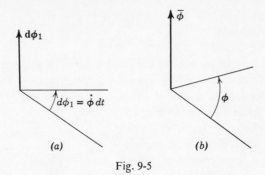

Fig. 9-5

As we can see in Fig. 9-5a, $\boldsymbol{\omega}_1 \, dt$ is the angular displacement $\mathbf{d\phi}_1$ when it is regarded as a directed quantity in the sense shown. Then (9-4) can be written

$$\mathbf{d\phi} = \mathbf{d\phi}_1 + \mathbf{d\phi}_2 \tag{9-5}$$

which shows that infinitesimal angular displacements as defined in this way also obey the vector law of addition and are therefore vectors.

It is an interesting and important fact that, although infinitesimal angular displacements are vectors, *finite* angular displacements are not vectors. We see from Fig. 9-5b that we can easily associate a directed quantity $\bar{\phi}$ with a finite angle of rotation ϕ; the magnitude of $\bar{\phi}$ can be set equal to the actual rotation angle ϕ, and its direction will be given by the familiar right-hand rule to be perpendicular to the plane formed by the two positions of the line which has been rotated through the angle ϕ. Now, if $\bar{\phi}$ were a vector, it would obey the parallelogram law of addition; a fundamental property of this law of addition of vectors is its commutative property (1-1), and hence the order of operation is immaterial. Thus, if $\bar{\phi}_1$ and $\bar{\phi}_2$ represented two finite rotations, and if they were vectors, we would have to have $\bar{\phi}_1 + \bar{\phi}_2 = \bar{\phi}_2 + \bar{\phi}_1$. However, a simple example easily shows that

$$\bar{\phi}_1 + \bar{\phi}_2 \neq \bar{\phi}_2 + \bar{\phi}_1 \tag{9-6}$$

and is illustrated in Fig. 9-6. Let us suppose that $\bar{\phi}_1$ represents a 90° rotation about the x axis and $\bar{\phi}_2$ represents a 90° rotation about the y axis. In (a), we show the result of performing $\bar{\phi}_1$ and then $\bar{\phi}_2$ on a body, i.e., $\bar{\phi}_1 + \bar{\phi}_2$; in ($b$), the result of performing $\bar{\phi}_2$ and then $\bar{\phi}_1$, i.e., $\bar{\phi}_2 + \bar{\phi}_1$, is also shown. The initial configuration is the same, and the final results are clearly different; therefore (9-6) is correct. Thus these directed quantities associated with finite angular displacements are not vectors. This result is the basic origin of many of the difficulties in discussing rigid body motion because it means that there is no set of angles which we can

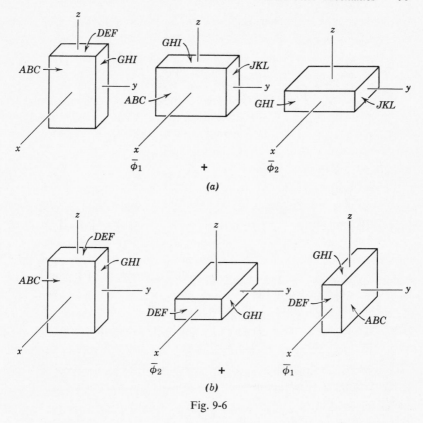

Fig. 9-6

simply differentiate (i.e., essentially divide by a scalar) in order to get vector angular velocities.

In connection with our basic result (9-2), we should note that $\boldsymbol{\omega}$ need not be a constant vector but may be changing both in magnitude and in direction.

9-3 Rotation about a fixed axis

Before we study the dynamics of rigid bodies in all its generality, it will be worth while to consider first a simple case which is comparatively familiar.

In general, the number of degrees of freedom will be reduced if the rigid body is constrained. For example, if the body is constrained to rotate about a fixed axis as shown in Fig. 9-7, only one coordinate ϕ is needed to specify its configuration completely. One way of constraining the body is to hold it in place by bearings O and O'. In general, if the bearings were not there, the body would tend to move; this tendency is obviated by the forces exerted on it by the bearings. In order to apply our theorems about the motion of systems of particles, we can replace the bearings by the forces $\mathbf{F}$ and $\mathbf{F}'$ that they exert. If we let $\mathbf{N}$ be the resultant torque due to external forces, then from (6-17) we have

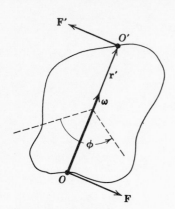

Fig. 9-7

$$\frac{d\mathbf{L}}{dt} = \mathbf{r} \times \mathbf{F} + \mathbf{r}' \times \mathbf{F}' + \mathbf{N} \quad (9\text{-}7)$$

where $\mathbf{r}$ and $\mathbf{r}'$ are the position vectors of O and O' with respect to the external coordinate system.

Although (9-7) is correct, we generally do not know the values of $\mathbf{F}$ and $\mathbf{F}'$, but they can be eliminated in the following way. First, we choose our origin at O and the z axis along the fixed axis, so that $\mathbf{r} = 0$, $\mathbf{r}' = r'\hat{\mathbf{k}}$ and (9-7) becomes

$$\frac{d\mathbf{L}}{dt} = r'\hat{\mathbf{k}} \times \mathbf{F}' + \mathbf{N} \quad (9\text{-}8)$$

The first term on the right is perpendicular to the z axis; consequently, if we consider the z component of (9-8), that is, the component along the fixed axis, we obtain

$$\dot{L}_z = r'(\hat{\mathbf{k}} \times \mathbf{F}')_z + N_z = N_z \quad (9\text{-}9)$$

so that only the z component of the external torque need be considered.

From (6-12), (9-2), and (1-21), we get

$$\mathbf{L} = \sum_i m_i \mathbf{r}_i \times \mathbf{v}_i = \sum_i m_i \mathbf{r}_i \times (\boldsymbol{\omega} \times \mathbf{r}_i)$$

$$= \sum_i m_i \boldsymbol{\omega}(\mathbf{r}_i \cdot \mathbf{r}_i) - \sum_i m_i \mathbf{r}_i(\boldsymbol{\omega} \cdot \mathbf{r}_i) \quad (9\text{-}10)$$

Now, in this case,

$$\boldsymbol{\omega} = \omega\hat{\mathbf{k}} = \dot{\phi}\hat{\mathbf{k}} \quad (9\text{-}11)$$

so that $\boldsymbol{\omega} \cdot \mathbf{r}_i = \omega z_i$. Also, $\mathbf{r}_i \cdot \mathbf{r}_i = r_i^2$, and (9-10) becomes

$$\mathbf{L} = \hat{\mathbf{k}}\omega \sum_i m_i r_i^2 - \omega \sum_i m_i z_i \mathbf{r}_i \quad (9\text{-}12)$$

and therefore

$$L_z = \mathbf{L} \cdot \hat{\mathbf{k}} = \omega \sum_i m_i(r_i^2 - z_i^2) = \omega \sum_i m_i(x_i^2 + y_i^2) \quad (9\text{-}13)$$

If we let

$$I_{zz} = \sum_i m_i(x_i^2 + y_i^2) = \text{moment of inertia about the } z \text{ axis}$$

then (9-13) and (9-11) together give

$$L_z = I_{zz}\omega = I_{zz}\dot{\phi} \tag{9-14}$$

and (9-9) becomes

$$\dot{L}_z = I_{zz}\ddot{\phi} = N_z \tag{9-15}$$

Since a knowledge of ϕ as a function of time gives the orientation of the body completely, (9-15) is the only equation which need be considered for this case, and in fact (9-15) is generally the only equation considered in elementary courses when rigid body motion is discussed. Now let us return to the general case.

9-4 Angular momentum and kinetic energy for a rigid body with one point fixed

The general expression for the angular momentum is given by (6-12); for a rigid body, the particle velocities are all given in terms of $\boldsymbol{\omega}$ by (9-2). When these are combined, we get (9-10) again; however, (9-11) no longer generally obtains, so that when we expand (9-10) we get

$$
\begin{aligned}
\mathbf{L} = \hat{\mathbf{i}} & \left[\omega_x \sum_i m_i r_i^2 - \sum_i m_i x_i (\omega_x x_i + \omega_y y_i + \omega_z z_i) \right] \\
+ \hat{\mathbf{j}} & \left[\omega_y \sum_i m_i r_i^2 - \sum_i m_i y_i (\omega_x x_i + \omega_y y_i + \omega_z z_i) \right] \\
+ \hat{\mathbf{k}} & \left[\omega_z \sum_i m_i r_i^2 - \sum_i m_i z_i (\omega_x x_i + \omega_y y_i + \omega_z z_i) \right]
\end{aligned}
$$

which becomes

$$L_x = I_{xx}\omega_x + I_{xy}\omega_y + I_{xz}\omega_z \tag{9-16a}$$

$$L_y = I_{yx}\omega_x + I_{yy}\omega_y + I_{yz}\omega_z \tag{9-16b}$$

$$L_z = I_{zx}\omega_x + I_{zy}\omega_y + I_{zz}\omega_z \tag{9-16c}$$

where

$$I_{xx} = \sum_i m_i(y_i^2 + z_i^2) \tag{9-17a}$$

$$I_{yy} = \sum_i m_i(z_i^2 + x_i^2) \tag{9-17b}$$

$$I_{zz} = \sum_i m_i(x_i^2 + y_i^2) \tag{9-17c}$$

$$I_{xy} = -\sum_i m_i x_i y_i = I_{yx} \tag{9-18a}$$

$$I_{yz} = -\sum_i m_i y_i z_i = I_{zy} \tag{9-18b}$$

$$I_{zx} = -\sum_i m_i z_i x_i = I_{xz} \tag{9-18c}$$

We can also write (9-16) as

$$L_a = \sum_{b=x,y,z} I_{ab}\omega_b, \quad a = x, y, z \qquad (9\text{-}19)$$

The quantities I_{xx}, I_{yy}, I_{zz} are called *moments of inertia* about the x, y, z axes, and the I_{xy}, etc., are called *products of inertia*. All can be calculated from (9-17) and (9-18) once the mass distribution is known, that is, if we know the positions of all the particles with respect to the system of axes we happen to be using.

We can similarly calculate the kinetic energy. Using (6-24), (9-2), (1-20), and (9-10), we obtain

$$2T = \sum_i m_i v_i^2 = \sum_i m_i (\boldsymbol{\omega} \times \mathbf{r}_i) \cdot (\boldsymbol{\omega} \times \mathbf{r}_i)$$

$$= \sum_i m_i \boldsymbol{\omega} \cdot [\mathbf{r}_i \times (\boldsymbol{\omega} \times \mathbf{r}_i)] = \boldsymbol{\omega} \cdot \sum_i m_i \mathbf{r}_i \times (\boldsymbol{\omega} \times \mathbf{r}_i) = \boldsymbol{\omega} \cdot \mathbf{L}$$

and, therefore, if we also use (9-19), we can express this as

$$T = \tfrac{1}{2}\boldsymbol{\omega} \cdot \mathbf{L} = \tfrac{1}{2} \sum_{a=x,y,z} \omega_a L_a = \tfrac{1}{2} \sum_a \sum_b I_{ab}\omega_a\omega_b \qquad (9\text{-}20)$$

If we write (9-20) out in detail and use (9-18) to combine some of the terms, we obtain

$$T = \tfrac{1}{2}(I_{xx}\omega_x^2 + I_{yy}\omega_y^2 + I_{zz}\omega_z^2 + 2I_{xy}\omega_x\omega_y + 2I_{yz}\omega_y\omega_z + 2I_{zx}\omega_z\omega_x)$$

$$(9\text{-}21)$$

Let us return to the relation (9-16) or, equivalently, (9-19); suppose we had a situation in which $\omega_x = \omega_y = 0$ while $\omega_z \neq 0$. Then we would have

$$L_x = I_{xz}\omega_z, \quad L_y = I_{yz}\omega_z, \quad L_z = I_{zz}\omega_z \qquad (9\text{-}22)$$

which shows that in general the angular momentum is not parallel to the angular velocity; the situation described by (9-22) is illustrated in Fig. 9-8. This general type of result differs from our previous example of linear momentum where the momentum was parallel to the velocity, i.e., $\mathbf{p} = m\mathbf{v}$.

Example. Two Masses Connected by a Rigid Massless Rod and Rotating about a Fixed Axis. See Fig. 9-9. If we use (9-10), it is clear from the construction of the system that the angular momentum $\mathbf{L}$ is perpendicular to the connecting rod and thus is not parallel to $\boldsymbol{\omega}$. As the system rotates, the angular momentum vector will turn in space and, if the velocities are constant in magnitude, the magnitude of $\mathbf{L}$ will be constant and its tip will trace out a circle which is perpendicular to the axis of rotation. Since the angular momentum is changing in time, our general result (6-17) tells us that there is an external torque acting on the

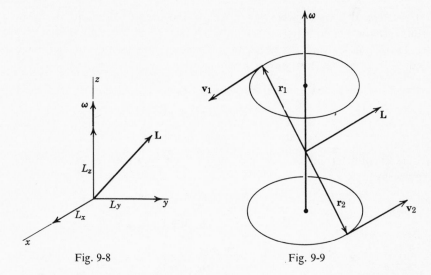

Fig. 9-8   Fig. 9-9

system. This torque is supplied by whatever bearings are constraining the rotation of this system to be along the fixed axis; similarly, by (3-10), the rotating system will in turn exert sideways forces on the bearings. As a general result, we can see that, when the angular momentum and angular velocity are not parallel, the angular momentum changes in time as the body rotates, so that the rotating system exerts forces on any restraining bearings. From a practical point of view, these forces can lead to undesirable wear on the bearings, so it would be nice if we somehow knew how to make **L** and **ω** parallel.

9-5 Principal axes of inertia

We now want to show how we can find an axis, or axes, of rotation for a given body such that, when **ω** is along such a *principal axis*, the angular momentum is parallel to the angular velocity; that is, the equation which defines a principal axis is

$$\mathbf{L} = I\boldsymbol{\omega} \qquad (9\text{-}23)$$

where I is a scalar. Combining (9-23) with the general relations (9-16) connecting **L** and **ω**, we find that we must have $L_x = I_{xx}\omega_x + I_{xy}\omega_y + I_{xz}\omega_z = I\omega_x$, etc., or

$$(I_{xx} - I)\omega_x + I_{xy}\omega_y + I_{xz}\omega_z = 0 \qquad (9\text{-}24a)$$

$$I_{yx}\omega_x + (I_{yy} - I)\omega_y + I_{yz}\omega_z = 0 \qquad (9\text{-}24b)$$

$$I_{zx}\omega_x + I_{zy}\omega_y + (I_{zz} - I)\omega_z = 0 \qquad (9\text{-}24c)$$

These are three simultaneous, linear, homogeneous equations for the three unknowns ω_x, ω_y, ω_z.

Let us consider first the properties of a more general set of simultaneous equations. Suppose we have the set

$$a_{11}x_1 + a_{12}x_2 + a_{13}x_3 = b_1$$

$$a_{21}x_1 + a_{22}x_2 + a_{23}x_3 = b_2$$

$$a_{31}x_1 + a_{32}x_2 + a_{33}x_3 = b_3$$

In terms of determinants, the solutions of these equations are known to be given by

$$x_1 = \frac{\begin{vmatrix} b_1 & a_{12} & a_{13} \\ b_2 & a_{22} & a_{23} \\ b_3 & a_{32} & a_{33} \end{vmatrix}}{\begin{vmatrix} a_{11} & a_{12} & a_{13} \\ a_{21} & a_{22} & a_{23} \\ a_{31} & a_{32} & a_{33} \end{vmatrix}} \tag{9-25}$$

with similar expressions for x_2 and x_3.

In the case of interest to us, which is given by (9-24), we have $b_1 = b_2 = b_3 = 0$, hence, if the determinant of the coefficients of the equations [the denominator of (9-25)] is different from zero, the only solutions are $x_1 = x_2 = x_3 = 0$. The corresponding solutions of (9-24) would be $\omega_x = \omega_y = \omega_z = 0$, which is of no interest to us, because we want the components of $\boldsymbol{\omega}$ to be different from zero.

Suppose, however, that the determinant of the coefficients a_{ij} is zero. Then both the numerator and denominator of (9-25) are zero, and the solution by determinants cannot be evaluated and we have to go back to the equations and solve them by straightforward algebraic methods. Hence we can say that the general condition for the existence of a nontrivial solution of the set of linear, homogeneous, equations of the type (9-24) is that the determinant of the coefficients vanishes.

Applying this condition to our case (9-24), we must have

$$\begin{vmatrix} I_{xx} - I & I_{xy} & I_{xz} \\ I_{yx} & I_{yy} - I & I_{yz} \\ I_{zx} & I_{zy} & I_{zz} - I \end{vmatrix} = 0 \tag{9-26}$$

When this determinant is expanded, the result will be a cubic equation for the unknown quantity I. When the equation is solved, there will be three roots: I_1, I_2, I_3; these are called the *principal moments of inertia*. Now let us go back to the original equations in order to see what use these values of I will be to us in finding the principal axes.

Dividing each of the equations (9-24) by ω_x, we obtain

$$(I_{xx} - I) + I_{xy}\left(\frac{\omega_y}{\omega_x}\right) + I_{xz}\left(\frac{\omega_z}{\omega_x}\right) = 0 \qquad (9\text{-}27a)$$

$$I_{yx} + (I_{yy} - I)\left(\frac{\omega_y}{\omega_x}\right) + I_{yz}\left(\frac{\omega_z}{\omega_x}\right) = 0 \qquad (9\text{-}27b)$$

$$I_{zx} + I_{zy}\left(\frac{\omega_y}{\omega_x}\right) + (I_{zz} - I)\left(\frac{\omega_z}{\omega_x}\right) = 0 \qquad (9\text{-}27c)$$

which shows us that what appeared to be three algebraic equations in three unknowns are really three equations for the two unknown *ratios*, ω_y/ω_x and ω_z/ω_x. Thus we can understand why there must exist fairly restrictive relations connecting the coefficients of these equations in order that they be compatible with each other; this is expressed by the fact that the determinant of the coefficients must vanish.

Suppose the axis of rotation has the direction angles a, b, c with corresponding direction cosines $\alpha = \cos a$, $\beta = \cos b$, $\gamma = \cos c$. Then the components of $\boldsymbol{\omega}$ with respect to the fixed set of axes are given by

$$\omega_x = \alpha\omega, \quad \omega_y = \beta\omega, \quad \omega_z = \gamma\omega \qquad (9\text{-}28)$$

and

$$\frac{\omega_y}{\omega_x} = \frac{\beta}{\alpha}, \quad \frac{\omega_z}{\omega_x} = \frac{\gamma}{\alpha} \qquad (9\text{-}29)$$

Thus the equations (9-27) can be written in terms of the ratios of the direction cosines of the axis of rotation by the use of (9-29). Suppose we now put one of our principal moments, for example, I_1, into the equations (9-27). We can solve the equations for the corresponding ratios β_1/α_1 and γ_1/α_1, and then, by using the relation $\alpha_1{}^2 + \beta_1{}^2 + \gamma_1{}^2 = 1$, we can find the whole set of direction cosines corresponding to I_1, that is, the direction of the principal axis of inertia along which **L** is parallel to $\boldsymbol{\omega}$ and the moment of inertia is I_1. In the same way, we can insert the values I_2 and I_3 of the other principal moments and find the directions of the corresponding principal axes of inertia. Thus there are *three* principal axes of inertia.

We want now to show that these principal axes have the interesting property of being mutually perpendicular. The method of showing this is straightforward.

Combining (9-24), (9-28), and the remarks above, we have

$$I_{xx}\alpha_1 + I_{xy}\beta_1 + I_{xz}\gamma_1 = I_1\alpha_1 \qquad (9\text{-}30a)$$

$$I_{yx}\alpha_1 + I_{yy}\beta_1 + I_{yz}\gamma_1 = I_1\beta_1 \qquad (9\text{-}30b)$$

$$I_{zx}\alpha_1 + I_{zy}\beta_1 + I_{zz}\gamma_1 = I_1\gamma_1 \qquad (9\text{-}30c)$$

$$I_{xx}\alpha_2 + I_{xy}\beta_2 + I_{xz}\gamma_2 = I_2\alpha_2 \qquad (9\text{-}31a)$$

$$I_{yx}\alpha_2 + I_{yy}\beta_2 + I_{yz}\gamma_2 = I_2\beta_2 \qquad (9\text{-}31b)$$

$$I_{zx}\alpha_2 + I_{zy}\beta_2 + I_{zz}\gamma_2 = I_2\gamma_2 \qquad (9\text{-}31c)$$

We multiply the equations of the set (9-30) by α_2, β_2, γ_2, respectively; the equations of the second set (9-31) by α_1, β_1, γ_1, respectively. We then add the three equations which we get from (9-30) by this procedure, do the same for those from (9-31), and then subtract the two equations obtained in this way. The result is

$$(I_1 - I_2)(\alpha_1\alpha_2 + \beta_1\beta_2 + \gamma_1\gamma_2) = 0 \qquad (9\text{-}32)$$

If $I_1 \neq I_2$, then $\alpha_1\alpha_2 + \beta_1\beta_2 + \gamma_1\gamma_2 = 0$ and the two axes 1 and 2 are perpendicular. The same result will be obtained for the other pairs of axes. If, however, $I_1 = I_2$, the value of $\alpha_1\alpha_2 + \beta_1\beta_2 + \gamma_1\gamma_2$ is not determined to be zero by (9-32), but it will certainly be compatible with (9-32) if we make it zero. In other words, if the principal moments are equal, we can always choose the corresponding principal axes to be perpendicular. Thus we can always take our principal axes to form a mutually perpendicular set.

As a result of the properties of the principal axes, it is convenient to use a coordinate system whose axes coincide with the principal axes of inertia. Designating components along these axes by 1, 2, 3, we have $\mathbf{L} = \mathbf{L}_1 + \mathbf{L}_2 + \mathbf{L}_3$, where

$$L_1 = I_1\omega_1, \quad L_2 = I_2\omega_2, \quad L_3 = I_3\omega_3 \qquad (9\text{-}33)$$

and, therefore,

$$T = \tfrac{1}{2}\boldsymbol{\omega} \cdot \mathbf{L} = \tfrac{1}{2}(I_1\omega_1{}^2 + I_2\omega_2{}^2 + I_3\omega_3{}^2) \qquad (9\text{-}34)$$

We see that the procedure of finding the principal axes is essentially one of finding a system of coordinates in which the products of inertia (9-18) all vanish. For a uniform body which has an axis of symmetry, we can see that the symmetry axis will be a principal axis, since for every positive value of x_i appearing for a given y_i in the sum (9-18a) there will be a negative contribution which is equal in magnitude and the whole sum will cancel in pairs with a net result of zero.

9-6 Ellipsoid of inertia

There is another interesting and instructive way of looking at these problems. If we substitute (9-28) into (9-21), we find that the kinetic energy has the form

$$T = \tfrac{1}{2}\omega^2(\alpha^2 I_{xx} + \beta^2 I_{yy} + \gamma^2 I_{zz} + 2\alpha\beta I_{xy} + 2\beta\gamma I_{yz} + 2\gamma\alpha I_{zx}) \quad (9\text{-}35)$$

The usual elementary expression for T is

$$T = \tfrac{1}{2}I\omega^2 \quad (9\text{-}36)$$

where I is the moment of inertia for rotation about the axis; hence we expect the quantity in parentheses in (9-35) to be this general moment of inertia I. Let us verify this.

By the elementary definition,

$$I = \sum_i m_i h_i^2 \quad (9\text{-}37)$$

where h_i is the perpendicular distance from the axis of rotation to m_i, as shown in Fig. 9-10. We see that $h_i = |\hat{n} \times r_i|$ where

$$\hat{n} = \alpha\hat{i} + \beta\hat{j} + \gamma\hat{k} \quad (9\text{-}38)$$

is the unit vector in the direction of the axis of rotation. Since $r_i = x_i\hat{i} + y_i\hat{j} + z_i\hat{k}$, (9-37) becomes

$$
\begin{aligned}
I &= \sum_i m_i(\hat{n} \times r_i)^2 \\
&= \sum_i m_i[(\beta z_i - \gamma y_i)\hat{i} + (\gamma x_i - \alpha z_i)\hat{j} + (\alpha y_i - \beta x_i)\hat{k}]^2 \\
&= \sum_i m_i[(\beta z_i - \gamma y_i)^2 + (\gamma x_i - \alpha z_i)^2 + (\alpha y_i - \beta x_i)^2] \\
&= \alpha^2 \sum_i m_i(y_i^2 + z_i^2) + 2\alpha\beta\left(-\sum_i m_i x_i y_i\right) + \cdots \\
&= \alpha^2 I_{xx} + \beta^2 I_{yy} + \gamma^2 I_{zz} + 2\alpha\beta I_{xy} + 2\beta\gamma I_{yz} + 2\gamma\alpha I_{zx} \quad (9\text{-}39)
\end{aligned}
$$

which agrees with (9-35) and (9-36). Thus we see by (9-39) that, if we know the moments and products of inertia with respect to some set of coordinate axes, we can find the moment of inertia for rotation about any axis once its direction is given with respect to the coordinate axes.

If we define a vector

$$\rho = \frac{\hat{n}}{\sqrt{I}} \quad (9\text{-}40)$$

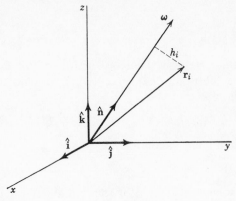

Fig. 9-10

so that $\rho_1 = n_x/\sqrt{I} = \alpha/\sqrt{I}$, etc., then (9-39) can be written

$$I_{xx}\rho_1{}^2 + I_{yy}\rho_2{}^2 + I_{zz}\rho_3{}^2 + 2I_{xy}\rho_1\rho_2 + 2I_{yz}\rho_2\rho_3 + 2I_{zx}\rho_3\rho_1 = 1 \quad (9\text{-}41)$$

If we consider this equation as a function of the three variables ρ_1, ρ_2, ρ_3, it is the equation of a surface in ρ space. In particular, since I is finite and thus ρ must be finite, it is the equation of an ellipsoid which is called the *ellipsoid of inertia*. In the geometric problem, we know that we can always transform this equation to a new set of axes $(\rho_1', \rho_2', \rho_3')$ such that the cross products vanish and the equation of the ellipsoid has its normal form,

$$I_1\rho_1'^2 + I_2\rho_2'^2 + I_3\rho_3'^2 = 1 \quad (9\text{-}42)$$

where the principal axes of the ellipsoid are the directions of the new coordinate axes. Therefore the principal axis transformation we have discussed is exactly the coordinate transformation which puts the equation of the ellipsoid into the form (9-42).

9-7   Euler's equations

It is advantageous to use the principal axes because then the relations among angular momentum, kinetic energy, and angular velocity become greatly simplified. However, the principal axes are fixed in the body and rotate as the body rotates, whereas our laws of motion refer to coordinate axes fixed in space (the inertial systems). Thus, in order to use the principal axes, we must learn how to express the laws of motion in this system; for example, a basic expression is $\mathbf{N} = d\mathbf{L}/dt$, but $d\mathbf{L}/dt$ gives the rate of change of $\mathbf{L}$ as seen by someone fixed in space.

We can write

$$\mathbf{L} = L_1\hat{\mathbf{e}}_1 + L_2\hat{\mathbf{e}}_2 + L_3\hat{\mathbf{e}}_3 \qquad (9\text{-}43)$$

where $\hat{\mathbf{e}}_1$, $\hat{\mathbf{e}}_2$, and $\hat{\mathbf{e}}_3$ are unit vectors along the principal axes as shown in Fig. 9-11. Differentiating (9-43) with respect to t, we obtain

$$\frac{d\mathbf{L}}{dt} = \frac{dL_1}{dt}\hat{\mathbf{e}}_1 + \frac{dL_2}{dt}\hat{\mathbf{e}}_2 + \frac{dL_3}{dt}\hat{\mathbf{e}}_3 + L_1\frac{d\hat{\mathbf{e}}_1}{dt} + L_2\frac{d\hat{\mathbf{e}}_2}{dt} + L_3\frac{d\hat{\mathbf{e}}_3}{dt} \quad (9\text{-}44)$$

We also see from Fig. 9-12 that

$$|d\hat{\mathbf{e}}_i| = |\hat{\mathbf{e}}_i| \sin \alpha \, d\phi = |\hat{\mathbf{e}}_i| \sin \alpha \cdot \omega \, dt$$

Hence

$$\frac{d\hat{\mathbf{e}}_i}{dt} = \boldsymbol{\omega} \times \hat{\mathbf{e}}_i \qquad (9\text{-}45)$$

and therefore (9-44) becomes

$$\frac{d\mathbf{L}}{dt} = \frac{dL_1}{dt}\hat{\mathbf{e}}_1 + \frac{dL_2}{dt}\hat{\mathbf{e}}_2 + \frac{dL_3}{dt}\hat{\mathbf{e}}_3 + \boldsymbol{\omega} \times \mathbf{L} \qquad (9\text{-}46)$$

with the help of (9-43). Since the principal moments I_1, I_2, I_3 are constant with respect to the principal axis system, we can differentiate (9-33) and obtain

$$\dot{L}_1 = I_1\dot{\omega}_1, \quad \dot{L}_2 = I_2\dot{\omega}_2, \quad \dot{L}_3 = I_3\dot{\omega}_3 \qquad (9\text{-}47)$$

which finally enables us to write (9-46) as

$$\frac{d\mathbf{L}}{dt} = I_1\dot{\omega}_1\hat{\mathbf{e}}_1 + I_2\dot{\omega}_2\hat{\mathbf{e}}_2 + I_3\dot{\omega}_3\hat{\mathbf{e}}_3 + \boldsymbol{\omega} \times \mathbf{L} \qquad (9\text{-}48)$$

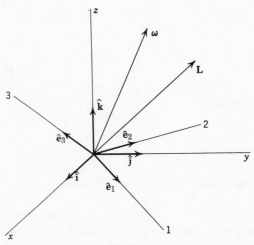

Fig. 9-11

We must be careful to note the meaning of the various derivatives in (9-46) and (9-48): $d\mathbf{L}/dt$ is the rate of change of $\mathbf{L}$ as observed by someone fixed in inertial space; dL_1/dt is the rate of change of L_1 as observed by someone fixed in the principal axis system, that is, the rate of change with respect to the principal axes for which the $\hat{\mathbf{e}}_i$ are constant; and the last term, $\boldsymbol{\omega} \times \mathbf{L}$, is the rate of change due to the rotation of the principal axes with respect to the inertial system. This term would still be observed in the inertial system even if the components of the angular momentum along the principal axes were constant; the rotating body is then carrying along a vector which is constant as far as the body is concerned.

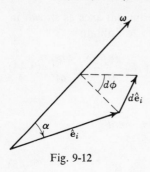

Fig. 9-12

Actually, of course, these relations apply for *any vector* $\mathbf{A}$, and we can say in general that

$$\left(\frac{d\mathbf{A}}{dt}\right)_{\text{space}} = \left(\frac{d\mathbf{A}}{dt}\right)_{\text{body}} + \boldsymbol{\omega} \times \mathbf{A} \qquad (9\text{-}49)$$

Now suppose we let N_1, N_2, N_3 be the components of the external torque along the moving principal axes; then

$$\mathbf{N} = N_1\hat{\mathbf{e}}_1 + N_2\hat{\mathbf{e}}_2 + N_3\hat{\mathbf{e}}_3 \qquad (9\text{-}50)$$

If we find the components of $\mathbf{N} = d\mathbf{L}/dt$ along the principal axes by using (9-48), (9-50), and (1-18), we obtain the following set of equations:

$$N_1 = I_1\dot{\omega}_1 + (I_3 - I_2)\omega_2\omega_3 \qquad (9\text{-}51a)$$

$$N_2 = I_2\dot{\omega}_2 + (I_1 - I_3)\omega_3\omega_1 \qquad (9\text{-}51b)$$

$$N_3 = I_3\dot{\omega}_3 + (I_2 - I_1)\omega_1\omega_2 \qquad (9\text{-}51c)$$

These equations are called *Euler's equations*. They tell us the time rate of change of the angular velocity, with respect to the principal axis system, if we know the external torque components in this system. By solving equations (9-51) to find the components of $\boldsymbol{\omega}$ as a function of time, we can find how the angular velocity and angular momentum move with respect to the principal axes.

9-8 Force-free motion of a symmetric rigid body

One of the problems to which Euler's equations can be conveniently applied is that in which there are no net forces or torques acting on the body; for example, the rotation of the earth can be described in this way as a fairly good first approximation. In this problem, the center of mass is at rest or moves uniformly so that the only angular momentum is due to motion about the center of mass. Then we can choose the center of mass as a fixed point and the origin for the principal axis system fixed in the body.

Since $N = 0$, $L = $ const., by (6-17), so that the angular momentum has a fixed direction in the inertial space. Also, when $N = 0$, Euler's equations (9-51) become

$$I_1\dot{\omega}_1 = (I_2 - I_3)\omega_2\omega_3 \tag{9-52a}$$

$$I_1\dot{\omega}_2 = (I_3 - I_1)\omega_3\omega_1 \tag{9-52b}$$

$$I_3\dot{\omega}_3 = (I_1 - I_2)\omega_1\omega_2 \tag{9-52c}$$

It is possible to integrate these equations completely and find $\boldsymbol{\omega}(t)$; however, the result involves elliptic functions and is not very illuminating for our purposes.

The analytical solution of (9-52) is very easy to obtain for a *symmetric body*; by this we mean a body having an axis of symmetry and uniform density. If we choose the symmetry axis as axis 3, it easily follows from (9-17) that

$$I_1 = I_2 \tag{9-53}$$

and (9-52) simplifies to

$$I_1\dot{\omega}_1 = (I_1 - I_3)\omega_3\omega_2 \tag{9-54a}$$

$$I_1\dot{\omega}_2 = -(I_1 - I_3)\omega_3\omega_1 \tag{9-54b}$$

$$I_3\dot{\omega}_3 = 0 \tag{9-54c}$$

We see at once from (9-54c) that

$$\omega_3 = \text{const.} \tag{9-55}$$

If we now let

$$\Omega = \frac{(I_1 - I_3)\omega_3}{I_1} = \text{const.} \tag{9-56}$$

we can write (9-54a) and (9-54b) more simply as

$$\dot{\omega}_1 = \Omega\omega_2, \quad \dot{\omega}_2 = -\Omega\omega_1 \tag{9-57}$$

If we differentiate the first equation of (9-57), we can eliminate ω_2 and obtain

$$\ddot{\omega}_1 = \Omega\dot{\omega}_2 = -\Omega^2\omega_1 \tag{9-58}$$

which is of the simple harmonic form (5-8). We can write the solution of (9-59) as

$$\omega_1 = \bar{\omega} \sin \Omega t \tag{9-59}$$

where $\bar{\omega}$ is a constant and we have chosen our time scale so that $\omega_1 = 0$ when $t = 0$. We can then find ω_2 by combining (9-59) with the first equation of (9-57); the result is that

$$\omega_2 = \frac{\dot{\omega}_1}{\Omega} = \bar{\omega} \cos \Omega t \qquad (9\text{-}60)$$

These results, (9-59) and (9-60), show us that the vector

$$\boldsymbol{\omega}_p = \omega_1 \hat{e}_1 + \omega_2 \hat{e}_2 = \bar{\omega} (\sin \Omega t \, \hat{e}_1 + \cos \Omega t \, \hat{e}_2) \qquad (9\text{-}61)$$

has a constant magnitude $\bar{\omega}$ and rotates about the 3 axis with constant angular frequency $-\Omega$ as illustrated in Fig. 9-13. Therefore the total angular velocity

$$\boldsymbol{\omega} = \omega_1 \hat{e}_1 + \omega_2 \hat{e}_2 + \omega_3 \hat{e}_3 = \boldsymbol{\omega}_p + \omega_3 \hat{e}_3 \qquad (9\text{-}62)$$

is also constant in magnitude and *precesses* about the 3 axis with the same angular frequency, $-\Omega$. This precessional motion is illustrated in Fig. 9-14, where we see that $\boldsymbol{\omega}$ sweeps out a cone about the 3 axis in the rigid body with the same constant angular frequency, $-\Omega$. This motion, of course, takes place with respect to the principal axes of the body, which are themselves rotating in space with the angular velocity $\boldsymbol{\omega}$.

The two constants, ω_3 and $\bar{\omega}$, can be evaluated in terms of two other constants of the motion—the kinetic energy and the magnitude of the angular momentum. Using (9-33), (9-34), (9-53), (9-55), (9-59), and (9-60), we find that

$$T = \tfrac{1}{2}(I_1\omega_1{}^2 + I_1\omega_2{}^2 + I_3\omega_3{}^2) = \tfrac{1}{2}I_1\bar{\omega}^2 + \tfrac{1}{2}I_3\omega_3{}^2$$

$$L^2 = I_1{}^2\omega_1{}^2 + I_1{}^2\omega_2{}^2 + I_3{}^2\omega_3{}^2 = I_1{}^2\bar{\omega}^2 + I_3{}^2\omega_3{}^2$$

so that

$$\omega_3{}^2 = -\frac{(L^2 - 2I_1 T)}{I_3(I_1 - I_3)}, \qquad \bar{\omega}^2 = \frac{L^2 - 2I_3 T}{I_1(I_1 - I_3)} \qquad (9\text{-}63)$$

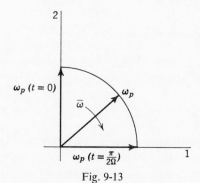

Fig. 9-13

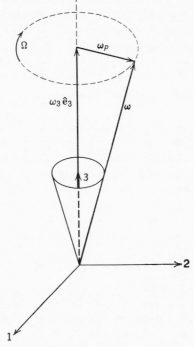

Fig. 9-14

We also see, from (9-56), that, the more nearly equal I_1 and I_3 are, the slower will be the precession frequency Ω as compared to ω_3.

As mentioned above, these results can be applied to the earth. The earth is nearly symmetric about the polar axis and slightly bulged at the equator, so that $I_1 < I_3$. It is found that $(I_3 - I_1) = 0.0033I_1$ and thus $|\Omega| = 0.0033\omega_3$. Therefore $1/|\Omega| = 300/\omega_3$; hence

$$\tau_\Omega = 300\tau_3 \qquad (9\text{-}64)$$

where the τ's are the periods associated with the circular frequencies Ω and ω_3. Since $|\Omega| \ll \omega_3$, ω_3 is approximately equal to the magnitude of the total angular velocity of the earth, $|\boldsymbol{\omega}|$, so that $\tau_3 \simeq 1$ day. Therefore (9-64) predicts a period for the precessional motion of about 300 days. In other words, an observer on the earth would find the axis of rotation of the earth tracing out a circle about the North Pole once every 300 days. What has actually been observed resembles this somewhat: The path is irregular and the amplitude is small, so that the rotational axis is never more than about fifteen feet from the North Pole. The period is also observed to be closer to 427 days than to 300. The differences in the period are ascribed to the fact that the earth is not completely rigid but is somewhat like steel in its elastic properties; the fluctuations in the motion are thought to arise from changes in the mass distribution of the earth, such as could arise from atmospheric motion.

9-9   Euler's angles and Lagrange's equations

What we have said above is about as much as we can easily and usefully get from Euler's equations for this problem. We can obtain a more useful set of equations by using Lagrange's equations, but in order to do this we shall require some generalized coordinates which can be used to describe the rotational motion. A useful set is known as *Euler's angles* and is illustrated in Fig. 9-15. This system entails the simultaneous use of three sets of rectangular coordinates. The *xyz* set is fixed in space, and the 123 set is the principal axis system fixed in the body. The $\xi\eta\zeta$ system is obtained as follows: The plane perpendicular to the 3 axis intersects the *xy* plane in a line called the line of nodes which we choose as the ξ axis; the 3 axis is also chosen as the ζ axis; then, the η axis is chosen to be perpendicular to the $\xi\zeta$ plane. The Euler angles, our generalized coordinates, are then the three angles ϕ, ψ, θ shown in the figure.

In order to see the significance of these angles, let us find what corresponds to their rates of change. With the help of Fig. 9-16, we see that, if $\dot{\psi} \neq 0$, $\dot{\phi} = \dot{\theta} = 0$, we have a rotation about the 3 axis; if $\dot{\phi} \neq 0$, $\dot{\theta} = \dot{\psi} = 0$, we have a rotation about the z axis, so that the 3 axis traces out a cone about the z axis (precession); if $\dot{\theta} \neq 0$, $\dot{\psi} = \dot{\phi} = 0$, we have a rotation

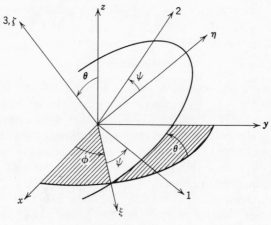

Fig. 9-15

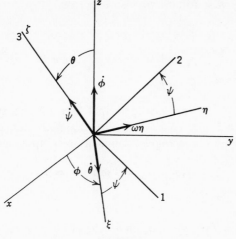

Fig. 9-16

about the ξ axis. Therefore $\dot\theta$, $\dot\phi$, and $\dot\psi$ are angular velocities about the ξ, z, and ζ axes, respectively; however, these axes are not mutually perpendicular.

Resolving along the $\xi\eta\zeta$ axes, with the aid of Fig. 9-16, we find the components of the angular velocity along these axes to be

$$\omega_\xi = \dot\theta, \quad \omega_\eta = \dot\phi \sin\theta, \quad \omega_\zeta = \dot\psi + \dot\phi \cos\theta \qquad (9\text{-}65)$$

Similarly, if we calculate the components along the principal axes, we obtain

$$\omega_1 = \omega_\xi \cos\psi + \omega_\eta \sin\psi = \dot\theta \cos\psi + \dot\phi \sin\theta \sin\psi \qquad (9\text{-}66a)$$

$$\omega_2 = -\omega_\xi \sin\psi + \omega_\eta \cos\psi = -\dot\theta \sin\psi + \dot\phi \sin\theta \cos\psi \qquad (9\text{-}66b)$$

$$\omega_3 = \omega_\zeta = \dot\psi + \dot\phi \cos\theta \qquad (9\text{-}66c)$$

We are now ready to start finding Lagrange's equations, which we shall use in the form (7-32). When (9-66) is substituted into (9-34) and (9-53) is used, the kinetic energy of the symmetric rigid body is found to be given in terms of our generalized coordinates by

$$T = \tfrac{1}{2}I_1(\dot\theta^2 + \dot\phi^2 \sin^2\theta) + \tfrac{1}{2}I_3(\dot\psi + \dot\phi \cos\theta)^2 \qquad (9\text{-}67)$$

The generalized momenta can now be found from (7-62) and (9-67):

$$p_\theta = \partial T/\partial\dot\theta = I_1\dot\theta \qquad (9\text{-}68a)$$

$$p_\phi = \partial T/\partial\dot\phi = I_1 \sin^2\theta\,\dot\phi + I_3 \cos\theta(\dot\psi + \dot\phi \cos\theta) \qquad (9\text{-}68b)$$

$$p_\psi = \partial T/\partial\dot\psi = I_3(\dot\psi + \dot\phi \cos\theta) \qquad (9\text{-}68c)$$

If we use (9-65), these results can also be written

$$p_\theta = I_1 \omega_\xi$$
$$p_\phi = I_1 \omega_\eta \sin \theta + I_3 \omega_\zeta \cos \theta \qquad (9\text{-}69)$$
$$p_\psi = I_3 \omega_\zeta$$

However, the $\xi\eta\zeta$ axes are also principal axes for this symmetric rigid body because the ξ and η axes lie in the same plane as the 1 and 2 axes; therefore we can write the angular momentum components as

$$L_\xi = I_1 \omega_\xi, \quad L_\eta = I_1 \omega_\eta, \quad L_\zeta = I_3 \omega_\zeta \qquad (9\text{-}70)$$

and (9-69) can be written

$$p_\theta = L_\xi, \quad p_\phi = L_\eta \sin \theta + L_\zeta \cos \theta, \quad p_\psi = L_\zeta \qquad (9\text{-}71)$$

We see from Fig. 9-17 that these results (9-71) show that the generalized momenta in this case are just the components of the angular momentum of the system along the axes which correspond to the directions of rotation described by the corresponding generalized coordinates θ, ϕ, and ψ.

We now want to find the generalized forces from (7-19) which we can write as

$$dW = \sum_i \mathbf{F}_i \cdot \mathbf{r}_i \, dt = \sum_j Q_j \, dq_j \qquad (9\text{-}72)$$

where F_i is the resultant force acting on the ith particle. If we substitute

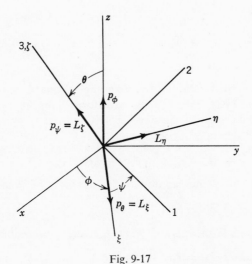

Fig. 9-17

(9-2) into (9-72) and use (1-8), (1-20), and (6-14), we get

$$dW = \sum_i \mathbf{F}_i \cdot (\mathbf{\omega} \times \mathbf{r}_i)\, dt = \mathbf{\omega} \cdot \sum_i \mathbf{r}_i \times \mathbf{F}_i\, dt = \mathbf{\omega} \cdot \mathbf{N}\, dt$$

$$= N_\xi \omega_\xi\, dt + N_\eta \omega_\eta\, dt + N_\zeta \omega_\zeta\, dt$$

$$= N_\xi\, d\theta + (N_\eta \sin\theta + N_\zeta \cos\theta)\, d\phi + N_\zeta\, d\psi \qquad (9\text{-}73)$$

where N_ξ, N_η, and N_ζ are the components of the total external torque along the $\xi\eta\zeta$ axes. Comparing (9-72) and (9-73), we see that the generalized forces are

$$Q_\theta = N_\xi = N_\theta \qquad\qquad (9\text{-}74a)$$

$$Q_\phi = N_\eta \sin\theta + N_\zeta \cos\theta = N_\phi \qquad (9\text{-}74b)$$

$$Q_\psi = N_\zeta = N_\psi \qquad\qquad (9\text{-}74c)$$

where N_θ is the component of the external torque along the ξ axis, the rotation about which is described by the angle θ, etc. Thus the generalized forces in this problem turn out to be the components of the external torque along the corresponding axes of rotation.

Substituting (9-67), (9-68), and (9-74) into (7-32), we find that Lagrange's equations for the symmetric rigid body become

$$\frac{dp_\theta}{dt} = \frac{\partial T}{\partial \theta} + Q_\theta = I_1 \ddot{\theta}$$

$$= I_1 \sin\theta \cos\theta \dot{\phi}^2 - I_3 \dot{\phi}(\dot{\psi} + \dot{\phi}\cos\theta)\sin\theta + N_\theta \qquad (9\text{-}75a)$$

$$\frac{dp_\phi}{dt} = \frac{\partial T}{\partial \phi} + Q_\phi = \frac{d}{dt}[I_1 \sin^2\theta \dot{\phi} + I_3 \cos\theta(\dot{\psi} + \dot{\phi}\cos\theta)] = N_\phi \quad (9\text{-}75b)$$

$$\frac{dp_\psi}{dt} = \frac{\partial T}{\partial \psi} + Q_\psi = \frac{d}{dt}[I_3(\dot{\psi} + \dot{\phi}\cos\theta)] = N_\psi \qquad (9\text{-}75c)$$

which are our desired equations of motion expressed in terms of the Euler angles. We can show that they are equivalent to Euler's equations (9-51) as, of course, they must be.

9-10 Force-free motion of a symmetric rigid body (concluded)

We recall that, when $\mathbf{N} = 0$, $\mathbf{L} = \text{const.}$ We can simplify our work by choosing our coordinate system so that $L_x = L_y = 0$ and $L_z = \text{const.}$ Then, with the help of Fig. 9-17 and (9-71), we see that

$$L_\xi = 0, \quad L_\eta = L_z \sin\theta, \quad L_\zeta = L_z \cos\theta$$

$$p_\theta = 0, \quad p_\phi = L_z, \quad p_\psi = L_z \cos\theta \qquad\qquad (9\text{-}76)$$

We also find from (9-68a) that $p_\theta = I_1\dot{\theta} = 0$, so that

$$\theta = \text{const.} \tag{9-77}$$

That is, the angle between the axis of symmetry and the fixed direction of the angular momentum is constant.

With $N = 0$, Lagrange's equations (9-75) become or lead to

$$\dot{\phi} \sin \theta \, [I_1 \, \dot{\phi} \cos \theta - I_3(\dot{\psi} + \dot{\phi} \cos \theta)] = 0 \tag{9-78}$$

$$p_\phi = L_z = \text{const.} = I_1 \sin^2 \theta \dot{\phi} + I_3 \cos \theta(\dot{\psi} + \dot{\phi} \cos \theta) \tag{9-79}$$

$$p_\psi = L_z \cos \theta = \text{const.} = I_3(\dot{\psi} + \dot{\phi} \cos \theta) = I_3\omega_3 \tag{9-80}$$

We see from (9-80) that

$$\omega_3 = \dot{\psi} + \dot{\phi} \cos \theta = \text{const.} \tag{9-81}$$

so that the component of the angular velocity along the symmetry axis remains constant.

From (9-78) and (9-81), we find that

$$I_1\dot{\phi} \cos \theta = I_3(\dot{\psi} + \dot{\phi} \cos \theta) = I_3\omega_3 = \text{const.}$$

so that

$$\dot{\phi} = \frac{I_3\omega_3}{I_1 \cos \theta} = \text{const.} \tag{9-82}$$

because of (9-77). Finally

$$\dot{\psi} = \omega_3 - \dot{\phi} \cos \theta = \frac{(I_1 - I_3)}{I_1} \omega_3 = \Omega = \text{const.} \tag{9-83}$$

and now we are in a position to describe the motion.

For definiteness, let us assume that $I_1 > I_3$. The z axis is along the direction of the constant angular momentum, and the axis of symmetry (3 axis) makes a constant angle θ with L_z. Since $\dot{\phi}$ is constant, the ξ axis (line of nodes) rotates about the z axis at a constant rate. Therefore the 3 (or ζ) axis sweeps out a cone in space around the z axis at this constant rate $\dot{\phi}$; this motion is called uniform precession. Meanwhile the body is spinning about the 3 axis with constant angular speed $\dot{\psi}$. These relations are indicated in Fig. 9-18.

Since $L_\xi = 0$, $\omega_\xi = 0$; also

$$L_\eta = I_1\omega_\eta, \quad L_\zeta = I_3\omega_\zeta = I_3\omega_3 \tag{9-84}$$

Hence the only non-zero components of $\boldsymbol{\omega}$ are ω_η and ω_ζ, and thus $\boldsymbol{\omega}$ lies in the same plane as the symmetry axis and $\mathbf{L}$, i.e., in the $z\zeta$ plane. Also

$$\frac{L_\eta}{L_\zeta} = \frac{I_1\omega_\eta}{I_3\omega_\zeta} > \frac{\omega_\eta}{\omega_\zeta}$$

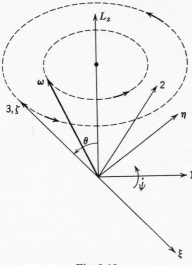

Fig. 9-18

since $I_1 > I_3$. This result means that **ω** is closer to the ζ axis than **L** is, as shown in Fig. 9-19. Therefore, since **ω** must remain in the $z\zeta$ plane, the direction of **ω** also sweeps out a smaller cone about the z axis than does the ζ axis as it sweeps out its cone about the z axis; this is shown in Fig. 9-18.

We also recall that our discussion in Sec. 9-8 based on Euler's equations showed us that, with respect to the axes *fixed in the body*, the direction of the angular velocity swept out still a third cone about the direction of the 3 axis. A very graphic way which has been found to describe this situation is illustrated in Fig. 9-20. We introduce two new cones—one fixed in space

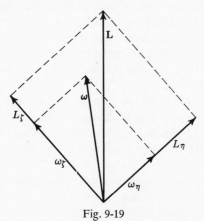

Fig. 9-19

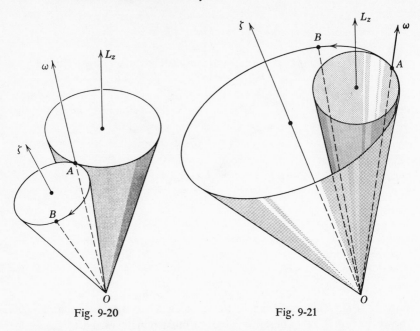

Fig. 9-20   Fig. 9-21

(shaded) and one fixed in the body. The cone fixed in the body has the axis of symmetry (ζ) of the body as its axis of symmetry. The cone fixed in space has as its axis of symmetry the fixed direction of the angular momentum. The positions of the cones are so chosen that the direction of the angular velocity is along their line of contact.

The motion can now be described as the body cone rolling without slipping on the space cone. We see that then both the ζ axis and ω trace out their cones about z, as well as stay in the same plane as they should. As this occurs, the angular velocity moves about the space cone, with the period associated with this motion given by that corresponding to $\dot{\phi}$. After one period, ω will be back to its original position with respect to the axes fixed in space, as will ζ. But, since the body cone rolls without slipping on the space cone, after one period the line of contact of the cones will have rotated a certain distance around the body cone, for example, from OA to OB, so that the direction of the angular velocity will have rotated with respect to the body cone. This is exactly the motion pictured in Fig. 9-14 and is associated with the angular frequency $-\Omega$. We must remember, of course, that the body is also spinning with constant angular speed ω_3 about the symmetry axis.

It will be left as an exercise to show that, when $I_1 < I_3$, the proper arrangement of body and space cones is that shown in Fig. 9-21, the direction of ω again going from OA to OB.

9-11   Mechanics in a rotating coordinate system

We have occasionally pointed out some effects which arose because we made our calculations in a coordinate system which is rotating with respect to an inertial system, and now we are at a convenient place to discuss these essentially kinematic effects in a more systematic manner. An extremely important example of this situation occurs when we discuss mechanical experiments performed on the earth because we almost always refer our measurements to coordinate systems fixed with respect to the earth, which in turn is rotating with respect to inertial axes fixed in space; and it is with respect to these inertial axes that our laws of motion are valid.

We therefore want to find relations between dynamical quantities observed in the inertial and rotating systems and we particularly need the acceleration. The basic equation we need is given by (9-49), and in order to emphasize that it describes a relation involving coordinate systems we write it in the form

$$\left(\frac{d\mathbf{A}}{dt}\right)_{\text{inertial}} = \left(\frac{d\mathbf{A}}{dt}\right)_{\text{rotating}} + \boldsymbol{\omega} \times \mathbf{A}$$

or simply

$$\left(\frac{d\mathbf{A}}{dt}\right)_{i} = \left(\frac{d\mathbf{A}}{dt}\right)_{r} + \boldsymbol{\omega} \times \mathbf{A} \tag{9-85}$$

If we let $\mathbf{r}$ be the radius vector from the origin of the rotating system to the particle, and let $\mathbf{A} = \mathbf{r}$ in (9-85), we obtain

$$\mathbf{v}_i = \mathbf{v}_r + \boldsymbol{\omega} \times \mathbf{r} \tag{9-86}$$

where $\mathbf{v}_i$ and $\mathbf{v}_r$ are the velocities of the particle relative to the inertial and rotating sets of axes, respectively.

We can now find the acceleration $\mathbf{a}_i$ from

$$\mathbf{a}_i = \left(\frac{d\mathbf{v}_i}{dt}\right)_i = \left(\frac{d\mathbf{v}_i}{dt}\right)_r + \boldsymbol{\omega} \times \mathbf{v}_i = \left[\frac{d}{dt}(\mathbf{v}_r + \boldsymbol{\omega} \times \mathbf{r})\right]_r + \boldsymbol{\omega} \times (\mathbf{v}_r + \boldsymbol{\omega} \times \mathbf{r})$$

$$= \left(\frac{d\mathbf{v}_r}{dt}\right)_r + \boldsymbol{\omega} \times \left(\frac{d\mathbf{r}}{dt}\right)_r + \boldsymbol{\omega} \times \mathbf{v}_r + \boldsymbol{\omega} \times (\boldsymbol{\omega} \times \mathbf{r})$$

$$= \mathbf{a}_r + 2\boldsymbol{\omega} \times \mathbf{v}_r + \boldsymbol{\omega} \times (\boldsymbol{\omega} \times \mathbf{r}) \tag{9-87}$$

In the inertial system the equation of motion is given by (4-1) as $\mathbf{F} = m\mathbf{a}_i$; therefore, from (9-87), we obtain

$$m\mathbf{a}_r = \mathbf{F} - 2m\boldsymbol{\omega} \times \mathbf{v}_r - m\boldsymbol{\omega} \times (\boldsymbol{\omega} \times \mathbf{r}) \tag{9-88}$$

If the observer in the rotating system insists upon continuing to write mass times acceleration as force, even in his non-inertial system where it is not, he can interpret (9-88) as saying that with respect to his system the particle is moving under the influence of an effective force given by

$$\mathbf{F}_{\text{eff}} = m\mathbf{a}_r = \mathbf{F} - 2m\boldsymbol{\omega} \times \mathbf{v}_r - m\boldsymbol{\omega} \times (\boldsymbol{\omega} \times \mathbf{r}) \qquad (9\text{-}89)$$

The second term on the right side of (9-89) is called the *Coriolis "force"* and the last term, the *centrifugal "force."* We see that they are not really forces at all but are correction terms which must be added to the actual force if we want to continue to set the force equal to mass times acceleration, even in this rotating system where (4-1) does not apply.

As seen in Fig. 9-22, the centrifugal force is a vector perpendicular to $\boldsymbol{\omega}$ and is directed out from the axis of rotation; its magnitude is $m\omega^2 r \sin\theta$, so that, for the earth, it is a maximum at the equator and zero at the poles. If the particle is at rest in the rotating system and thus $\mathbf{v}_r = 0$, we see by (9-88) that the centrifugal force is the only correction term needed to describe the motion with respect to the rotating system.

When the particle is moving with respect to the rotating system so that $\mathbf{v}_r \neq 0$, the Coriolis force $-2m\boldsymbol{\omega} \times \mathbf{v}_r$ must be considered as well. This correction term is always perpendicular to both $\boldsymbol{\omega}$ and $\mathbf{v}_r$. In the northern hemisphere, $\boldsymbol{\omega}$ points out from the earth's surface and, as shown in Fig. 9-23, the effect of the Coriolis force is to deflect the path of a *horizontally* moving particle to the *right* of the path it would otherwise have with respect to the earth's surface. In the southern hemisphere, the direction of the horizontal Coriolis force is opposite to this, and it is zero at the equator for horizontal motion because $\boldsymbol{\omega}$ is also horizontal.

The Coriolis force is very important in meteorology in the discussion of the problems of wind directions and air flow. Although the Coriolis force is quite small the time that it can act on the moving air masses is very long, and it can make an appreciable change in the momentum of the air. If the Coriolis effect were not present, the air would flow from regions of high to low pressure along the direction of the pressure gradient, as shown by the dashed arrow in Fig. 9-24a. The Coriolis forces deflect the air to the

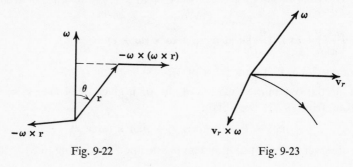

Fig. 9-22   Fig. 9-23

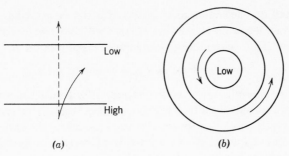

Fig. 9-24

right of this direction in the northern hemisphere. At equilibrium, the net force on a given air mass is zero; hence the Coriolis force must be oppositely directed to the pressure gradient. The net effect is that the wind direction will be parallel to the equal pressure lines or isobars. If we now consider the air flow around a cyclone, which is a region of low pressure with approximately circular isobars about it, we see that the air flow will be counterclockwise as shown in Fig. 9-24b; the direction of flow will be clockwise around a low in the southern hemisphere. These general effects can also be observed by watching water run down a drain, or by walking radially on a merry-go-round.

Coriolis forces are also important in the classical problem of a freely falling particle. The particle velocity is nearly vertical, $\boldsymbol{\omega}$ lies in the north-south vertical plane, and therefore the force $2m\mathbf{v}_r \times \boldsymbol{\omega}$ is in the east-west direction. A body falling toward the surface of the earth will then be deflected to the *east*, as shown in Fig. 9-25a. We can calculate the

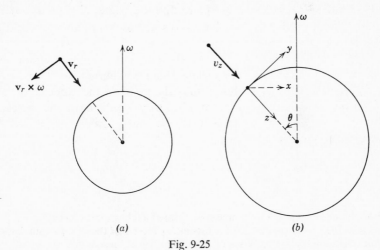

Fig. 9-25

magnitude of this deflection quite easily with the help of the coordinate system of Fig. 9-25b, in which the x axis is chosen to point west, y north, and z down. The x component of the equation of motion (9-89) is

$$m\ddot{x} = -2m(\boldsymbol{\omega} \times \mathbf{v}_r)_x = -2m\omega v_z \sin \theta \qquad (9\text{-}90)$$

Although the Coriolis force would have an effect on v_z, it would be so small that it would constitute only a small correction to the eastward deflection, which itself is very small. Thus, as a first approximation, we can calculate v_z as if the particle were falling freely with constant acceleration g. If we drop it from rest,

$$v_z = gt \quad \text{and} \quad T = \sqrt{2h/g} \qquad (9\text{-}91)$$

where T is the total time required to fall the distance h. If we substitute for v_z in (9-90), we obtain

$$m\ddot{x} = -2m\omega gt \sin \theta$$

We can easily integrate this equation to obtain the total deflection from the vertical with the result that

$$x = -\tfrac{1}{3}\omega gT^3 \sin \theta = -\tfrac{1}{3}\omega g\left(\frac{2h}{g}\right)^{3/2} \sin \theta \qquad (9\text{-}92)$$

Thus the deflection is eastward and is proportional to the cube of the total time of fall. As a numerical example, suppose we consider a fall at the equator where $\theta = \pi/2$, and take $h = 100$ meters. Since

$$\omega = \frac{2\pi}{24 \times 3600} = 7.29 \times 10^{-5}\,(\text{second})^{-1}$$

is the angular velocity of the earth, we find that (9-92) yields $x = -0.022$ meter $= -2.2$ centimeters. Needless to say, this is a difficult experiment to perform.

Centrifugal and Coriolis terms are also important in atomic and molecular physics. The atoms can oscillate about equilibrium positions while the molecule rotates as a whole; thus the paths of the atoms and their separations will be different from what they would be if the molecule were at rest. Noticeable effects in the various possible energies of the molecule are produced in this way.

Exercises

9-1. Three particles of equal mass are located at the points $(a, 0, 0)$, $(0, a, 2a)$, and $(0, 2a, a)$. Find the principal moments of inertia of the system with respect to the origin, and also find a set of principal axes of inertia.

9-2. What is the relation between the discussion of Fig. 9-9 and the necessity of getting the wheels of an automobile balanced?

9-3. Show that the ellipsoid of inertia of a cube of uniform density is a sphere.

9-4. Suppose that the pulley of the Atwood's machine of Fig. 7-3 has a constant density and a total mass M. Find the moment of inertia of the pulley about its axis of rotation. Then find the kinetic energy of the pulley, and show how the Lagrangian and Lagrange equations of motion of the whole system are altered. Find the new acceleration of the masses.

9-5. Show the equivalence of Lagrange's equations (9-75) and Euler's equations.

9-6. Verify the correctness of Fig. 9-21.

9-7. Calculate the eastward deflection of a freely falling body from the point of view of an observer who is fixed in an inertial system and sees the earth rotating and carrying along a tower of height h from which the body is dropped, thereby showing that the result is again (9-92).

10 Hamilton's equations

We now want to turn to another formulation of the laws of motion which is due to Hamilton. In doing this, we add nothing new to mechanics, of course, but, as a means of increasing our understanding, it turns out to be a particularly valuable way of considering the problem, and it is useful for obtaining even more powerful methods for attacking some problems.

We recall that, in the Lagrangian formulation of the mechanics of a system of n degrees of freedom, we defined the Lagrangian $L(q_1, \ldots, q_n, \dot{q}_1, \ldots, \dot{q}_n) = T - V$ in (7-38) and found the equations of motion as given by (7-39) to be

$$\frac{d}{dt}\left(\frac{\partial L}{\partial \dot{q}_j}\right) - \frac{\partial L}{\partial q_j} = 0 \qquad (10\text{-}1)$$

where $j = 1, 2, \ldots, n$. In this formulation, we completely specify the state of the system by giving all the values of the q_j and the $\dot{q}_j$ at a given time—a total of $2n$ quantities.

We also defined the n generalized momenta in (7-62) as

$$p_j = \frac{\partial L}{\partial \dot{q}_j} \qquad (10\text{-}2)$$

Now we could equally well describe the complete mechanical state of the system by giving the p_j and q_j as functions of the time; thus we would be putting the generalized momenta on an equal footing with the generalized coordinates, rather than using the $\dot{q}_j$. If we are going to do this, we would certainly like to write the equations of motion directly and entirely in terms of the p's and q's. The way in which this can be done was first developed by Hamilton.

We define a new function of the p_j and q_j:

$$H = H(p_1, \ldots, p_n, q_1, \ldots, q_n) = \sum_j p_j \dot{q}_j - L(q_1, \ldots, q_n, \dot{q}_1, \ldots, \dot{q}_n)$$

(10-3)

In (10-3), we have asserted that H is really a function of the p_j and q_j, although from the defining equation it looks like a function of the q_j and $\dot{q}_j$. We can verify our assertion by calculating the differential of H from (10-3):

$$dH = \sum_j p_j \, d\dot{q}_j + \sum_j \dot{q}_j \, dp_j - \sum_j \frac{\partial L}{\partial q_j} \, dq_j - \sum_j \frac{\partial L}{\partial \dot{q}_j} \, d\dot{q}_j$$

$$= \sum_j \dot{q}_j \, dp_j - \sum_j \frac{\partial L}{\partial q_j} \, dq_j$$

(10-4)

where we used (10-2) as the basis of cancelling the first and fourth terms. On the other hand, if H is truly a function only of the p_j and q_j, we can write

$$dH = \sum_j \frac{\partial H}{\partial p_j} \, dp_j + \sum_j \frac{\partial H}{\partial q_j} \, dq_j$$

(10-5)

and upon comparison with (10-4) we see that this actually obtains, as was asserted. Equating coefficients in (10-4) and (10-5), we find that

$$\frac{\partial L}{\partial q_j} = -\frac{\partial H}{\partial q_j}, \quad \dot{q}_j = \frac{\partial H}{\partial p_j}$$

(10-6)

We have not used the equations of motion (10-1) yet; from them we see that

$$\frac{\partial L}{\partial q_j} = \frac{d}{dt}\left(\frac{\partial L}{\partial \dot{q}_j}\right) = \frac{dp_j}{dt} = \dot{p}_j$$

so that (10-6) finally becomes

$$\dot{p}_j = -\frac{\partial H}{\partial q_j}, \quad \dot{q}_j = \frac{\partial H}{\partial p_j}$$

(10-7)

This set of $2n$ first order differential equations is known as *Hamilton's canonical equations*. We shall still obtain $2n$ constants of integration upon integrating the equations of motion (10-7); as usual, these constants can be evaluated in terms of the initial conditions.

We also recall that, by definition, if q_j is a cyclic coordinate, q_j does not appear in L and $p_j = $ const., by (7-64). From the point of view of Hamilton's equations (10-7), if $p_j = $ const., then $\dot{p}_j = 0$ and $\partial H/\partial q_j = 0$, and q_j does not appear in H. Thus, if a given coordinate is cyclic in the

Lagrangian formulation, it is also cyclic in the Hamiltonian formulation. In this case, we can easily see why a cyclic coordinate is also called "ignorable." If q_n, for example, is cyclic, p_n will be some constant α, and we can write $H = H(q_1, \ldots, q_{n-1}, p_1, \ldots, p_{n-1}, \alpha)$; we are really dealing with a problem of only $2(n - 1)$ variables. Thus we can solve the problem, *ignoring* q_n, except for the constant of integration, α. Once all this is done, q_n can be found as a function of time from $\dot{q}_n = \partial H/\partial p_n = \partial H/\partial \alpha$ .Such simplifications are not possible in the Lagrangian formulation, however, because, even if q_j does not appear in L, $\dot{q}_j$ generally does, so that one has to continue to consider the problem for all the variables.

We also recall that, in our discussion of conservation theorems, we were able to show that the quantity

$$h = \sum_j p_j \dot{q}_j - L \tag{10-8}$$

was a constant of the motion and, in fact, was equal to the total energy E of our conservative system. Comparing (10-8) and (10-3), we see that the physical significance of the Hamiltonian function H is that, for a conservative system, it is exactly the *total energy expressed as a function of the p's and q's.* [In (10-8), h is *not* the Hamiltonian, even though it is numerically equal to the energy, for it is written as a function of the q's and $\dot{q}$'s.]

Example. Linear Harmonic Oscillator. From (7-40),

$$E = T + V = \tfrac{1}{2}m\dot{x}^2 + \tfrac{1}{2}kx^2 \tag{10-9}$$

and, therefore, $p = \partial L/\partial \dot{x} = \partial T/\partial \dot{x} = m\dot{x}$. Expressing (10-9) as a function of p and x, we get

$$H = H(p, x) = T + V = \tfrac{1}{2}m\left(\frac{p}{m}\right)^2 + \tfrac{1}{2}kx^2 = \frac{p^2}{2m} + \tfrac{1}{2}kx^2 \tag{10-10}$$

The equations of motion (10-7) become

$$\dot{p} = -\frac{\partial H}{\partial x} = -kx, \quad \dot{x} = \frac{\partial H}{\partial p} = \frac{p}{m} \tag{10-11}$$

These two can be combined to yield $m\ddot{x} = -kx$, which is, of course, the same as (7-42).

Example. Particle Moving Near the Surface of the Earth. From (7-43) and (7-45), we have

$$T = \tfrac{1}{2}m(\dot{x}^2 + \dot{y}^2 + \dot{z}^2), \quad V = mgz \tag{10-12}$$

Therefore, by (10-2),

$$p_x = m\dot{x}, \quad p_y = m\dot{y}, \quad p_z = m\dot{z} \tag{10-13}$$

so that, if we use $H = T + V$ with (10-12) and (10-13), we obtain

$$H = H(p_x, p_y, p_z, x, y, z) = \frac{1}{2m}(p_x^2 + p_y^2 + p_z^2) + mgz \quad (10\text{-}14)$$

The equations of motion (10-7) become

$$\dot{p}_x = \dot{p}_y = 0, \quad \dot{p}_z = -mg$$

$$\dot{x} = \frac{p_x}{m}, \quad \dot{y} = \frac{p_y}{m}, \quad \dot{z} = \frac{p_z}{m}$$

Again we can eliminate the momenta from these equations to give the more common equations $\ddot{x} = \ddot{y} = 0, \ddot{z} = -g$, as found before in (7-47).

Example. Particle in a Central Field. From (8-18), we have

$$L = \tfrac{1}{2}m(\dot{r}^2 + r^2\dot{\theta}^2) - V(r) = T - V \quad (10\text{-}15)$$

We find at once that

$$p_r = \frac{\partial L}{\partial \dot{r}} = m\dot{r}, \quad p_\theta = \frac{\partial L}{\partial \dot{\theta}} = mr^2\dot{\theta} \quad (10\text{-}16)$$

Hence the Hamiltonian is

$$H = T + V = \frac{p_r^2}{2m} + \frac{p_\theta^2}{2mr^2} + V(r) \quad (10\text{-}17)$$

The equations of motion (10-7) then become

$$\dot{p}_r = -\frac{\partial H}{\partial r} = \frac{p_\theta^2}{mr^3} - \frac{dV}{dr} = \frac{p_\theta^2}{mr^3} + f(r)$$

$$\dot{p}_\theta = -\frac{\partial H}{\partial \theta} = 0, \quad \dot{r} = \frac{\partial H}{\partial p_r} = \frac{p_r}{m}, \quad \dot{\theta} = \frac{\partial H}{\partial p_\theta} = \frac{p_\theta}{mr^2}$$

which are easily seen to be equivalent to (8-20) and (8-21).

As we look back over these examples, we see that the differential equations of motion which we finally obtain are essentially the same ones we would have obtained if we had simply used Lagrange's equations in the first place, and that the use of Hamilton's equations has not made the problems easier to solve. As this is fairly generally true, in actually solving problems there is little choice between the two formulations and, in fact, the Lagrangian method is often easier to use.

The principal advantages of the Hamiltonian formulation arise from the fact that it gives equal status to "coordinates" and "momenta." This gives one a great deal more freedom in choosing what one will call coordinates or momenta, and this greater freedom is efficiently exploited in more abstract and profound formulations of mechanics whose natural starting point is based on the Hamiltonian method. From the point of view of atomic physics, the Hamiltonian formulation of mechanics is the natural and usual way of beginning the development of quantum mechanics, and the identification of the numerical value of the Hamiltonian with the energy of a conservative system is very important in the study of energy changes which are possible in atoms and molecules. The relation between the energy and the Hamiltonian is also of vital importance in statistical mechanics in which the macroscopic properties of systems are calculated as averages of atomic and molecular properties; the characteristics of the description in terms of generalized coordinates and momenta are essential for the formulation of the probability concepts required to evaluate these averages.

Exercises

10-1. Show that the Hamiltonian for the particle in spherical coordinates described in Exercise 7-4 is

$$H = \frac{1}{2m}\left(p_r{}^2 + \frac{p_\theta{}^2}{r^2} + \frac{p_\varphi{}^2}{r^2 \sin^2 \theta}\right) + V$$

Find the Hamiltonian equations of motion for a central force. How are the results modified if $r = $ const., as for a spherical pendulum?

10-2. Find the Hamiltonian function and Hamiltonian equations of motion for the symmetric rigid body whose kinetic energy is given by (9-67).

11 *Hamilton's principle*

In this chapter, we discuss the relation of Lagrange's equations of motion to a quite different formulation of the laws of motion which has been of great historical and practical importance. In order to do this, we shall first digress somewhat to consider a particular class of mathematical problems.

11-1 Calculus of variations

The fundamental problem of the calculus of variations can be stated as follows: If we form the definite integral

$$I = \int_{x_1}^{x_2} F\left(x, y, \frac{dy}{dx}\right) dx = \int_{x_1}^{x_2} F(x, y, y') dx \qquad (11\text{-}1)$$

for what function, $y = y(x)$, is the value of this integral a maximum or a minimum, for the *given* function $F(x, y, y')$ and the *fixed* end points x_1 and x_2? With the aid of Fig. 11-1, we also see that the problem can be reworded: What path should one follow in order to make the value of the integral a maximum or a minimum?

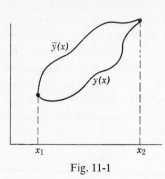

Fig. 11-1

To solve this problem, we see that, if we could somehow make I a function of a single variable, we could use a basic calculus result to determine the condition for a maximum or minimum by equating to zero the derivative of I with respect to this variable. These considerations lead to the reasons for the introduction of the *varied path*. Suppose $y(x)$ is the path for which I has its extreme value; then we define the varied path $\bar{y}(x)$ as

$$\bar{y}(x) = y(x) + \epsilon\eta(x) \tag{11-2}$$

where ϵ is a small quantity and $\eta(x)$ is an arbitrary continuous function of x subject only to the requirements that

$$\eta(x_1) = \eta(x_2) = 0 \tag{11-3}$$

so that

$$\bar{y}(x_1) = y(x_1), \quad \bar{y}(x_2) = y(x_2) \tag{11-4}$$

If we keep ϵ small, we can speak of $\bar{y}(x)$ as a varied path which is only slightly different from $y(x)$ and whose end points coincide with those of $y(x)$; this is also shown in Fig. 11-1.

We shall also have

$$\frac{d\bar{y}}{dx} = \frac{dy}{dx} + \epsilon\frac{d\eta}{dx} = \bar{y}' = y' + \epsilon\eta' \tag{11-5}$$

If (11-2) and (11-5) are substituted into (11-1), then I as determined by integrating along the varied path is

$$I = \int_{x_1}^{x_2} F(x, y + \epsilon\eta, y' + \epsilon\eta') \, dx = I(\epsilon) \tag{11-6}$$

so that I is now a function of the parameter ϵ. We now require that y and ϵ be chosen so that $I(\epsilon)$ is an extremum (maximum or minimum) for $\epsilon = 0$, that is, for the path $y(x)$; this condition is simply that

$$\left(\frac{dI}{d\epsilon}\right)_{\epsilon=0} = 0 \tag{11-7}$$

The simplest way of carrying out this procedure is to expand F in a Taylor series; then (11-6) becomes

$$I(\epsilon) = \int_{x_1}^{x_2} \left[F(x, y, y') + \epsilon\eta \frac{\partial F}{\partial y} + \epsilon\eta' \frac{\partial F}{\partial y'} + \cdots \right] dx \qquad (11\text{-}8)$$

where the terms in the integrand which are not written out are proportional to $\epsilon^2, \epsilon^3, \ldots$. Therefore

$$\frac{dI}{d\epsilon} = \int_{x_1}^{x_2} \left[\eta \frac{\partial F}{\partial y} + \eta' \frac{\partial F}{\partial y'} + \cdots \right] dx \qquad (11\text{-}9)$$

where the terms in the integrand which are not written out are proportional to $\epsilon, \epsilon^2, \ldots$. When we set $\epsilon = 0$, the only terms remaining in the integrand will be those shown, and we obtain

$$\left(\frac{dI}{d\epsilon}\right)_{\epsilon=0} = \int_{x_1}^{x_2} \left[\eta \frac{\partial F}{\partial y} + \eta' \frac{\partial F}{\partial y'} \right] dx = 0 \qquad (11\text{-}10)$$

This can be put into a more useful form by integrating the last integral in (11-10) by parts and using (11-3):

$$\int_{x_1}^{x_2} \eta' \frac{\partial F}{\partial y'} dx = \left[\eta(x) \frac{\partial F}{\partial y'} \right]_{x_1}^{x_2} - \int_{x_1}^{x_2} \eta \frac{d}{dx}\left(\frac{\partial F}{\partial y'}\right) dx$$

$$= -\int_{x_1}^{x_2} \eta \frac{d}{dx}\left(\frac{\partial F}{\partial y'}\right) dx \qquad (11\text{-}11)$$

When (11-11) is substituted into (11-10), we get

$$\int_{x_1}^{x_2} \eta(x)\left[\frac{\partial F}{\partial y} - \frac{d}{dx}\left(\frac{\partial F}{\partial y'}\right) \right] dx = 0 \qquad (11\text{-}12)$$

The function $\eta(x)$ is completely arbitrary, however, and therefore the integral in (11-12) can always be zero only if the term in brackets vanishes, so that we must have

$$\frac{d}{dx}\left(\frac{\partial F}{\partial y'}\right) - \frac{\partial F}{\partial y} = 0 \qquad (11\text{-}13)$$

Since the form of F is assumed to be given, the result (11-13) is a differential equation for y from which we can find $y(x)$. We know that, for this form of $y(x)$, that is, this path of integration, the integral I will have a maximum or minimum value, since (11-13) is equivalent to (11-7).

This result can be easily generalized. Suppose that F is now a function of n variables $y_1, \ldots, y_j, \ldots, y_n$ and their first derivatives $y_1', \ldots, y_j', \ldots, y_n'$. We can proceed as before by defining a new set of functions

$\bar{y}_j = y_j + \epsilon_j \eta_j$ and substituting them into the defining equation for I. The conditions to be fulfilled would then be that

$$\frac{\partial I(\epsilon_1, \ldots, \epsilon_j, \ldots, \epsilon_n)}{\partial \epsilon_j} = 0 \qquad (11\text{-}14)$$

when $\epsilon_1 = \cdots = \epsilon_j = \cdots = \epsilon_n = 0$; there would be n equations like (11-14), one for each value of j. The final result will clearly be that the functions y_j must satisfy the n equations

$$\frac{d}{dx}\left(\frac{\partial F}{\partial y_j{}'}\right) - \frac{\partial F}{\partial y_j} = 0, \quad j = 1, 2, \ldots, n \qquad (11\text{-}15)$$

which are the generalizations of (11-13).

When ϵ is small, the quantity

$$I(\epsilon) - I(0) = \epsilon \frac{dI}{d\epsilon} \qquad (11\text{-}16)$$

is called the *variation* of the integral and is also written

$$I(\epsilon) - I(0) = \delta I = \delta \int_{x_1}^{x_2} F(x, y, y') \, dx \qquad (11\text{-}17)$$

It is obviously the difference between the integrals as evaluated over the two paths. Our requirement that the integral be an extremum can now, with the help of (11-16) and (11-17), be seen to be the same as requiring that the variation vanish:

$$\delta \int_{x_1}^{x_2} F(x, y, y') \, dx = \int_{x_1}^{x_2} \delta F(x, y, y') \, dx = 0 \qquad (11\text{-}18)$$

We can make the replacement shown in (11-18) because the integral has fixed end points and therefore

$$\delta \int_{x_1}^{x_2} F \, dx = \int_{x_1}^{x_2} F(\epsilon) \, dx - \int_{x_1}^{x_2} F(0) \, dx = \int_{x_1}^{x_2} [F(\epsilon) - F(0)] \, dx$$

$$= \int_{x_1}^{x_2} \delta F \, dx \qquad (11\text{-}19)$$

Example. Shortest Distance between Two Points in a Plane. If we let s be the distance along the curve connecting the two points P_1 and P_2 shown in Fig. 11-2, then

$$s = \int_{x_1}^{x_2} \sqrt{(dx)^2 + (dy)^2} = \int_{x_1}^{x_2} \sqrt{1 + \left(\frac{dy}{dx}\right)^2} \, dx = \int_{x_1}^{x_2} \sqrt{1 + y'^2} \, dx \quad (11\text{-}20)$$

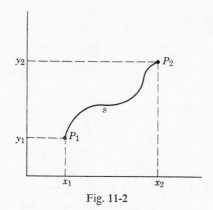

Fig. 11-2

Comparing (11-20) and (11-1), we see that here

$$F = \sqrt{1 + y'^2} \qquad (11\text{-}21)$$

and (11-13) becomes

$$\frac{d}{dx}\left(\frac{\partial F}{\partial y'}\right) = 0$$

and

$$\frac{\partial F}{\partial y'} = \frac{y'}{\sqrt{1 + y'^2}} = \text{const.} = \alpha \qquad (11\text{-}22)$$

Solving (11-22) for y', we find that

$$y' = \frac{dy}{dx} = \frac{\alpha}{\sqrt{1 - \alpha^2}} = \text{const.}$$

and therefore

$$y = \frac{\alpha}{\sqrt{1 - \alpha^2}} x + \beta \qquad (11\text{-}23)$$

where β is another constant. This result is exactly the equation of a straight line; thus we have obtained the well-known result that the shortest distance between two points in a plane is along the straight line connecting them.

The constants α and β can be determined from the condition that the straight line (11-23) pass through the points P_1 and P_2. Therefore

$$y_1 = \frac{\alpha}{\sqrt{1 - \alpha^2}} x_1 + \beta, \quad y_2 = \frac{\alpha}{\sqrt{1 - \alpha^2}} x_2 + \beta$$

so that

$$\frac{\alpha}{\sqrt{1 - \alpha^2}} = \frac{y_2 - y_1}{x_2 - x_1}, \quad \beta = \frac{y_1 x_2 - y_2 x_1}{x_2 - x_1}$$

and (11-23) can be written

$$y = \left(\frac{y_2 - y_1}{x_2 - x_1}\right) x + \left(\frac{y_1 x_2 - y_2 x_1}{x_2 - x_1}\right)$$

11-2 Hamilton's principle

At this point, we return to mechanics; if we make the replacements

$$x \to t, \quad y_j \to q_j, \quad y_j' \to \dot{q}_j, \quad F \to L \qquad (11\text{-}24)$$

we see at once that the equations (11-15) become exactly Lagrange's equations (7-39). Therefore we can say that the fact that the laws of motion can be written as Lagrange's equations means that the actual (or dynamical) paths followed by the particles of the system are such that the integral

$$I = \int_{t_1}^{t_2} L(q_1, \ldots, q_n, \dot{q}_1, \ldots, \dot{q}_n)\, dt \qquad (11\text{-}25)$$

has a maximum or a minimum value as compared with the value obtained for any other path which has the same end points in time. Or, to say it another way, the natural motion of the system is such that the time integral of the Lagrangian, taken between any two configurations of the system, has an extreme value. This result is called *Hamilton's principle*.

Thus we have seen that we have these two alternative, yet equivalent, ways of describing the motion of the system: Lagrange's equations (7-39), or

$$\delta \int_{t_1}^{t_2} L(q_1, \ldots, q_n, \dot{q}_1, \ldots, \dot{q}_n)\, dt = 0 \qquad (11\text{-}26)$$

which follows from (11-18). The integral would have to be evaluated by choosing definite forms of the functions $q_j(t)$. In principle, then, the way in which one would solve a problem in mechanics by using Hamilton's principle would be to *guess* various forms for $q_j(t)$, put them into the integral and evaluate it, and then keep using this procedure until all the $q_j(t)$ which result in an extreme value for the integral have been found. In this way, the solution to the problem would have been obtained because the q's would then be known as functions of the time.

In the use of (11-26), it is important to remember that the functions q_j are chosen to have the same end points. In Fig. 11-3, we illustrate the situation for a system of two degrees of freedom and coordinates q_1 and q_2. The *actual*, or dynamical, path is labeled D, and a possible varied, or nondynamical, path is labeled N. The projections of these paths, D' and N',

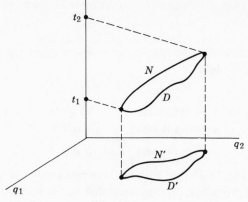

Fig. 11-3

on the q_1q_2 plane are also shown; these projections are the spatial points traced out by the system and therefore are the *geometrical* paths or orbits. We see from the figure that it would be perfectly possible for the non-dynamical path to be different in q_1q_2t space but have the same geometrical path, i.e., projection, in the q_1q_2 space. A possible example of this sort of situation could be the free fall of a body under gravity: the actual path which follows from the law of motion is one of *constant acceleration*; a non-dynamical path could be chosen as one of *constant speed*; in both cases, the body would cover the same geometrical path, or points in space.

Let us discuss this last example in some detail and show that the integrals (11-25) for the two paths are really different. For this one-dimensional problem, the Lagrangian as obtained from (7-46) is

$$L = \tfrac{1}{2}m\dot{z}^2 - mgz \tag{11-27}$$

Suppose the body is released from rest at $t = 0$ and $z = 0$ and falls a total distance h in a time T, as illustrated in Fig. 11-4a.

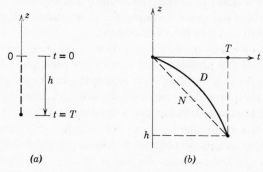

(a)   (b)

Fig. 11-4

We know, from (7-47) and (4-8), that on the dynamical path (D)

$$z = -\tfrac{1}{2}gt^2 \tag{11-28}$$

and that $z = 0$ when $t = t_1 = 0$ and $z = -h$ when $t = t_2 = T$, so that from (11-28) we obtain

$$h = \tfrac{1}{2}gT^2 \quad \text{or} \quad T = \sqrt{2h/g} \tag{11-29}$$

We choose the non-dynamical path (N) to be the one for which the particle falls with a constant speed v_0. Therefore

$$z = -v_0 t \quad \text{and} \quad h = v_0 T \tag{11-30}$$

We see from Fig. 11-4b that both of these paths have the same end points and the same projection on the z axis, that is, the same geometrical path.

On the dynamical path, $\dot{z} = -gt$ and, from (11-27) and (11-28), we find that $L = \tfrac{1}{2}mg^2t^2 + \tfrac{1}{2}mg^2t^2 = mg^2t^2$ and (11-25) becomes

$$I_D = \int_{t_1}^{t_2} L \, dt = \int_0^T mg^2t^2 \, dt = \tfrac{1}{3}mg^2T^3 = \frac{2^{3/2}mg^{1/2}h^{3/2}}{3} \tag{11-31}$$

with the aid of (11-29).

On the non-dynamical path, $\dot{z} = -v_0$ and, from (11-27) and (11-30), we find that $L = \tfrac{1}{2}mv_0^2 + mgv_0t$ so that (11-25) becomes

$$I_N = \int_0^T (\tfrac{1}{2}mv_0^2 + mgv_0t) \, dt = \tfrac{1}{2}mv_0^2 T + \tfrac{1}{2}mgv_0 T^2 = \tfrac{9}{8}I_D \tag{11-32}$$

with the use of (11-29), (11-30), and (11-31). Therefore we see that $I_N > I_D$, or

$$\underset{\text{non-dynam}}{\int_{t_1}^{t_2}} L \, dt > \underset{\text{dynam}}{\int_{t_1}^{t_2}} L \, dt \tag{11-33}$$

Thus, here the integral over the actual path is a minimum as compared with that over the non-dynamical path. This is actually the usual situation, as it generally turns out that the integral $\int L \, dt$ is a minimum, as compared to the varied paths, rather than a maximum.

It is evident from our previous discussion of the procedure one would need to use in solving problems that Hamilton's principle is not of much practical value for this purpose. The principal advantages of Hamilton's principle are that it provides us with a quite different point of view toward mechanics and thus broadens our understanding of it, and it enables us to write a basic law of mechanics in a form which is independent of any special coordinate system, in contrast to Lagrange's equations which have to be written explicitly in terms of the coordinates. Hamilton's principle is only one of several "variational principles" which can be formulated for mechanics; for example, (11-26) can be expressed in terms of an integral of the Hamiltonian function rather than the Lagrangian, and it is this form which is so useful in developing the more advanced aspects of mechanics.

Exercises

11-1. Show that the shortest distance between two points in three dimensions is a straight line.

11-2. Solve the problem of the freely falling body by using a path of the form $z = -at^n$, where n is to be found. Start with (11-27) and evaluate the integral I. Then find the condition $dI/dn = 0$ for the extreme value of I, and thus show that $n = 2$.

12 Normal modes of coupled systems

We have already discussed some aspects of the mechanics of systems of particles to the extent of considering some general theorems and also the motion of the system as a whole when it is treated as a rigid body. Now we want to consider what is essentially the internal motion of the system since no body is really rigid, and also we want to discuss situations in which the motion of a given particle is influenced by the motions of all the other particles in the system. An example of the latter case would be the double pendulum discussed in Exercise 7-3. Although there were only two particles in the system, the general equations of motion were quite complicated. Hence, when we come to consider systems of very many particles, we can expect to find that the equations of motion will be exceedingly involved and a general solution very difficult, if not impossible, to obtain.

As a result of these considerations, we are going to make a strong limiting assumption about the motion, namely, that the displacements of the particles are restricted to small deviations from positions of *stable* equilibrium. We shall then find that the forces depend only on the first powers of the displacements, and we shall obtain a set of equations of motion which can be solved, in principle at least, and we shall be able to make some interesting and useful statements about the general motion. In spite of the fairly restrictive nature of these assumptions, the method of treatment we shall develop is applicable to a wide variety of problems, in modern atomic and molecular physics as well as in classical physics, and it is very important that one get a good understanding of the method, its applications, and its results.

Since we are considering a system of n degrees of freedom, we shall have a total of n equations of motion. If n is very large, as it would be for a large number of particles, we could have a very unwieldy situation. Fortunately, it is possible to define variables known as *normal coordinates* whose characteristic feature is that *all particle coordinates oscillate with the same frequency*. The special motions corresponding to these *normal frequencies* are called the *normal modes* of the system. We shall learn the extremely important fact that the general motion of the system can be regarded as an appropriate *superposition* of the normal modes. This is a general result, and we shall illustrate it for a great variety of situations as we proceed.

12-1   Equations of motion of a coupled system

The system is in equilibrium for the values $q_{01}, q_{02}, \ldots, q_{0n}$ of the generalized coordinates when the generalized forces vanish:

$$Q_j = -\left(\frac{\partial V}{\partial q_j}\right)_0 = 0 \tag{12-1}$$

Therefore, if we assume the equilibrium to be stable, the potential energy is a minimum when evaluated at these q_{0j}.

If we introduce the displacements u_j of the generalized coordinates from their equilibrium values, we can write

$$q_j = q_{0j} + u_j \tag{12-2}$$

and we see that we can take the u_j as equally good generalized coordinates for the system. Since we shall be interested only in motions for which the displacements are small, it will be appropriate to expand every relevant dynamical quantity in a Taylor's series about equilibrium and keep only the lowest order non-vanishing terms. If we do this for the potential energy, we obtain

$$V(q_1, \ldots, q_n) = V(u_1, \ldots, u_n) = V(q_{01}, \ldots, q_{0n}) + \sum_{j=1}^{n}\left(\frac{\partial V}{\partial q_j}\right)_0 u_j$$

$$+ \frac{1}{2}\sum_{j=1}^{n}\sum_{k=1}^{n}\left(\frac{\partial^2 V}{\partial q_j\,\partial q_k}\right)_0 u_j u_k + \cdots \tag{12-3}$$

The second term of (12-3) vanishes because of (12-1). Since $V(q_{01}, \ldots, q_{0n})$ is a constant, we can change the zero of our potential energy and this term can be dropped from (12-3); and we obtain for the potential energy the approximation

$$V = \frac{1}{2}\sum_{j}\sum_{k}\left(\frac{\partial^2 V}{\partial q_j\,\partial q_k}\right)_0 u_j u_k = \frac{1}{2}\sum_{j,k} v_{jk} u_j u_k \tag{12-4}$$

which is quadratic in the displacements. We see that the v_{jk} depend only on the equilibrium values q_{0j} and are constants; they can be calculated from a knowledge of the properties of the system at equilibrium. We also see that the v_{jk} are symmetric in the indices; that is,

$$v_{jk} = v_{kj} \tag{12-5}$$

If we calculate the generalized force from (12-4) and (12-2), we get

$$Q_j = -\frac{\partial V}{\partial q_j} = -\frac{\partial V}{\partial u_j} = -\sum_k v_{jk} u_k \tag{12-6}$$

which shows that the force tending to change any generalized coordinate depends on the displacement of *all* the others—this is, of course, exactly what we have in mind when we call this a coupled system.

We can obtain a similar expansion for the kinetic energy. If we use (7-59) and (12-2), we get

$$T = \tfrac{1}{2} \sum_{j=1}^{n} \sum_{k=1}^{n} a_{jk} \dot{q}_j \dot{q}_k = \tfrac{1}{2} \sum_{j,k} a_{jk} \dot{u}_j \dot{u}_k \tag{12-7}$$

where the coefficients of this homogeneous quadratic function of the velocities are given by (7-60) to be

$$a_{jk} = a_{kj} = \sum_{i=1}^{N} m_i \left(\frac{\partial \mathbf{r}_i}{\partial q_j}\right) \cdot \left(\frac{\partial \mathbf{r}_i}{\partial q_k}\right) = a_{jk}(q_1, \dots, q_n) \tag{12-8}$$

for a system of N particles.

If we expand the coefficients a_{jk}, we obtain

$$a_{jk}(q_1, \dots, q_n) = a_{jk}(q_{01}, \dots, q_{0n}) + \sum_{l=1}^{n} \left(\frac{\partial a_{jk}}{\partial q_l}\right)_0 u_l + \cdots \tag{12-9}$$

Since T is already quadratic in the small quantities $\dot{u}_j$, we can get the lowest order non-vanishing approximation to T by taking

$$a_{jk}(q_1, \dots, q_n) \simeq a_{jk}(q_{01}, \dots, q_{0n}) = t_{jk} = t_{kj} \tag{12-10}$$

The symmetric quantities t_{jk} depend only on the equilibrium configuration and are constants characteristic of the given system. Thus, for small displacements, the kinetic energy is obtained by substituting (12-10) into (12-7) with the result that

$$T = \tfrac{1}{2} \sum_{j,k} t_{jk} \dot{u}_j \dot{u}_k \tag{12-11}$$

From (12-4) and (12-11), we find the Lagrangian to be

$$L = T - V = \tfrac{1}{2} \sum_{j,k} (t_{jk} \dot{u}_j \dot{u}_k - v_{jk} u_j u_k) \tag{12-12}$$

and the Lagrangian equations of motion (7-39) will be

$$\frac{d}{dt}\left(\frac{\partial L}{\partial \dot{u}_j}\right) - \frac{\partial L}{\partial u_j} = 0 \qquad (12\text{-}13)$$

Using (12-12), (12-5), and (12-10), we find that

$$\frac{\partial L}{\partial \dot{u}_j} = \frac{1}{2}\sum_k (t_{jk}\dot{u}_k + t_{kj}\dot{u}_k) = \sum_k t_{jk}\dot{u}_k$$

$$\frac{\partial L}{\partial u_j} = -\frac{1}{2}\sum_k (v_{jk}u_k + v_{kj}u_k) = -\sum_k v_{jk}u_k$$

and (12-13) becomes

$$\sum_{k=1}^{n}(t_{jk}\ddot{u}_k + v_{jk}u_k) = 0 \qquad (12\text{-}14)$$

where $j = 1, 2, \ldots, n$. These are the equations of motion of our coupled system.

Each of the n equations (12-14) will generally involve all the coordinates, and it is this set which must be solved to find the motion of the system. In general, one cannot solve these equations directly; we note, however, that it would be a great simplification if we could somehow replace the set (12-14) by another system of n equations each of which involves only a single variable. This is basically the reason for the introduction of the normal coordinates and normal frequencies; we could, then, approach the problem by trying to find a transformation of coordinates which will separate the set of equations (12-14) into another set in which only one variable is involved in each equation. We shall not do this, however, but shall use another method instead.

12-2   Normal frequencies of oscillation

The equations (12-14) are reminiscent of harmonic oscillator equations because of the dependence of the force on the first powers of the displacements. This fact leads us to begin by trying to see if we can possibly find a solution in which all coordinates oscillate sinusoidally with the same circular frequency ω. Hence we assume a solution of the form

$$u_j = Ca_j e^{-i\omega t} \qquad (12\text{-}15)$$

where $i = \sqrt{-1}$; the amplitude is written Ca_j, where C is a scale factor which is the same for each coordinate; it is introduced here because it will be convenient in results to be obtained later.

The use of the complex notation in (12-15) requires a few words of comment since this is an almost universal procedure and is one which we shall be constantly following. Since the coordinates, of course, are real, the expression (12-15) must somehow give us a real value for u_j. To see how this can be done, suppose we write u_j as

$$u_j = R_j + iI_j \tag{12-16}$$

where both R_j and I_j are real quantities, called the real and imaginary parts of u_j, respectively. Also, let us suppose that u_j satisfies a linear differential equation with *real coefficients* and, to be specific, of the form

$$A\ddot{u}_j + B\dot{u}_j + Cu_j = 0 \tag{12-17}$$

When (12-16) is substituted into (12-17), we obtain

$$(A\ddot{R}_j + B\dot{R}_j + CR_j) + i(A\ddot{I}_j + B\dot{I}_j + CI_j) = 0 \tag{12-18}$$

A complex quantity can be zero only if the real and imaginary parts are separately zero; therefore (12-18) tells us that

$$A\ddot{R}_j + B\dot{R}_j + CR_j = 0 \quad \text{and} \quad A\ddot{I}_j + B\dot{I}_j + CI_j = 0 \tag{12-19}$$

Hence we see from (12-19) that, if u_j is a complex solution of a linear differential equation with real coefficients, of which (12-17) is an example, the real and imaginary parts are *separately* solutions of the same differential equation. Thus we could choose either the real part *or* the imaginary part to represent the solution for the real physical quantity. The standard convention for the choice to be made (and the one we shall follow) is that, if the solution is obtained in complex form, the *real part* shall be chosen to represent the solution.

Therefore it may well turn out that Ca_j is complex, so that

$$Ca_j = \alpha_j + i\beta_j \tag{12-20}$$

When this is substituted into (12-15), we get

$$u_j = (\alpha_j + i\beta_j)e^{-i\omega t} = (\alpha_j \cos \omega t + \beta_j \sin \omega t) + i(-\alpha_j \sin \omega t + \beta_j \cos \omega t) \tag{12-21}$$

and, in accordance with our convention, we would choose

$$u_j = \alpha_j \cos \omega t + \beta_j \sin \omega t \tag{12-22}$$

as our solution for the real physical displacement. Sometimes it is more convenient to write

$$Ca_j = \rho_j e^{i\varphi_j} \tag{12-23}$$

where ρ_j and φ_j are real. When this is substituted into (12-15), and the real part taken, the displacement has the form

$$u_j = \rho_j \cos (\omega t - \varphi_j) \qquad (12\text{-}24)$$

With these results in mind, we shall go on, calculating the displacements as complex, but always remembering to take the real part before making any interpretations of the results.

Using (12-15), we find that $\ddot{u}_j = -\omega^2 C a_j e^{-i\omega t} = -\omega^2 u_j$, and (12-14) becomes

$$\sum_k [-\omega^2 C t_{jk} a_k e^{-i\omega t} + v_{jk} C a_k e^{-i\omega t}] = 0$$

or

$$\sum_k (v_{jk} - \omega^2 t_{jk}) a_k = 0 \qquad (12\text{-}25)$$

where $j = 1, 2, \ldots, n$. Written out, these equations (12-25) are

$(j = 1)$ $(v_{11} - \omega^2 t_{11})a_1 + (v_{12} - \omega^2 t_{12})a_2 + \cdots + (v_{1n} - \omega^2 t_{1n})a_n = 0$

$(j = 2)$ $(v_{21} - \omega^2 t_{21})a_1 + (v_{22} - \omega^2 t_{22})a_2 + \cdots + (v_{2n} - \omega^2 t_{2n})a_n = 0$

$$(12\text{-}26)$$

$\cdots\cdots \quad \cdots\cdots\cdots\cdots\cdots\cdots\cdots\cdots\cdots\cdots\cdots\cdots\cdots\cdots \quad \cdots\cdot$

$(j = n)$ $(v_{n1} - \omega^2 t_{n1})a_1 + (v_{n2} - \omega^2 t_{n2})a_2 + \cdots + (v_{nn} - \omega^2 t_{nn})a_n = 0$

These are n simultaneous linear homogeneous equations for the n unknowns a_j, and they are similar to the equations we discussed in connection with the determination of the principal axes of inertia in Chapter 9. We saw there that these equations (12-26) will have solutions different from the trivial ones $a_1 = a_2 = \cdots = a_n = 0$ only if the determinant of the coefficients vanishes; that is, if

$$\begin{vmatrix} v_{11} - \omega^2 t_{11} & v_{12} - \omega^2 t_{12} & \cdots & v_{1n} - \omega^2 t_{1n} \\ v_{21} - \omega^2 t_{21} & v_{22} - \omega^2 t_{22} & \cdots & \cdots \\ \cdots & \cdots & \cdots & \cdots \\ v_{n1} - \omega^2 t_{n1} & \cdots & \cdots & v_{nn} - \omega^2 t_{nn} \end{vmatrix} = 0 \qquad (12\text{-}27)$$

Because the values of the v_{jk} and the t_{jk} are known from the characteristics of the system, when this determinant (12-27) is expanded the result is an algebraic equation of the nth degree for the unknown ω^2. This equation will have n roots and thus will give us n values of ω^2 for which our solution (12-15) represents a possible solution of the equations of motion (12-14); these values of ω are called the *normal frequencies*. Of course, it may not be easy to solve (12-27) for the actual roots, but that is another problem; in any case, we can label these roots ω^2 in some arbitrary way, for example, in the order of increasing size, so that we can write these n values of ω^2 as $\omega_1{}^2, \omega_2{}^2, \ldots, \omega_l{}^2, \ldots, \omega_n{}^2$. For *each* of these roots the equations (12-26) can be solved for the $n - 1$ ratios of the amplitudes a_j; thus, at this point, we are left with a certain amount of arbitrariness in the determination of the displacements u_j. We shall come back to this point later.

12-3 Normal modes

We now discuss some important properties of these solutions of the equations of motion. Let us consider the lth root, $\omega_l{}^2$. If we substitute this back into (12-26), we obtain the corresponding *set* of a_j's: call them $a_{jl}(j = 1, 2, \ldots, n)$. This whole *set* of n numbers a_{jl} corresponding to the lth normal frequency ω_l is called the lth *normal mode*. Then, *for each l*, the equations of motion (12-25) can be written

$$\sum_k v_{jk}a_{kl} = \omega_l{}^2 \sum_k t_{jk}a_{kl} \tag{12-28}$$

We now want to show that all the roots $\omega_l{}^2$ are real because the v_{jk} and t_{jk} are real and symmetric as given in (12-5) and (12-10).

Let $(\omega_l{}^2)^* = $ complex conjugate of $\omega_l{}^2$, and

$$a_{jl}{}^* = (c_{jl} + id_{jl})^* = c_{jl} - id_{jl} \tag{12-29}$$

If we take the complex conjugate of (12-28) and replace l by m, we obtain

$$\sum_k v_{jk}a_{km}{}^* = (\omega_m{}^2)^* \sum_k t_{jk}a_{km}{}^* \tag{12-30}$$

since v_{jk} and t_{jk} are real.

If we multiply (12-28) by $a_{jm}{}^*$ and sum over j, we get

$$\sum_{j,k} v_{jk}a_{jm}{}^*a_{kl} = \omega_l{}^2 \sum_{j,k} t_{jk}a_{jm}{}^*a_{kl} \tag{12-31}$$

Also, if we multiply (12-30) by a_{jl}, sum over j, interchange j and k, use (12-5) and (12-10), we obtain

$$\sum_{j,k} v_{jk}a_{km}{}^*a_{jl} = (\omega_m{}^2)^* \sum_{j,k} t_{jk}a_{km}{}^*a_{jl} = \sum_{j,k} v_{kj}a_{jm}{}^*a_{kl}$$

$$= \sum_{j,k} v_{jk}a_{jm}{}^*a_{kl} = (\omega_m{}^2)^* \sum_{j,k} t_{kj}a_{jm}{}^*a_{kl}$$

$$= (\omega_m{}^2)^* \sum_{j,k} t_{jk}a_{jm}{}^*a_{kl} = \omega_l{}^2 \sum_{j,k} t_{jk}a_{jm}{}^*a_{kl}$$

where we used (12-31) in the last step. Since the last two terms of the preceding equation are equal, we can subtract them and obtain

$$[(\omega_l{}^2) - (\omega_m{}^2)^*] \sum_{j,k} t_{jk}a_{jm}{}^*a_{kl} = 0 \tag{12-32}$$

Let us consider (12-32) a little more closely, and first of all for the case $m = l$, for which it becomes

$$[(\omega_l^2) - (\omega_l^2)^*] \sum_{j,k} t_{jk} a_{jl}^* a_{kl} = 0 \tag{12-33}$$

Using (12-29), we find that the sum in (12-33) can be written

$$\sum_{j,k} t_{jk} a_{jl}^* a_{kl} = \sum_{j,k} t_{jk}(c_{jl} - id_{jl})(c_{kl} + id_{kl})$$

$$= \sum_{j,k} t_{jk} c_{jl} c_{kl} + \sum_{j,k} t_{jk} d_{jl} d_{kl} + i \sum_{j,k} t_{jk} c_{jl} d_{kl}$$

$$- i \sum_{j,k} t_{jk} c_{kl} d_{jl} \tag{12-34}$$

However, if we interchange j and k in the last sum and use (12-10), we find that

$$\sum_{j,k} t_{jk} c_{kl} d_{jl} = \sum_{j,k} t_{kj} c_{jl} d_{kl} = \sum_{j,k} t_{jk} c_{jl} d_{kl}$$

so that the imaginary terms of (12-34) cancel and we are left with only the first two terms on the right of (12-34). If we now use (12-11), we see that $\sum_{j,k} t_{jk} c_{jl} c_{kl}$ equals twice the kinetic energy which the system would have if the velocities were c_{jl} and c_{kl}; but, since kinetic energy is intrinsically a positive quantity, this double sum must be positive and different from zero. Similarly, the second sum in (12-34) is positive because it equals twice the kinetic energy if the velocities were d_{jl} and d_{kl}. Therefore, from (12-34), we must have

$$\sum_{j,k} t_{jk} a_{jl}^* a_{kl} \neq 0$$

and (12-33) tells us that

$$(\omega_l^2)^* = \omega_l^2 \tag{12-35}$$

Thus we have proved that all the ω_l^2 are *real*, for, if we write $\omega_l^2 = \delta + i\epsilon = (\omega_l^2)^* = \delta - i\epsilon$, we see that upon subtraction we find that $2i\epsilon = 0$, or $\epsilon = 0$, and hence the imaginary part is zero. We can go even further than (12-35), however.

We have assumed for generality that the a_{jl} may be complex. Since we have just shown that all the ω_l^2 are real, we see that the equations (12-28) which determine the a_{jl} have all real coefficients. Because these equations are linear, when we solve them for the $n - 1$ ratios of the a's we shall use only the linear algebraic operations of addition, subtraction, multiplication, and division. Since there will be no necessity of taking any square roots, no complex quantities will be obtained, and we can conclude that the $n - 1$ ratios will also be real. If we now further require that the last arbitrary component of the a_{jl} be chosen to be real, we can say that *all the*

a_{jl} *are real.* [Any complex part of the amplitude of (12-15) is thus put into the common amplitude factor C.]

If we multiply (12-28) by a_{jl} and sum over j, we obtain

$$\omega_l^2 = \frac{\sum\limits_{j,k} v_{jk} a_{jl} a_{kl}}{\sum\limits_{j,k} t_{jk} a_{jl} a_{kl}} = \text{a positive quantity} \qquad (12\text{-}36)$$

since by (12-11) the denominator is twice the value the kinetic energy would have if the velocities were the a_{jl} and is therefore positive, and since by (12-4) the numerator is twice the value the potential energy would have if the displacements were the a_{jl}; this potential energy is positive because we have assumed the equilibrium potential energy to be a minimum. Since $\omega_l^2 > 0$, ω_l itself is *real*; hence all the normal frequencies are real and the motion for a given ω_l will be completely oscillatory about the positions of stable equilibrium.

Taking account of the real nature of all the quantities involved, we can now write our previous result (12-32) as

$$(\omega_l^2 - \omega_m^2) \sum_{j,k} t_{jk} a_{jm} a_{kl} = 0 \qquad (12\text{-}37)$$

If $\omega_l^2 \neq \omega_m^2$, we obtain

$$\sum_{j,k} t_{jk} a_{jm} a_{kl} = 0 \qquad (12\text{-}38)$$

which is called the *orthogonality condition* (or property).

If $l = m$, (12-37) gives us no new information. However, we recall that our solutions for the a_{jl} gave only the $n - 1$ ratios a_{2l}/a_{1l}, etc., so that the values of the a_{jl} are still indeterminate. We can remove this indeterminacy in a way which is completely consistent with (12-37) by *requiring* that

$$\sum_{j,k} t_{jk} a_{jl} a_{kl} = 1 \qquad (12\text{-}39)$$

This equation, plus the equations of motion, completely determines the set of the $n\, a_{jl}$ for each of the n values of ω_l. The reason for this particular requirement (12-39) is the simplification to be obtained later.

These results can be summarized very compactly if we define the *Kronecker delta* symbol δ_{jk} by

$$\delta_{jk} = \begin{cases} 1, & \text{if } j = k \\ 0, & \text{if } j \neq k \end{cases} \qquad (12\text{-}40)$$

Then (12-38) and (12-39) can be written as the single equation

$$\sum_{j,k} t_{jk} a_{jm} a_{kl} = \delta_{ml} \qquad (12\text{-}41)$$

This is called the *orthogonality and normalization* condition, or simply the *orthonormal* condition; it is an extremely important result, as we shall see many times. Strictly speaking, we have not proved that (12-41) is also correct if $l \neq m$ but $\omega_l^2 = \omega_m^2$. This is similar to the situation we found when we were discussing principal axes of inertia, and we shall simply content ourselves with saying that, in this case also, one can show that it is still possible to choose the a_{jl} so that they will be orthogonal.

The reason for the terminology that has been used is that one can give a sort of geometrical interpretation to these results. This is most easily seen if we use rectangular coordinates as our generalized coordinates. For a system of N particles, we would need the $3N$ coordinates $x_1, y_1, z_1, x_2, \ldots,$ z_{N-1}, x_N, y_N, z_N. For convenience, we shall relabel these coordinates $x_1, x_2, x_3, \ldots, x_{n-1}, x_n$ where $n = 3N$. Then we can write the kinetic energy as

$$T = \tfrac{1}{2} \sum_{j=1}^{n} m_j \dot{x}_j^2$$

where $m_1 = m_2 = m_3 =$ mass of the first particle, etc. Comparing this with (12-11), we see that, when rectangular coordinates are used,

$$t_{jk} = m_j \, \delta_{jk} \tag{12-42}$$

so that our general result (12-41) becomes

$$\sum_{j,k} m_j \, \delta_{jk} a_{jm} a_{kl} = \delta_{ml} = \sum_j m_j a_{jm} a_{jl} \tag{12-43}$$

Suppose we now introduce an n-dimensional space with vectors $\mathbf{A}_l$ in it which are defined so that

$$\sqrt{m_j} \, a_{jm} = j\text{th component of } \mathbf{A}_m$$

$$\sqrt{m_j} \, a_{jl} = j\text{th component of } \mathbf{A}_l$$

In this space, then, the scalar product of $\mathbf{A}_m$ and $\mathbf{A}_l$ would be defined as the natural generalization of (1-11) and therefore

$$\mathbf{A}_m \cdot \mathbf{A}_l = \sum_j A_{jm} A_{jl} = \sum_j m_j a_{jm} a_{jl} \tag{12-44}$$

Upon comparing (12-44) and (12-43) we see that, when $m \neq l$, $\mathbf{A}_m \cdot \mathbf{A}_l = 0$; since the scalar product is zero, we can say that the vectors $\mathbf{A}_m$ and $\mathbf{A}_l$ are "perpendicular" or orthogonal. On the other hand, if $m = l$, we see that $\mathbf{A}_l \cdot \mathbf{A}_l = 1$ and these vectors are "unit" vectors. Thus our orthonormal condition (12-43) simply expresses the fact that these unit vectors are all mutually perpendicular. A similar interpretation can be given to the more general orthonormal condition (12-41), but it is more complicated and less easy to visualize.

12-4 The general motion

We have now seen that the equations of motion are satisfied by an oscillatory motion like (12-15) for a set of n frequencies ω_k, and not only by a single frequency. Thus a possible solution to the problem is $u_j = C_k a_{jk} e^{-i\omega_k t}$. Of course, this is not the general solution, but, since the differential equations are linear, an arbitrary sum of special solutions is also a solution. We now assert that the general solution of the problem can be written

$$u_j = \sum_{k=1}^{n} C_k a_{jk} e^{-i\omega_k t} \qquad (12\text{-}45)$$

In other words, the general motion is a superposition of n simple harmonic motions. We know that (12-45) is a solution of the equations of motion, and thus in order to show that it is actually the general solution we must show that it has the appropriate number of arbitrary constants. Now each C_k is complex and therefore equivalent to two constants; since there are n C's, there are a total of $2n$ constants, as there should be for a system of n degrees of freedom. As usual, these $2n$ constants can be determined from the $2n$ initial values of the displacements and velocities. Of course, we must still remember that the real part of (12-45) is to be taken as our actual solution.

We are now able to show that the orthonormal property (12-41) enables us to determine the arbitrary constants in our solution in terms of the initial conditions in a simple and direct way. If we write

$$C_k = c_k + i d_k \qquad (12\text{-}46)$$

the real part of (12-45) is

$$u_j = \sum_k a_{jk}(c_k \cos \omega_k t + d_k \sin \omega_k t) \qquad (12\text{-}47)$$

The initial conditions at $t = 0$ are found from (12-47) to be

$$u_j(0) = \sum_k a_{jk} c_k, \quad \dot{u}_j(0) = \sum_k a_{jk} \omega_k d_k, \qquad (12\text{-}48)$$

If we multiply each side of the first of these by $t_{jl} a_{lm}$, sum over j and l, and use (12-41) and (12-40), we obtain

$$\sum_{j,l} u_j(0) t_{jl} a_{lm} = \sum_k c_k \left[\sum_{j,l} t_{jl} a_{jk} a_{lm} \right] = \sum_k c_k \delta_{mk} = c_m$$

If we replace m by k, we can also write this

$$c_k = \sum_{j,l} u_j(0) t_{jl} a_{lk} \qquad (12\text{-}49)$$

Similarly, we can show that

$$d_k = \frac{1}{\omega_k} \sum_{j,l} \dot{u}_j(0) t_{jl} a_{lk} \tag{12-50}$$

and these two formulas permit the direct computation of the constants needed in the general solution (12-47) in terms of the initial conditions.

12-5 Normal coordinates

We previously remarked that it would be helpful if we could put the equations of motion into such a form that each equation involved only one coordinate. This is what we shall now proceed to do by properly defining a set of *n normal coordinates* ζ_j. We shall not learn anything really new about the nature of the motion, but our description of it will be put into a form which is quite illuminating and very useful for other purposes.

The normal coordinates are related to the original coordinates by the defining equation

$$u_j = \sum_k a_{jk} \zeta_k \tag{12-51}$$

We can find the ζ_j in terms of the u_j by using the orthonormal property; multiplying both sides of (12-51) by $t_{jl}a_{lm}$, summing over j and l, and using (12-41), we obtain

$$\sum_{j,l} u_j t_{jl} a_{lm} = \sum_k \zeta_k \sum_{j,l} t_{jl} a_{jk} a_{lm} = \sum_k \zeta_k \, \delta_{km} = \zeta_m$$

Thus we see that, if (12-51) holds, we have

$$\zeta_l = \sum_{j,k} u_j t_{jk} a_{kl} \tag{12-52}$$

Let us look at the form of the potential and kinetic energies when they are expressed in terms of the normal coordinates. Using (12-4), (12-51), (12-28), (12-41), and (12-40), we obtain

$$V = \tfrac{1}{2} \sum_{j,k} v_{jk} u_j u_k = \tfrac{1}{2} \sum_{j,k} \sum_{l,m} v_{jk} a_{jl} \zeta_l a_{km} \zeta_m$$

$$= \tfrac{1}{2} \sum_{l,m} \zeta_l \zeta_m \sum_j a_{jl} \sum_k v_{jk} a_{km}$$

$$= \tfrac{1}{2} \sum_{l,m} \zeta_l \zeta_m \sum_j a_{jl} \sum_k \omega_m{}^2 t_{jk} a_{km}$$

$$= \tfrac{1}{2} \sum_{l,m} \omega_m{}^2 \zeta_l \zeta_m \sum_{j,k} t_{jk} a_{jl} a_{km}$$

$$= \tfrac{1}{2} \sum_{l,m} \omega_m{}^2 \zeta_l \zeta_m \, \delta_{lm}$$

and, since the sum over m in the last term has a non-vanishing value only when $m = l$, the final result is

$$V = \tfrac{1}{2} \sum_l \omega_l^2 \zeta_l^2 \tag{12-53}$$

Thus we see that, when the potential energy is written in terms of the normal coordinates, it becomes a sum of terms each of which involves only the square of a given normal coordinate.

In the same manner, the kinetic energy becomes

$$T = \tfrac{1}{2} \sum_{j,k} t_{jk} \dot{u}_j \dot{u}_k = \tfrac{1}{2} \sum_{l,m} \dot{\zeta}_l \dot{\zeta}_m \sum_{j,k} t_{jk} a_{jl} a_{km}$$

$$= \tfrac{1}{2} \sum_l \dot{\zeta}_l^2 \tag{12-54}$$

and is given by a sum of squares of "velocities." Thus we see that when normal coordinates are used the cross-product terms, which previously appeared in both the potential and the kinetic energy, no longer appear in (12-53) and (12-54).

The Lagrangian now is

$$L = T - V = \tfrac{1}{2} \sum_l (\dot{\zeta}_l^2 - \omega_l^2 \zeta_l^2) \tag{12-55}$$

and the Lagrangian equations of motion (7-39) become

$$\ddot{\zeta}_k + \omega_k^2 \zeta_k = 0 \tag{12-56}$$

where $k = 1, 2, \ldots, n$. Now, since (12-56) is the equation of motion of a linear harmonic oscillator, we can write the solution as

$$\zeta_k = C_k e^{-i\omega_k t} \tag{12-57}$$

so that (12-51) becomes $u_j = \sum_k a_{jk} C_k e^{-i\omega_k t}$, which we already know to be the correct general solution to our problem. We see from (12-57) that each of the normal coordinates is a periodic function involving only one of the normal frequencies.

We can get a better idea of the meaning of the normal coordinates by seeing what sort of situation is described if only one is different from zero. Let us assume that $\zeta_l \neq 0$ while $\zeta_k = 0$ if $k \neq l$; then (12-51) becomes $u_j = a_{jl} \zeta_l \sim a_{jl}$, so that each displacement is proportional to the corresponding displacement for the lth normal mode. In other words, the existence of only one normal coordinate is equivalent to producing a normal mode for the whole system. If we now look at the Lagrangian (12-55), we see that by introducing the normal coordinates we have put the Lagrangian in a form which describes a system of *independent* oscillators because each term in the sum involves only one normal coordinate, as does the corresponding equation of motion (12-56). Thus we no longer need to deal with the system of coupled oscillators with which we started in (12-12), and we can consider the complete motion for small oscillations as being obtained by exciting these various independent harmonic oscillators (the normal coordinates) with different intensities and phases.

12-6   Example: two coupled pendulums

In order to illustrate and clarify all the many results which we have obtained for a general system up to this point, we want to consider a specific example in great detail. This system consists of two simple pendulums which move in two parallel vertical planes perpendicular to a common flexible support such as a string from which they are suspended, as shown in Fig. 12-1. The coupling between the two is provided by the twisting motion of the support.

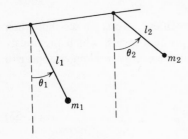

Fig. 12-1

If we choose the angles θ_1 and θ_2 as generalized coordinates, the equilibrium values are $\theta_{j0} = 0$, and therefore, from (12-2), we can let $u_j = \theta_j$. Since there is no twist of the support, or coupling between the two pendulums, if the angles are the same, the potential energy of interaction can depend only on the difference of the angles, $\theta_1 - \theta_2$, and we must have

$$V_{\text{int}} = V_{\text{int}}(\theta_1 - \theta_2), \quad V_{\text{int}}(0) = 0 \tag{12-58}$$

where the last statement is in accord with (12-4).

From (7-54), we obtain

$$T = \tfrac{1}{2}m_1 l_1^2 \dot{\theta}_1^2 + \tfrac{1}{2}m_2 l_2^2 \dot{\theta}_2^2 \tag{12-59}$$

and when we compare (12-59) and (12-11) we see that

$$t_{11} = m_1 l_1^2, \quad t_{22} = m_2 l_2^2, \quad t_{12} = t_{21} = 0 \tag{12-60}$$

Using (7-45), (12-58), and Fig. 12-1, we find the potential energy to be given by

$$V = m_1 g l_1 (1 - \cos \theta_1) + m_2 g l_2 (1 - \cos \theta_2) + V_{\text{int}}(\theta_1 - \theta_2)$$

$$\simeq \tfrac{1}{2}m_1 g l_1 \theta_1^2 + \tfrac{1}{2}m_2 g l_2 \theta_2^2 + \tfrac{1}{2}K(\theta_1 - \theta_2)^2$$

$$= \tfrac{1}{2}(m_1 l_1^2 \omega_1^2 + K)\theta_1^2 + \tfrac{1}{2}(m_2 l_2^2 \omega_2^2 + K)\theta_2^2 - K\theta_1\theta_2 \tag{12-61}$$

where $K = \partial^2 V_{int}/\partial(\theta_1 - \theta_2)^2$ and

$$\omega_1{}^2 = \frac{g}{l_1}, \quad \omega_2{}^2 = \frac{g}{l_2} \tag{12-62}$$

Comparing (12-61) and (12-4), we find that

$$v_{11} = m_1 l_1{}^2 \omega_1{}^2 + K$$

$$v_{22} = m_2 l_2{}^2 \omega_2{}^2 + K \tag{12-63}$$

$$v_{12} = v_{21} = -K$$

since $-K\theta_1\theta_2 = -\tfrac{1}{2}K\theta_1\theta_2 - \tfrac{1}{2}K\theta_2\theta_1$.

The equations (12-26) then become

$$[(m_1 l_1{}^2 \omega_1{}^2 + K) - m_1 l_1{}^2 \omega^2]a_1 - Ka_2 = 0 \tag{12-64a}$$

$$-Ka_1 + [(m_2 l_2{}^2 \omega_2{}^2 + K) - m_2 l_2{}^2 \omega^2]a_2 = 0 \tag{12-64b}$$

If we let

$$\frac{K}{m_1 l_1{}^2} = K_1, \quad \frac{K}{m_2 l_2{}^2} = K_2 \tag{12-65}$$

the equations (12-64) become

$$(\omega_1{}^2 - \omega^2 + K_1)a_1 - K_1 a_2 = 0 \tag{12-66a}$$

$$-K_2 a_1 + (\omega_2{}^2 - \omega^2 + K_2)a_2 = 0 \tag{12-66b}$$

Let us first review the case of no coupling, for which $K = 0$ and hence $K_1 = K_2 = 0$; then (12-66) give $(\omega_1{}^2 - \omega^2)a_1 = 0$ and $(\omega_2{}^2 - \omega^2)a_2 = 0$. This result shows that the two pendulums oscillate with their known natural frequencies and there are no restrictions on the relative values of a_1 and a_2; this statement simply describes the fact that they are independent.

In order to find the normal frequencies, we compare (12-27) and (12-66) and obtain the equation

$$\begin{vmatrix} (\omega_1{}^2 - \omega^2 + K_1) & -K_1 \\ -K_2 & (\omega_2{}^2 - \omega^2 + K_2) \end{vmatrix}$$

$$= (\omega_1{}^2 - \omega^2 + K_1)(\omega_2{}^2 - \omega^2 + K_2) - K_1 K_2 = 0 \tag{12-67}$$

When this is expanded, it is a quadratic equation in ω^2 whose roots are

$$\omega^2 = \tfrac{1}{2}(\omega_1{}^2 + \omega_2{}^2 + K_1 + K_2) \pm \tfrac{1}{2}[(\omega_1{}^2 - \omega_2{}^2)^2$$

$$+ 2(\omega_1{}^2 - \omega_2{}^2)(K_1 - K_2) + (K_1 + K_2)^2]^{1/2} \tag{12-68}$$

Thus, corresponding to the two possible normal modes of this system of two degrees of freedom, we have the two solutions ω_+^2 and ω_-^2 obtained by choosing the plus or minus sign, respectively, in (12-68).

Because it is difficult to see the qualitative effect of the interaction from the general result (12-68), we shall look for an approximation corresponding to K_1 and K_2 being small. If we assume $\omega_1^2 \neq \omega_2^2$, and keep only terms which are linear in K_1 and K_2, we can approximate the square root in (12-68) by

$$[(\omega_1^2 - \omega_2^2)^2 + 2(\omega_1^2 - \omega_2^2)(K_1 - K_2)]^{\frac{1}{2}}$$

$$= (\omega_1^2 - \omega_2^2)\left[1 + \frac{2(K_1 - K_2)}{(\omega_1^2 - \omega_2^2)}\right]^{\frac{1}{2}}$$

$$\simeq (\omega_1^2 - \omega_2^2)\left[1 + \frac{(K_1 - K_2)}{(\omega_1^2 - \omega_2^2)}\right] = (\omega_1^2 + K_1) - (\omega_2^2 + K_2)$$

so that (12-68) itself can be written

$$\omega_\pm^2 \simeq \tfrac{1}{2}[(\omega_1^2 + K_1) + (\omega_2^2 + K_2)] \pm \tfrac{1}{2}[(\omega_1^2 + K_1) - (\omega_2^2 + K_2)]$$

and therefore

$$\omega_+^2 \simeq \omega_1^2 + K_1 = \omega_1^2 + \frac{K}{m_1 l_1^2} \tag{12-69a}$$

$$\omega_-^2 \simeq \omega_2^2 + K_2 = \omega_2^2 + \frac{K}{m_2 l_2^2} \tag{12-69b}$$

We see from (12-69) that the general effect of the interaction is to make the normal frequencies slightly different from the natural frequencies of the uncoupled system. In this particular case, both of the frequencies are increased; this is not always what occurs, however.

There is one simple case for which the normal frequencies can be easily and exactly found. Let us assume the two pendulums have the same length, so that $l_1 = l_2 = l_0$ and then

$$\omega_1^2 = \omega_2^2 = \frac{g}{l_0} = \omega_0^2 \tag{12-70}$$

according to (12-62). When (12-70) is substituted into (12-68), we find the normal frequencies to be given by

$$\omega_+^2 = \omega_0^2 + K_1 + K_2 = \omega_0^2 + \frac{K}{l_0^2}\left(\frac{1}{m_1} + \frac{1}{m_2}\right) \tag{12-71a}$$

$$\omega_-^2 = \omega_0^2 \tag{12-71b}$$

Hence one of the normal frequencies equals the natural frequency, while the other is larger; we can understand these results better if we find the normal modes. From (12-66) and (12-70), we see that

$$\frac{a_{2k}}{a_{1k}} = \frac{\omega_0^2 - \omega_k^2 + K_1}{K_1} = \frac{K_2}{\omega_0^2 - \omega_k^2 + K_2} \tag{12-72}$$

and, when we substitute into (12-72), in turn, the normal frequencies given in (12-71), we find that

$$\frac{a_{2+}}{a_{1+}} = -\frac{K_2}{K_1} = -\frac{m_1}{m_2}, \quad a_{2-} = a_{1-} \tag{12-73}$$

The latter result in (12-73) shows that for $\omega_-^2 = \omega_0^2$ the pendulums oscillate in phase and with equal amplitude; thus there is no interaction between them because in the common support there is no twist due to a relative displacement, and therefore the natural frequency is not changed. On the other hand, for ω_+^2, the particles oscillate out of phase with opposite signs of the amplitude, resulting in considerable interaction because of the twisting of the support which makes the normal frequency considerably different from the uncoupled natural frequency. In the special case of equal masses, we see that $a_{2+} = -a_{1+}$ while $a_{2-} = a_{1-}$ and hence the magnitudes of the normal mode amplitudes are equal. However, if $m_2 \gg m_1$, we see that $|a_{2+}| \ll |a_{1+}|$ and, although the phase relations remain the same, the amplitude for particle 2 is always much smaller than that for particle 1, as could be expected from the relatively larger inertia of 2.

We recall that the general motion of this system is some sort of superposition of the normal modes—the exact superposition being determined by the initial conditions. In order to discuss this, we shall find the a_{jk} explicitly where we take j and k as $+$ or $-$, etc. The basic relation is given by (12-41) but, in our case, $t_{jk} = 0$ if $j \neq k$, according to (12-60), and (12-41) can be written

$$\sum_j t_{jj} a_{jm} a_{jl} = \delta_{ml} \tag{12-74}$$

As a check, if we take $m = +$ and $l = -$, (12-74) tells us that

$$\sum_j t_{jj} a_{j+} a_{j-} = 0 = t_{11} a_{1+} a_{1-} + t_{22} a_{2+} a_{2-} \tag{12-75}$$

If we substitute from (12-73) and (12-60) into (12-75), we find that

$$m_1 l_0^2 a_{1+} a_{1-} + m_2 l_0^2 \left(-\frac{m_1}{m_2} a_{1+} \right) a_{1-} = 0$$

as it should; thus we have shown directly that the normal modes are orthogonal, as we first saw in (12-38). We now take $m = l = +$ so that we can use the normalization condition to determine the a's exactly; using (12-74) and (12-73), we find that

$$\sum_j t_{jj} a_{j+} a_{j+} = 1 = t_{11} a_{1+}{}^2 + t_{22} a_{2+}{}^2$$

$$= m_1 l_0{}^2 a_{1+}{}^2 + m_2 l_0{}^2 \left(\frac{m_1{}^2 a_{1+}{}^2}{m_2{}^2} \right)$$

and

$$a_{1+} = \frac{1}{l_0} \left[\frac{m_2}{m_1(m_1 + m_2)} \right]^{1/2}, \quad a_{2+} = -\frac{1}{l_0} \left[\frac{m_1}{m_2(m_1 + m_2)} \right]^{1/2} \quad (12\text{-}76)$$

Similarly, by using $m = l = -$, we find that

$$a_{1-} = a_{2-} = \frac{1}{l_0 \sqrt{m_1 + m_2}} \quad (12\text{-}77)$$

Using (12-76) and (12-77), we see that the general solution as given by (12-47) is

$$\theta_1 = a_{1+}(c_+ \cos \omega_+ t + d_+ \sin \omega_+ t) + a_{1-}(c_- \cos \omega_- t + d_- \sin \omega_- t)$$

$$= \frac{1}{l_0 \sqrt{m_1 + m_2}} \left[\sqrt{\frac{m_2}{m_1}} (c_+ \cos \omega_+ t + d_+ \sin \omega_+ t) \right.$$

$$\left. + (c_- \cos \omega_- t + d_- \sin \omega_- t) \right] \quad (12\text{-}78a)$$

$$\theta_2 = \frac{1}{l_0 \sqrt{m_1 + m_2}} \left[-\sqrt{\frac{m_1}{m_2}} (c_+ \cos \omega_+ t + d_+ \sin \omega_+ t) \right.$$

$$\left. + (c_- \cos \omega_- t + d_- \sin \omega_- t) \right] \quad (12\text{-}78b)$$

As an example of evaluating the constants from the initial conditions, let us assume that pendulum 1 is pulled to one side and released from rest at the angle θ_0; therefore, for $t = 0$,

$$\theta_1 = \theta_0, \quad \theta_2 = 0, \quad \dot{\theta}_1 = \dot{\theta}_2 = 0 \quad (12\text{-}79)$$

Equations (12-78) then become

$$\theta_0 = \frac{1}{l_0 \sqrt{m_1 + m_2}} \left[\sqrt{\frac{m_2}{m_1}} c_+ + c_- \right]$$

$$0 = \frac{1}{l_0 \sqrt{m_1 + m_2}} \left[-\sqrt{\frac{m_1}{m_2}} c_+ + c_- \right]$$

$$0 = \frac{1}{l_0 \sqrt{m_1 + m_2}} \left[\sqrt{\frac{m_2}{m_1}} \omega_+ d_+ + \omega_- d_- \right]$$

$$0 = \frac{1}{l_0 \sqrt{m_1 + m_2}} \left[-\sqrt{\frac{m_1}{m_2}} \omega_+ d_+ + \omega_- d_- \right]$$

which can be solved for the constants; the results are

$$c_+ = l_0\theta_0\left[\frac{m_1m_2}{m_1 + m_2}\right]^{\frac{1}{2}}, \quad c_- = \frac{l_0\theta_0 m_1}{\sqrt{m_1 + m_2}}, \quad d_+ = d_- = 0 \quad (12\text{-}80)$$

so that the equations in (12-78) become

$$\theta_1 = \frac{\theta_0}{m_1 + m_2}\,[m_2\cos\omega_+t + m_1\cos\omega_-t] \qquad (12\text{-}81a)$$

$$\theta_2 = \frac{\theta_0 m_1}{m_1 + m_2}\,[-\cos\omega_+t + \cos\omega_-t] \qquad (12\text{-}81b)$$

which are the general solutions of the problem which satisfy the initial conditions (12-79). We calculated the results given in (12-80) by straightforward algebraic means from the general equations, but we could equally well have obtained them from the general results (12-49) and (12-50). Let us illustrate this process for c_+, for which (12-49) becomes

$$c_+ = \sum_j \theta_j(0)t_{jj}a_{j+} = \theta_1(0)t_{11}a_{1+} + \theta_2(0)t_{22}a_{2+}$$
$$= \theta_0 t_{11}a_{1+} = l_0\theta_0\left[\frac{m_1m_2}{m_1 + m_2}\right]^{\frac{1}{2}}$$

which agrees with the first result given in (12-80). Similarly, the remaining results in (12-80) can be obtained in the same way, thus verifying our general results (12-49) and (12-50) when applied in detail to this special simple case.

As an additional special case, we now assume that $m_1 = m_2 = m$, so that (12-81) gives

$$\theta_1 = \tfrac{1}{2}\theta_0(\cos\omega_+t + \cos\omega_-t) = \theta_0\cos\tfrac{1}{2}(\omega_+ - \omega_-)t\cos\tfrac{1}{2}(\omega_+ + \omega_-)t$$
$$(12\text{-}82a)$$

$$\theta_2 = \tfrac{1}{2}\theta_0(-\cos\omega_+t + \cos\omega_-t) = \theta_0\sin\tfrac{1}{2}(\omega_+ - \omega_-)t\sin\tfrac{1}{2}(\omega_+ + \omega_-)t$$
$$(12\text{-}82b)$$

In this case, we find from (12-71) that $\omega_+^2 = \omega_0^2 + (2K/ml_0^2)$, $\omega_-^2 = \omega_0^2$; hence $\omega_- = \omega_0$ and

$$\omega_+ = \omega_0\left[1 + \left(\frac{2K}{ml_0^2\omega_0^2}\right)\right]^{\frac{1}{2}} \simeq \omega_0\left[1 + \frac{K}{ml_0^2\omega_0^2}\right] = \omega_0 + \frac{K}{ml_0^2\omega_0}$$

for small coupling. To this approximation, then, we find from (12-82) that

$$\theta_1 \simeq \theta_0\cos\left(\frac{Kt}{ml_0^2\omega_0}\right)\cos\omega_0t \qquad (12\text{-}83a)$$

$$\theta_2 \simeq \theta_0\sin\left(\frac{Kt}{ml_0^2\omega_0}\right)\sin\omega_0t \qquad (12\text{-}83b)$$

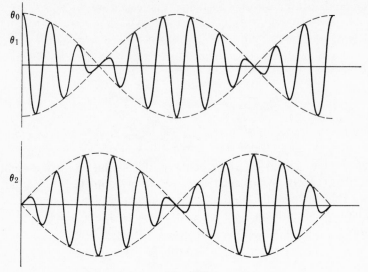

Fig. 12-2

As a check, we can let $K \to 0$ and we find that $\theta_1 \to \theta_0 \cos \omega_0 t$ and $\theta_2 \to 0$, as we expect for the uncoupled situation.

The motions described by (12-83) are illustrated in Fig. 12-2. We see that each pendulum oscillates with approximately the uncoupled frequency but is modulated by a term which depends on the coupling. The net result is that the energy of the total system flows back and forth between the two pendulums, for, as shown in the figure, as the displacement of 1 decreases, that of 2 increases until finally θ_1 has zero value and θ_2 has its maximum amplitude; then the coupling starts 1 oscillating again with increasing amplitude so that, as 2 loses its energy to 1, the value of θ_2 decreases again. This whole interchange is then repeated indefinitely.

There is still one more thing we can do for this example, and that is to find the normal coordinates. They are given in general by (12-52), which, with the help of (12-60), becomes

$$\zeta_l = \sum_j \theta_j t_{jj} a_{jl} \tag{12-84}$$

If we choose $l = +$, use (12-60), (12-70), and (12-76), we find that

$$\zeta_+ = \theta_1 t_{11} a_{1+} + \theta_2 t_{22} a_{2+} = l_0 \left[\frac{m_1 m_2}{m_1 + m_2} \right]^{1/2} (\theta_1 - \theta_2) \tag{12-85}$$

Similarly, we find the other normal coordinate to be given by

$$\zeta_- = \theta_1 t_{11} a_{1-} + \theta_2 t_{22} a_{2-} = \frac{l_0}{\sqrt{m_1 + m_2}} (m_1 \theta_1 + m_2 \theta_2) \tag{12-86}$$

Although θ_1 and θ_2 oscillate simultaneously with both frequencies ω_+ and ω_-, the combinations of θ_1 and θ_2 which form ζ_+ and ζ_- oscillate only with the single frequency ω_+ or ω_-. We can solve these directly for θ_1 and θ_2 in terms of the normal coordinates, and the result is the same as obtained from (12-51):

$$\theta_1 = a_{1+}\zeta_+ + a_{1-}\zeta_- = \frac{1}{l_0\sqrt{m_1 + m_2}}\left[\sqrt{\frac{m_2}{m_1}}\,\zeta_+ + \zeta_-\right] \quad (12\text{-}87a)$$

$$\theta_2 = a_{2+}\zeta_+ + a_{2-}\zeta_- = \frac{1}{l_0\sqrt{m_1 + m_2}}\left[-\sqrt{\frac{m_1}{m_2}}\,\zeta_+ + \zeta_-\right] \quad (12\text{-}87b)$$

If we substitute (12-87) into (12-61) and use (12-71), we find after a straightforward calculation that $V = \frac{1}{2}(\omega_+^2\zeta_+^2 + \omega_-^2\zeta_-^2)$, thus verifying our general result (12-53) that the potential energy becomes a sum of squares when written in terms of the normal coordinates.

12-7 External forces

The normal coordinate description of coupled oscillators is especially useful when external forces are applied to the system, and we shall discuss these effects very briefly.

Suppose that in addition to the linear restoring forces, the coordinate u_j is subject to an additional external force F_j. We want to find the generalized force Q_k associated with the kth normal coordinate ζ_k. In the notation of this chapter, our previous general result (7-20) becomes

$$Q_k = \sum_j F_j \frac{\partial u_j}{\partial \zeta_k} = \sum_j F_j a_{jk} \quad (12\text{-}88)$$

since we see from (12-51) that $\partial u_j/\partial \zeta_k = a_{jk}$. When these generalized forces are included, Lagrange's equations (12-56) become

$$\ddot{\zeta}_k + \omega_k^2\zeta_k = Q_k \quad (12\text{-}89)$$

which is analogous to the equation for the forced motion of an oscillator as discussed in Chapter 5.

We see from (12-88) that the effectiveness of a force F_j acting on one of the coordinates in exciting the kth normal mode is proportional to the amplitude a_{jk} which that coordinate would have if the system were in that mode. This means that a force which is applied to a particle cannot excite a mode in which that particle is not displaced, i.e., for which $a_{jk}=0$, but the force will be very effective in exciting a mode in which the particle has a comparatively large displacement.

As an example, let us suppose that all the forces F_j are proportional to $e^{-i\omega t}$, where ω is arbitrary. Then we see from (12-88) that $Q_k \sim e^{-i\omega t}$ and we can write (12-89) as

$$\ddot{\zeta}_k + \omega_k{}^2 \zeta_k = Q_{k0} e^{-i\omega t} \tag{12-90}$$

If we look for the solution in which $\zeta_k = \zeta_{k0} e^{-i\omega t}$, we find from (12-90) that the forced motion of the normal coordinate is given by

$$\zeta_k = \frac{Q_k}{\omega_k{}^2 - \omega^2} \tag{12-91}$$

and, therefore, the actual displacement as found from (12-51) is

$$u_j = \sum_k \frac{a_{jk} Q_k}{\omega_k{}^2 - \omega^2} \tag{12-92}$$

so that $u_j \sim e^{-i\omega t}$ as well. We see from (12-92) that, if we consider u_j a function of ω, there are now n separate resonances, corresponding to the frequencies ω_k of the normal modes, rather than only the single resonance we found for the simple oscillator in Chapter 5.

Actually, the displacement for a real system will not be infinite at resonance, as it would appear to be by (12-92). What has happened is that we have neglected the frictional damping forces which will occur for any real system. We can introduce these forces in a manner similar to that we used in Sec. 5-2 by introducing damping forces proportional to $\dot{u}_j$. The discussion becomes somewhat complicated, but the results are qualitatively much like those we found before; the effect of the friction is to make the resonant amplitude finite, and at the same time to give a finite breadth to the resonance curve.

Exercises

12-1. Find the normal modes and normal frequencies of small oscillations of the double pendulum of Exercise 7-3. In particular, consider the limiting cases $m_1 \gg m_2$ and $m_1 \ll m_2$, and interpret the results physically. In the special case of equal masses and equal lengths show that the frequencies are $[g(2 \pm \sqrt{2})/l]^{1/2}$.

12-2. A mass m_1 is suspended from a spring of stiffness constant k_1, and another mass m_2 is suspended from m_1 by means of a spring of stiffness constant k_2. If the mass m_1 is subject to an external vertical force $F_0 \sin \omega t$, find the amplitude of the steady motion of m_2.

13 The weighted string

Many concepts and results associated with normal modes and their superposition to form general solutions, which are very important in other branches of physics such as electromagnetic theory and quantum mechanics, can be illustrated very well by studying the simple mechanical system formed by a vibrating string. We do not begin by considering the string to be a system of atoms or molecules, but instead we consider the simpler system known as the weighted string. In this system the mass is concentrated in a set of equally spaced mass points imagined to be held together by massless springs of equal tension T, as illustrated schematically in Fig. 13-1. We shall study only the transverse motions of the particles of this system, and we shall assume that the displacements from the horizontal equilibrium configuration are so small that the tension T can be assumed to remain constant.

If we have N particles, each of mass m, and spaced a distance d apart, then, as shown, the coordinates of the particles will be $x = d, 2d, \ldots, jd,$ $\ldots, Nd$. We shall let u_j be the transverse displacement of the jth mass at the distance jd from the left end; all these relations are also illustrated in Fig. 13-1. We have a new feature associated with this problem, however: we require that the *end points be held rigidly fixed*; that is, that the displacement be always zero when $x = 0$ or $(N + 1)d$. This is an example of a particular kind of a constraint known as a *boundary condition*, and it has important consequences, as we shall see.

As a first step in finding the equations of motion, we find the force acting on a particular mass. We can do this directly with the aid of Fig. 13-2a, and if we let F_j be the resultant transverse force on the jth mass, we see that

$$F_j = T \sin \beta - T \sin \alpha \simeq T \tan \beta - T \tan \alpha$$

$$= T \left[\frac{(u_{j+1} - u_j)}{d} - \frac{(u_j - u_{j-1})}{d} \right] \tag{13-1}$$

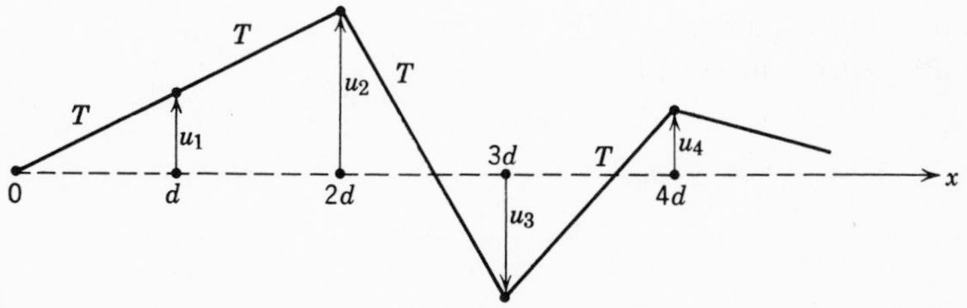

Fig. 13-1

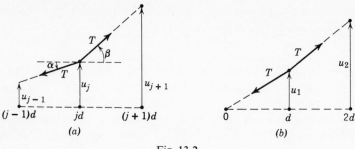

Fig. 13-2

for the small angles β and α. If we equate the force and the mass times acceleration, the equation of motion of the jth mass as found from (13-1) is

$$\frac{T}{d}(u_{j+1} - 2u_j + u_{j-1}) = m\frac{d^2u_j}{dt^2} = m\ddot{u}_j \tag{13-2}$$

We do, however, have to consider the first and last particles separately, that is, for $j = 1$ and N, since each of them has only one neighbor. In Fig. 13-2b, we have the situation for $j = 1$, and we see that, to the same approximation,

$$F_1 = T\frac{(u_2 - u_1)}{d} - T\frac{u_1}{d} = \frac{T}{d}(u_2 - 2u_1) \tag{13-3}$$

which is exactly what we get from the general result (13-1) if we define $u_0 = 0$. Similarly, the correct force on the Nth particle can also be obtained from (13-1) if we define $u_{N+1} = 0$, so that (13-2) can then be used for all values of j from 1 through N.

Before going on to look for the normal modes, let us show first that we can also find a Lagrangian for this system which gives the correct equations of motion. We easily see that

$$\text{Kinetic energy} = \sum_{j=1}^{N}\tfrac{1}{2}m\dot{u}_j{}^2 = \sum_{j=0}^{N}\tfrac{1}{2}m\dot{u}_j{}^2 \tag{13-4}$$

in which the last step is possible because $u_0 = 0$. We now assert that the potential energy is given by

$$V = \frac{T}{2d}[(u_1 - u_0)^2 + (u_2 - u_1)^2 + \cdots + (u_{N+1} - u_N)^2]$$

$$= \frac{T}{2d}\sum_{j=0}^{N}(u_{j+1} - u_j)^2 \tag{13-5}$$

In order to verify this assertion, we calculate the force:

$$F_j = -\frac{\partial V}{\partial u_j} = -\frac{T}{d}\left[-(u_{j+1} - u_j) + (u_j - u_{j-1})\right]$$

$$= \frac{T}{d}(u_{j+1} - 2u_j + u_{j-1})$$

which is correct, as shown by (13-1). Subtracting (13-4) and (13-5), we obtain the Lagrangian:

$$L = \tfrac{1}{2}\sum_{j=0}^{N}\left[m\dot{u}_j^{\,2} - \frac{T}{d}(u_{j+1} - u_j)^2\right] \tag{13-6}$$

If we use (13-6) in the Lagrangian equations of motion

$$\frac{d}{dt}\left(\frac{\partial L}{\partial \dot{u}_j}\right) - \frac{\partial L}{\partial u_j} = 0$$

we find that we get the equations (13-2); therefore (13-6) is a correct Lagrangian for the weighted string.

In order to find the normal modes and frequencies, we follow (12-15) and substitute

$$u_j = Ca_j e^{-i\omega t} \tag{13-7}$$

into (13-2) and find that they yield

$$-\frac{T}{d}a_{j-1} + \left(\frac{2T}{d} - m\omega^2\right)a_j - \frac{T}{d}a_{j+1} = 0 \tag{13-8}$$

where $j = 1, 2, \ldots, N$. Rather than writing out all N of these equations and setting the determinant of the coefficients of the a's equal to zero, we are able to solve the general equations for this problem quite easily by assuming an exponential solution of the form

$$a_j = Ae^{ijk} \tag{13-9}$$

where $i = \sqrt{-1}$ and k *is to be found.* If we substitute (13-9) into (13-8), we obtain

$$-\frac{T}{d}e^{i(j-1)k} + \left(\frac{2T}{d} - m\omega^2\right)e^{ijk} - \frac{T}{d}e^{i(j+1)k} = 0$$

from which we can solve for ω^2 to get

$$\omega^2 = \frac{2T}{md}(1 - \cos k) = \omega_k^{\,2} \tag{13-10}$$

if we use $e^{ik} + e^{-ik} = 2\cos k$, which follows from (5-33) and (5-34). Thus we see from (13-10) that for any k we can find the corresponding frequency for which (13-7) is a possible solution of the equations of motion (13-2). This may not appear to have helped us because we still do not know how to determine k. We have not yet considered one important factor, however, as we have only solved the equations of motion *but* we have not yet made our solutions satisfy the boundary conditions $u_0 = u_{N+1} = 0$, that is,

$$a_0 = a_{N+1} = 0 \qquad (13\text{-}11)$$

which follows from (13-7).

It is clear that the individual exponential solutions (13-9) will not satisfy (13-11), but since the equations of motion are linear and thus a sum of solutions is still a solution, we can hope to satisfy (13-11) with a suitable linear combination of terms of the form (13-9). We see that

$$a_j = \frac{A}{2i}(e^{ijk} - e^{-ijk}) = A \sin jk \qquad (13\text{-}12)$$

is also a solution corresponding to the frequency ω_k. This form automatically satisfies the first part of (13-11) in that $a_0 = 0$. We must also have $a_{N+1} = A \sin (N + 1)k = 0$, and this means that $(N + 1)k = n\pi$, where n is any integer, or

$$k = \frac{n\pi}{(N + 1)} \qquad (13\text{-}13)$$

Thus we see that the satisfying of the boundary conditions has *determined* that our previously arbitrary k can have only these definite values in (13-13). The normal frequencies (13-10) can now be written

$$\omega_n{}^2 = \frac{2T}{md}\left(1 - \cos \frac{n\pi}{N + 1}\right) \qquad (13\text{-}14)$$

and the normal modes which satisfy both the equations of motion and the boundary conditions are found from (13-12) and (13-13) to be

$$a_{jn} = A_n \sin \frac{n\pi j}{N + 1} \qquad (13\text{-}15)$$

where we are labeling the modes with the index n.

It may appear, however, that our results are incorrect. Since we have a system of N particles with N degrees of freedom, we expect from the general results obtained in the last chapter that there should be N normal modes. However, the way in which n entered as any integer in (13-13) makes it appear that we have found an infinite number of normal modes and frequencies. Actually, the values of n we need to use do not go on indefinitely, as there are only a finite number of normal modes corresponding to $n = 1, 2, 3, \ldots, N$. For values of n different from these, we simply repeat solutions already considered; hence there are only N different normal modes. We show this by example:

Suppose $n = N + 1$; then $\cos (n\pi/N + 1) = \cos \pi = -1$ and

$$\omega_{N+1}^2 = \frac{4T}{md} = (\omega_n^2)_{max} \tag{13-16}$$

The normal mode as obtained from (13-15), however, is proportional to $\sin (n\pi j/N + 1) = \sin j\pi = 0$ since j is an integer. Thus the case $n = N + 1$ does not really correspond to a normal mode at all, but rather to equilibrium.

Suppose $n = N + 2$; then

$$\cos \frac{n\pi}{N + 1} = \cos \frac{(N + 1 + 1)\pi}{N + 1} = \cos \left(\pi + \frac{\pi}{N + 1}\right)$$

$$= \cos \left(-\pi + \frac{\pi}{N + 1}\right) = \cos \frac{N\pi}{N + 1}$$

where we used the fact that $\cos \alpha = \cos (\alpha - 2\pi)$. We now see from (13-14) that $\omega_{N+2}^2 = \omega_N^2$. In a similar manner, we can easily show that

$$\sin \frac{(N + 2)\pi j}{N + 1} = -\sin \frac{N\pi j}{N + 1}$$

so that $a_{j,N+2} = -a_{jN}$ if we choose A_n to be positive for both cases. Thus for the mode $n = N + 2$, the frequency is the same as for $n = N$, but all displacements are of opposite sign. The latter does not correspond to a real difference, however, since the relative displacements of the particles remain the same.

In the same way, we can show that, if $n = N + 3$, we obtain the same solution as for $n = N - 1$, etc. Thus, as we said, there are only N *different* modes, and we can restrict n to the values $n = 1, 2, \ldots, N$.

Example. Three Particles. If $N = 3$, we find that

$$\omega_n{}^2 = \frac{2T}{md}\left(1 - \cos \frac{n\pi}{4}\right), \quad a_{jn} = A_n \sin \frac{n\pi j}{4}, \quad n = 1, 2, 3 \tag{13-17}$$

In order to compare the shape of the string in the various normal modes we need only look at the factor $\sin (n\pi j/4)$ for $j = 0, 1, 2, 3, 4$. These functions are illustrated in Fig. 13-3 for the values of n from 1 through 6, in order to show explicitly how the modes for larger n are the same as those for $n = 1, \ldots, N$. The dotted curve is $\sin x$ plotted as a function of a continuous variable; it is helpful in evaluating the displacements for the finite values of jd.

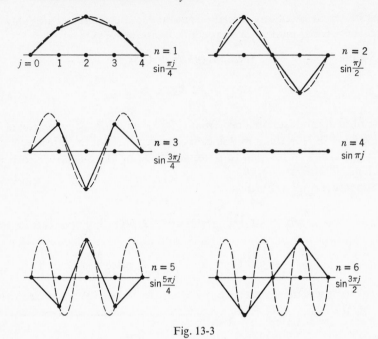

Fig. 13-3

The normal modes (13-15) were written with the factor A_n because they must still satisfy the orthonormal condition (12-41), which can be written in terms of our present notation as

$$\sum_{j,l} t_{jl} a_{jn} a_{lp} = \delta_{np} \tag{13-18}$$

From (13-4) and (12-11), we see that for the weighted string $t_{jl} = m \, \delta_{jl}$ so that (13-18) becomes

$$\sum_j m a_{jn} a_{jp} = \delta_{np} \tag{13-19}$$

Substituting (13-15), we find that (13-19) becomes

$$m A_n A_p \sum_{j=1}^{N} \sin\left(\frac{n\pi j}{N+1}\right) \sin\left(\frac{p\pi j}{N+1}\right) = \delta_{np} \tag{13-20}$$

The sum can be evaluated directly, and it will be left as an exercise to show that

$$\sum_{j=1}^{N} \sin\left(\frac{n\pi j}{N+1}\right) \sin\left(\frac{p\pi j}{N+1}\right) = \tfrac{1}{2}(N+1)\,\delta_{np} \tag{13-21}$$

Therefore, if $n \neq p$, $\sum_j m a_{jn} a_{jp} = 0$, verifying the orthogonality property.

The case $n = p$ enables us to evaluate the normalization factor A_n, because, when (13-20) and (13-21) are combined, we find that

$$mA_n{}^2 \cdot \tfrac{1}{2}(N + 1) = 1,$$

or

$$A_n = \sqrt{\frac{2}{m(N+1)}} \tag{13-22}$$

which is independent of n. When (13-22) is substituted into (13-15), we find that our final expressions for the normal modes of the weighted string are

$$a_{jn} = \sqrt{\frac{2}{m(N+1)}} \sin\left(\frac{n\pi j}{N+1}\right) \tag{13-23}$$

We can now write the general solution for the displacements of the weighted string by substituting (13-23) into (12-47); we find that

$$u_j = \sum_{n=1}^{N} \sqrt{\frac{2}{m(N+1)}} \sin\left(\frac{n\pi j}{N+1}\right)(c_n \cos \omega_n t + d_n \sin \omega_n t) \tag{13-24}$$

where the frequencies ω_n can be found from (13-14) and the c_n and d_n are $2N$ constants of integration whose values can be found from the initial displacements and velocities.

We can also find the normal coordinates for the weighted string from (12-52), (13-4), and (13-23) to be given by

$$\zeta_n = \sum_{j,l} u_j t_{jl} a_{ln} = \sum_j m u_j a_{jn}$$

$$= \sqrt{\frac{2m}{N+1}} \sum_{j=1}^{N} u_j \sin\left(\frac{n\pi j}{N+1}\right) \tag{13-25}$$

Exercises

13-1. Verify (13-21). [This is most easily done by using

$$\sin x = (e^{ix} - e^{-ix})/2i.]$$

13-2. What sort of initial conditions will be necessary to get the string oscillating in the normal mode corresponding to $n = 3$ in Fig. 13-3?

13-3. As was done in Fig. 13-3, sketch the shapes of the normal modes for four particles.

14 The continuous string

Many of the systems we want to consider can be described as continuous systems in the sense that various properties are continuous functions of the coordinates. For example, the mass of the system may be distributed continuously throughout space rather than be concentrated in the discrete particles which we have assumed to be the constituents of all the systems we have studied up to now. The methods of treating continuous systems also find applications as well in fields such as electromagnetic theory and quantum theory, and we shall find that the normal mode concept is very useful in discussing general continuous systems. The system we consider first is the uniform continuous string—a string of constant density and uniform tension T. Our first approach is to treat it simply as a limiting case of the weighted string, and later we shall attack the problem from quite a different point of view which is forthrightly based on the fact that the system is continuous.

14-1   Continuous string as limiting case of the weighted string

To go to the limit, we can let the number of particles, N, become infinite while the mass of each particle approaches zero and the distance between particles also approaches zero—all this being done in such a way that we are left with a string of length L and mass per unit length, μ. The string is also to be held rigidly at the ends, that is, at $x = 0$ and $x = L$, where x is the continuous position variable of each point. Therefore we want

$$(N + 1) d \xrightarrow[\substack{N \to \infty \\ d \to 0}]{} L \quad \text{and} \quad mN = \text{total mass} \xrightarrow[\substack{N \to \infty \\ m \to 0}]{} \mu L \qquad (14\text{-}1)$$

Since $N + 1 \simeq N$ when N is large, we see that we can simply make the replacement

$$\frac{m}{d} \to \mu \qquad (14\text{-}2)$$

to make weighted string results become those appropriate for the continuous string. Similarly, we can make the replacements

$$jd \to x \quad \text{and} \quad \frac{j}{N + 1} \to \frac{x}{L} \qquad (14\text{-}3)$$

the latter following with the help of (14-1). The displacement $u_j(t)$ of the jth mass now becomes the transverse displacement of the string at the point x at the time t, which we shall simply write as u; thus we also make the replacement

$$u_j(t) \to u_x(t) = u(x, t) \tag{14-4}$$

The displacement now becomes a function of *two* continuous variables.

Since the normal modes of the weighted string are given by (13-23), we can use (14-1) and (14-3) to find that the normal modes of the continuous string are

$$u_n(x) = \sqrt{\frac{2}{\mu L}} \sin \frac{n\pi x}{L} \tag{14-5}$$

since $m(N + 1) \simeq mN = \mu L$ when $N \to \infty$. From (13-14), we find that the expression for the normal frequencies becomes

$$\begin{aligned}
\omega_n{}^2 &= \frac{2T}{md}\left(1 - \cos\frac{n\pi}{N+1}\right) \to \frac{2T}{\mu d^2}\left(1 - \cos\frac{n\pi d}{L}\right) \\
&= \lim_{d \to 0} \frac{2T}{\mu d^2}\left[\frac{1}{2}\left(\frac{n\pi d}{L}\right)^2 + \text{terms of order } d^4 + \cdots\right] \\
&= \left(\frac{n\pi}{L}\right)^2 \frac{T}{\mu}
\end{aligned}$$

and the normal frequencies of the continuous string are

$$\omega_n = \frac{n\pi}{L}\sqrt{\frac{T}{\mu}} \tag{14-6}$$

where $n = 1, 2, 3, \ldots$. Thus we see that the continuous string has an infinite number of normal modes and frequencies corresponding to its infinite number of degrees of freedom.

It is interesting to compare the dependence of ω_n on n for the weighted and continuous string. The curve given by (14-6) is a straight line with an indefinite increase in ω_n. The curve obtained from (13-14) has a maximum given by $\omega_{\max} = \omega_{N+1} = 2\sqrt{T/md}$. These curves are shown in Fig. 14-1.

The orthonormal condition for the weighted string is given by (13-21) and (14-1) as

$$\frac{2}{L}\sum_j \sin\left(\frac{n\pi x}{L}\right) \sin\left(\frac{m\pi x}{L}\right)(\Delta j)d = \delta_{nm} \tag{14-7}$$

where we were able to insert Δj because the sum is over only integral values of j so that $\Delta j = 1$ always. Since $jd \to x$, then, as $d \to 0$, we can replace

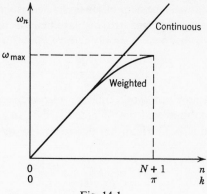

Fig. 14-1

$(\Delta j)\, d$ by the increment of distance dx and replace a summation over j by an integral over x as follows:

$$\sum_j f_j\, d \xrightarrow[\substack{N\to\infty \\ d\to 0}]{} \int_0^L f(x)\, dx \tag{14-8}$$

Therefore for the continuous string the orthonormal condition (14-7) becomes

$$\frac{2}{L}\int_0^L \sin\left(\frac{n\pi x}{L}\right) \sin\left(\frac{m\pi x}{L}\right) dx = \delta_{nm} \tag{14-9}$$

which is a result that can also be verified directly. This equation can be written in terms of the normal modes if we use (14-5); we find that it becomes

$$\int_0^L \mu u_n(x) u_m(x)\, dx = \delta_{nm} \tag{14-10}$$

which we shall meet again in the same form, for an even more general case in which μ is not constant.

We shall also have an infinite number of normal coordinates ζ_n. If we use (12-51), (14-4), and (14-5), we can write the equation connecting the displacement and the normal coordinates as

$$u(x, t) = \sum_n \zeta_n u_n(x) = \sum_n \zeta_n(t)\sqrt{\frac{2}{\mu L}}\sin\left(\frac{n\pi x}{L}\right) \tag{14-11}$$

Again, we see how we can interpret the normal coordinates as essentially the amplitude with which each normal mode of the vibrating string goes into the superposition which makes up the general displacement for all x and t.

For the continuous uniform string, it is of interest to verify explicitly that the normal coordinates reduce the problem to one of a system of independent oscillators. Using (13-4), (14-11), and (14-9), we find that the kinetic energy becomes

$$T = \sum_j \tfrac{1}{2} m \dot{u}_j{}^2 = \int_0^L \tfrac{1}{2} \mu \left(\frac{\partial u}{\partial t}\right)^2 dx = \frac{\mu}{2} \int_0^L \left[\sum_n \dot{\zeta}_n \sqrt{\frac{2}{\mu L}} \sin\left(\frac{n\pi x}{L}\right)\right]^2 dx$$

$$= \frac{1}{L} \sum_n \sum_m \dot{\zeta}_n \dot{\zeta}_m \int_0^L \sin\left(\frac{n\pi x}{L}\right) \sin\left(\frac{m\pi x}{L}\right) dx$$

$$= \tfrac{1}{2} \sum_n \sum_m \dot{\zeta}_n \dot{\zeta}_m \, \delta_{nm} = \tfrac{1}{2} \sum_n \dot{\zeta}_n{}^2 \qquad (14\text{-}12)$$

which is exactly what is expected from our general results. Similarly, if we use (13-5), (14-11), (14-6), (14-8), and

$$\frac{2}{L} \int_0^L \cos\left(\frac{n\pi x}{L}\right) \cos\left(\frac{m\pi x}{L}\right) dx = \delta_{nm} \qquad (14\text{-}13)$$

we find that the potential energy becomes

$$V = \frac{T}{2} \sum_j \left(\frac{u_{j+1} - u_j}{d}\right)^2 d = \frac{T}{2} \int_0^L \left(\frac{\partial u}{\partial x}\right)^2 dx$$

$$= \frac{T}{2} \int_0^L \left[\sum_n \zeta_n \frac{n\pi}{L} \sqrt{\frac{2}{\mu L}} \cos\left(\frac{n\pi x}{L}\right)\right]^2 dx$$

$$= \frac{T\pi^2}{2\mu L^2} \sum_n \sum_m nm \zeta_n \zeta_m \, \delta_{nm} = \tfrac{1}{2} \sum_n \frac{T}{\mu}\left(\frac{n\pi}{L}\right)^2 \zeta_n{}^2$$

$$= \tfrac{1}{2} \sum_n \omega_n{}^2 \zeta_n{}^2 \qquad (14\text{-}14)$$

Then the Lagrangian is

$$L = T - V = \tfrac{1}{2} \sum_n (\dot{\zeta}_n{}^2 - \omega_n{}^2 \zeta_n{}^2) \qquad (14\text{-}15)$$

which is exactly that for a system of independent harmonic oscillators.

The Lagrangian equations of motion then are $\ddot{\zeta}_n + \omega_n{}^2 \zeta_n = 0$, for which we have the solution $\zeta_n = C_n e^{-i\omega_n t}$, where C_n is a constant. If we insert this into (14-11), write $C_n = c_n + id_n$, and take the real part of the resulting expression, we obtain the general solution for the displacement of the continuous string in the form

$$u(x, t) = \sum_n \sqrt{\frac{2}{\mu L}} \sin\left(\frac{n\pi x}{L}\right)(c_n \cos \omega_n t + d_n \sin \omega_n t) \qquad (14\text{-}16)$$

where ω_n is given by (14-6). The doubly infinite set of constants of integration, c_n and d_n, can be obtained from the initial conditions by using the orthonormal relations. We shall defer the detailed discussion of this, however, since we shall be able to discuss it again in another context.

14-2   Equation of motion of a continuous string

Although we have just found the general solution for the motion of the continuous string in (14-16), we had first to solve the problem of a discrete number of coupled systems, the weighted string, and then go to the limit. What we want to do now is to start all over for the continuous string, treat it completely as a continuous system from the *very first*, and then *apply the normal mode concept* to it. In so doing, we shall have basically extended the range of utility of the normal mode concept from the system of coupled particles with which we started and shall thus be encouraged to use the idea more freely in the future.

Again the system we consider is a string stretched between rigid supports. The horizontal equilibrium position is shown dashed in Fig. 14-2, which also shows a possible position at a given time, as if we had taken a photograph of it. We let u be the displacement from equilibrium of an element of string at the distance x from the end, and, since we know that the shape can vary with position along the string at a fixed time and with time at a fixed point, we must write $u = u(x, t)$. Our first problem is to find the equation of motion, that is, to write $F = ma$ in a form appropriate to the string. The result which we obtain below is called the *wave equation*, for reasons which will become clear later.

We let $\mu =$ mass per unit length and $T =$ tension; we neglect gravity, i.e., the weight of the string. If we consider the element dx of the string at the time t, we see from Fig. 14-3 that

$$\text{Resultant force on } dx = T_{x+dx} \sin \theta_{x+dx} - T_x \sin \theta_x \qquad (14\text{-}17)$$

We shall assume small displacements and therefore small values of θ, so that we can make the approximation

$$\sin \theta \simeq \tan \theta = \frac{\partial u}{\partial x} \qquad (14\text{-}18)$$

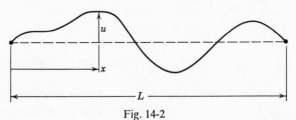

Fig. 14-2

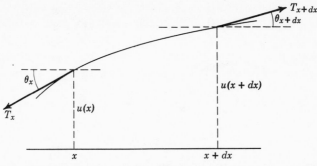

Fig. 14-3

Making this substitution in (14-17) and equating the resultant force on the element dx to the time rate of change of the momentum of this element of mass $\mu \, dx$, we obtain

$$\left(T\frac{\partial u}{\partial x}\right)_{x+dx} - \left(T\frac{\partial u}{\partial x}\right)_{x} = \frac{\partial}{\partial t}\left(\mu \, dx \, \frac{\partial u}{\partial t}\right) = \frac{\partial}{\partial x}\left(T\frac{\partial u}{\partial x}\right) dx$$

and, upon canceling out the constant factor dx, we obtain the equation of motion for the continuous string in the form

$$\frac{\partial}{\partial x}\left(T\frac{\partial u}{\partial x}\right) = \frac{\partial}{\partial t}\left(\mu\frac{\partial u}{\partial t}\right) \tag{14-19}$$

We have left (14-19) in this form because in general we could have T and μ given as functions of x and t; for example, μ could be a function of the time if we were spraying paint on the string and thereby changing its mass distribution.

For the present, however, we assume that both T and μ are constant; then (14-19) becomes

$$\frac{\partial^2 u}{\partial x^2} = \frac{\mu}{T}\frac{\partial^2 u}{\partial t^2} \tag{14-20}$$

which is the equation of motion for the uniform string and is known as the wave equation in one dimension. We also note that now our equation of motion is a *partial* differential equation; this is a characteristic feature of continuous systems, and we shall meet other examples as we go along.

14-3 Normal modes and boundary conditions

Suppose we try to find normal modes in which all parts of the string are oscillating with the same frequency. Accordingly, we try a solution of the form

$$u(x, t) = X(x)e^{-i\omega t} \tag{14-21}$$

so that

$$\frac{\partial^2 u}{\partial x^2} = \frac{d^2 X}{dx^2} e^{-i\omega t}, \quad \frac{\partial^2 u}{\partial t^2} = -\omega^2 X e^{-i\omega t}$$

and therefore (14-20) becomes

$$\frac{d^2 X}{dx^2} = -\frac{\omega^2}{v^2} X \tag{14-22}$$

where we have set

$$v = \sqrt{T/\mu} \tag{14-23}$$

There are two possible solutions for X which we can write as $\cos(\omega x/v)$ and $\sin(\omega x/v)$. Since the two real parts of the time factor in (14-21) are $\cos \omega t$ and $\sin \omega t$, we see that there are four possible real forms for $u(x, t)$ of unit amplitude which satisfy the equation of motion (14-20):

$$u_1 = \sin\left(\frac{\omega x}{v}\right) \sin \omega t, \quad u_2 = \sin\left(\frac{\omega x}{x}\right) \cos \omega t$$

$$u_3 = \cos\left(\frac{\omega x}{v}\right) \sin \omega t, \quad u_4 = \cos\left(\frac{\omega x}{v}\right) \cos \omega t \tag{14-24}$$

Since the differential equation is linear, an arbitrary sum of these four results will also be a solution, and the general solution of (14-20) for a given ω has the form

$$u(x, t) = a_1 u_1 + a_2 u_2 + a_3 u_3 + a_4 u_4 \tag{14-25}$$

where a_1, a_2, a_3, a_4 are constants. We note here that (14-25) is the general solution to the partial differential equation without reference to the fact that we are considering the particular problem of a string fixed rigidly at its ends; in this connection, it is important to realize that in the derivation of (14-19) we made no mention of how the string was fastened, or even if it were fastened at all!

Now we must apply our boundary conditions, that is, we must make sure that our solution is such that we always have

$$u(0, t) = u(L, t) = 0 \tag{14-26}$$

Since $\cos 0 \neq 0$, the first condition of (14-26) as applied to (14-25) tells us that we must have $a_3 = a_4 = 0$. The second part of (14-26), combined with (14-24), now tells us that we must have $\sin(\omega L/v) = 0$; this can be satisfied only for certain values of ω because everything else is fixed. Therefore we must have

$$\frac{\omega L}{v} = n\pi, \quad n = 1, 2, 3, \ldots \tag{14-27}$$

Thus the application of the boundary conditions of our special case has told us two things: first, the solutions involving $\cos(\omega x/v)$ can not enter because they do not satisfy the boundary condition at $x = 0$, and, second, only certain normal frequencies are possible and they were determined from the boundary condition at $x = L$. Hence only a certain discrete set of frequencies is allowed and they are found, by combining (14-27) and (14-23), to be

$$\omega_n = \frac{n\pi v}{L} = \frac{n\pi}{L}\sqrt{\frac{T}{\mu}} \qquad (14\text{-}28)$$

[Comparing with (14-6), we see that these frequencies are the same as obtained from the limit of the weighted string.]

Therefore to each normal frequency ω_n there correspond two solutions of the general form

$$u_{ns} = \sin\left(\frac{n\pi x}{L}\right)\sin\omega_n t, \quad u_{nc} = \sin\left(\frac{n\pi x}{L}\right)\cos\omega_n t \qquad (14\text{-}29)$$

which are known as *standing waves*. When $\sin(n\pi x/L) = 0$, the point x is always at rest; such a point is called a *node*. When $\sin(n\pi x/L) = \pm 1$, the point x oscillates with maximum amplitude; such a point is called an *antinode*. As an example, in Fig. 14-4, we show the solution u_{ns} corresponding to $n = 3$; that is

$$\sin\left(\frac{3\pi x}{L}\right)\sin\omega_3 t$$

The three curves show the position of the string at three different times. In all of them, the nodes at $x = \frac{1}{3}L, \frac{2}{3}L$ remain undisturbed; the antinodes are evenly spaced between the nodes.

A possible solution corresponding to ω_n is an arbitrary sum of the two special solutions given in (14-29), or

$$u_n = (A_n\cos\omega_n t + B_n\sin\omega_n t)\sin\left(\frac{n\pi x}{L}\right) \qquad (14\text{-}30)$$

where A_n and B_n are constants. Again, since the differential equation is

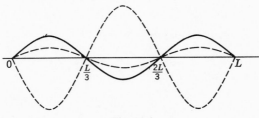

Fig. 14-4

linear, the general solution is a superposition of these particular solutions for all possible frequencies, and the general solution can be written

$$u(x, t) = \sum_{n=1}^{\infty} (A_n \cos \omega_n t + B_n \sin \omega_n t) \sin \left(\frac{n\pi x}{L} \right) \qquad (14\text{-}31)$$

which is, of course, the same solution found in (14-16) from the limit of the weighted string, where $A_n = \sqrt{2/\mu L} \, c_n$, etc. We now have a doubly infinite set of arbitrary constants A_n and B_n to be determined from the initial conditions:

$$u(x, 0) = u_0(x) \quad \text{and} \quad \left(\frac{\partial u}{\partial t} \right)_{t=0} = \dot{u}(x, 0) = \dot{u}_0(x) \qquad (14\text{-}32)$$

where $u_0(x)$ and $\dot{u}_0(x)$ are two given functions of position along the string which give us the initial displacement and velocity of each point of the string.

In order to find these constants, we make use of what we know now is essentially an orthonormal condition, namely, (14-9), and which can also be proved by straightforward elementary integrations. The initial conditions as obtained from (14-31) by setting $t = 0$ are

$$u_0(x) = \sum_n A_n \sin \left(\frac{n\pi x}{L} \right) \qquad (14\text{-}33)$$

$$\dot{u}_0(x) = \sum_n \omega_n B_n \sin \left(\frac{n\pi x}{L} \right) \qquad (14\text{-}34)$$

If we multiply (14-34) by $\sin (m\pi x/L)$, integrate over the length of the string, and use (14-9), we find that

$$\int_0^L \dot{u}_0(x) \sin \left(\frac{m\pi x}{L} \right) dx = \sum_n \omega_n B_n \int_0^L \sin \left(\frac{m\pi x}{L} \right) \sin \left(\frac{n\pi x}{L} \right) dx$$

$$= \sum_n \omega_n B_n \tfrac{1}{2} L \, \delta_{nm} = \tfrac{1}{2} L \omega_m B_m$$

Then

$$B_m = \frac{2}{\omega_m L} \int_0^L \dot{u}_0(x) \sin \left(\frac{m\pi x}{L} \right) dx \qquad (14\text{-}35)$$

Similarly, one can show from (14-33) that

$$A_m = \frac{2}{L} \int_0^L u_0(x) \sin \left(\frac{m\pi x}{L} \right) dx \qquad (14\text{-}36)$$

Thus, if we are given the initial conditions as a function of x, we can calculate the coefficients A_n and B_n from (14-35) and (14-36); when they are then inserted into (14-31), we obtain the general solution which tells us how the shape of the string changes in time after having been started in the given way, and which is, of course, the complete solution to the problem. These results naturally agree exactly with what we obtained in the first section of this chapter by treating the uniform continuous string as the limiting case of the weighted string. Of more importance than this, however, is that we have seen that we can usefully apply normal mode concepts to mechanical systems which depend continuously on position and time.

14-4 External forces

The string provides us with a good example for illustrating the use of normal coordinates and Lagrange's equations in treating the effect of external forces on a coupled system. Suppose that there is a force $F(x, t)\, dx$ acting on the element dx of the string at x and t, so that $F(x, t)$ is the force per unit length. We want to find the corresponding generalized force.

In order to apply (12-88) to the continuous string, we should replace a_{jk} by u_{jn} and convert the sum to an integral with the help of (14-8); in this way we get

$$Q_n = \sum_j \left(\frac{F_j}{d}\right) u_{jn}\, d \to \int_0^L F(x, t) u_n(x)\, dx \qquad (14\text{-}37)$$

since $F_j/d \to$ force per unit length $= F(x, t)$. If we now combine (14-5) and (14-37), we find that the generalized force associated with the normal coordinate ζ_n is

$$Q_n = \int_0^L F(x, t) \sqrt{\frac{2}{\mu L}} \sin\left(\frac{n\pi x}{L}\right) dx \qquad (14\text{-}38)$$

and Lagrange's equations become

$$\ddot{\zeta}_n + \omega_n^2 \zeta_n = Q_n \qquad (14\text{-}39)$$

If, for instance, $F(x, t) \sim e^{-i\omega t}$, then $Q_n \sim e^{-i\omega t}$ and the forced motion obtained from (14-39) is

$$\zeta_n = \frac{Q_n}{\omega_n^2 - \omega^2}$$

and, when this is substituted into (14-11), the forced motion of the whole string is found to be

$$u(x, t) = \sum_n \left(\frac{Q_n}{\omega_n^2 - \omega^2}\right) \sqrt{\frac{2}{\mu L}} \sin\left(\frac{n\pi x}{L}\right) \qquad (14\text{-}40)$$

which shows that an infinite number of resonances are possible because the displacement will become very large whenever the applied frequency approaches one of the natural frequencies ω_n of the system.

Now let us suppose that the string is also subject to a damping force proportional to the velocity; we could get such a force by immersing the whole string in a fluid such as air or water. We can write the frictional force per unit length as

$$F_{\text{fric}}(x, t) = -k\dot{u}(x, t) = -k \sum_m \zeta_m \sqrt{\frac{2}{\mu L}} \sin\left(\frac{m\pi x}{L}\right) \quad (14\text{-}41)$$

where k is a constant and where we have used (14-11). When (14-41) is put into (14-38) and (14-9) is used, the result is that

$$Q_{n,\text{fric}} = -k \sum_m \zeta_m \frac{2}{\mu L} \int_0^L \sin\left(\frac{m\pi x}{L}\right) \sin\left(\frac{n\pi x}{L}\right) dx = -\left(\frac{k}{\mu}\right)\zeta_n \quad (14\text{-}42)$$

Then, if $Q_n{}'$ is any additional force, (14-39) becomes

$$\ddot{\zeta}_n + \frac{k}{\mu}\dot{\zeta}_n + \omega_n{}^2\zeta_n = Q_n{}' \quad (14\text{-}43)$$

We see that this equation is still separated in the sense that only one normal coordinate is involved, so we can still think of the normal co-ordinates as representing independent oscillators, even in the presence of friction. This equation (14-43) is now in the standard form of a damped harmonic oscillator which we discussed at length in Secs. 5-2 and 5-3. If $Q_n{}' \sim e^{-i\omega t}$, we can find the forced motion of ζ_n by assuming $\zeta_n \sim e^{-i\omega t}$; the solution obtained in this way from (14-43) is

$$\zeta_n = \frac{Q_n{}'}{\omega_n{}^2 - \omega^2 - i\omega(k/\mu)}$$

We can obtain the complete steady state forced motion of the string by using this expression for ζ_n in (14-11); the result is

$$u(x, t) = \sqrt{\frac{2}{\mu L}} \sum_n \frac{Q_n{}' \sin(n\pi x/L)}{\omega_n{}^2 - \omega^2 - i\omega(k/\mu)} \quad (14\text{-}44)$$

We must still take the real part of this expression, and, in order to satisfy arbitrary initial conditions, we must still add to it a general solution of the equation of motion for $Q_n{}' = 0$, that is, the sum given by (14-16) or (14-31).

Exercises

14-1. Verify (14-36).

14-2. Beginning with (14-15), find the Hamiltonian and Hamiltonian equations of motion for the continuous string and show that they also lead to the general solution (14-16).

14-3. A uniform string of length L is pulled aside a distance d at a point $x = a$ and then released from rest, so that its initial shape is made up of two straight line segments. Find its subsequent displacement as a function of position and time. Consider the special case $a = \frac{1}{2}L$, and explain the physical significance of the result.

14-4. A uniform string is undisplaced and at rest at $t = 0$. Thereafter, it is subjected to a force $F_0 \sin \omega t$ applied in a very small region about the point $x = a$. Find the displacement for all future times.

15 *Waves on the string*

We can describe the displacement of a uniform string in another way by using the concepts associated with *traveling waves*. In order to do this, let us temporarily disregard the fact that the string must be somehow held at the ends, and consider only the differential equation appropriate for the uniform continuous string. As given by (14-20) and (14-23), this equation is

$$\frac{\partial^2 u}{\partial x^2} = \frac{1}{v^2} \frac{\partial^2 u}{\partial t^2} \tag{15-1}$$

where $v = \sqrt{T/\mu}$. The method of solution based on normal modes which we used in the last chapter is the convenient method for obtaining the standing waves which are appropriate for a string rigidly fixed at both ends.

We now want to show that a perfectly general solution of (15-1) is

$$u(x, t) = f(x - vt) + g(x + vt) \tag{15-2}$$

where f and g are two completely arbitrary functions. In order to prove this, we let $w = x - vt$; then we can write $f = f(w)$ and find that

$$\frac{\partial f}{\partial x} = \frac{df}{dw} \frac{\partial w}{\partial x} = \frac{df}{dw}$$

and

$$\frac{\partial^2 f}{\partial x^2} = \frac{d^2 f}{dw^2} \frac{\partial w}{\partial x} = \frac{d^2 f}{dw^2}$$

and

$$\frac{\partial f}{\partial t} = \frac{df}{dw} \frac{\partial w}{\partial t} = -v \frac{df}{dw}$$

and

$$\frac{\partial^2 f}{\partial t^2} = -v \frac{d^2 f}{dw^2} \frac{\partial w}{\partial t} = v^2 \frac{d^2 f}{dw^2}$$

so that

$$\frac{d^2f}{dw^2} = \frac{\partial^2 f}{\partial x^2} = \frac{1}{v^2}\frac{\partial^2 f}{\partial t^2}$$

which shows that $f(x - vt)$ is a solution of (15-1). Similarly, we can show that $g(x + vt)$ is also a solution of (15-1), and therefore the sum (15-2) is also a solution of the linear differential equation (15-1).

We interpret this result by saying that $f(x - vt)$ is a *wave* of arbitrary form traveling to the right with velocity v; that is, it is traveling in the direction of the positive x axis. In order to show this, let us consider a particular value of f at $t = 0$ and $x = 0$, which we call f_0; then $f_0 = f(0)$. At a later time t_0, f will also equal the same value f_0 at a new position x_0 such that the argument is again zero; that is,

$$f(x_0 - vt_0) = f_0 = f(0)$$

so tha

$$x_0 = vt_0 \tag{15-3}$$

Thus the particular feature $f = f_0$, which appeared at $x = 0$ and $t = 0$, now has moved to a new point x_0 given by (15-3), i.e., a point reached by traveling to the right at constant velocity v. These relations are illustrated in Fig. 15-1. Similarly, one can show that $g(x + vt)$ represents a wave of arbitrary form traveling to the left with velocity v.

The form of solution given in (15-2) therefore says that any displacement of the string can be written as the superposition of two waves—one traveling to the right and the other traveling to the left, but both with the same velocity v which is determined by the properties of the system. We might wonder how this can be reconciled with our results of the last chapter in which we found solutions in terms of standing waves. In order to see that the two treatments are compatible we consider the particular solution u_1 of (14-24), which we can transform with known trigonometric identities as follows:

$$u_1 = \sin\left(\frac{\omega}{v}x\right)\sin\omega t = \left[\tfrac{1}{2}\cos\frac{\omega}{v}(x - vt)\right] - \left[\tfrac{1}{2}\cos\frac{\omega}{v}(x + vt)\right] \tag{15-4}$$

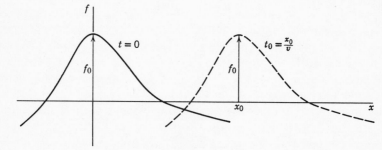

Fig. 15-1

so that we see that this particular solution can be written as a sum of oppositely traveling waves, as asserted by (15-2).

At a given time, the first sinusoidal wave on the right of (15-4) repeats its value whenever $(\omega x/v)$ increases by 2π; calling this distance λ, we get $(\omega\lambda/v) = 2\pi$. Thus this particular traveling wave is periodic in space with a spatial period λ which is called the *wavelength*; we see that

$$\lambda \frac{\omega}{2\pi} = v \qquad (15\text{-}5)$$

At a given point in space, the displacement is periodic in time, and whenever the quantity ωt increases by 2π, the displacement repeats itself. If we let τ be the *period*, we have $\omega\tau = 2\pi$ or

$$\tau = \frac{1}{\nu} = \frac{2\pi}{\omega} \qquad (15\text{-}6)$$

where ν is the *frequency*. Therefore we can also write $\nu = \omega/2\pi$, and (15-5) becomes

$$\lambda\,\nu = v \qquad (15\text{-}7)$$

which is a simple and useful relation for a wave.

We also note the interesting fact that the velocity v given by (14-23) for the continuous uniform string is independent of the frequency. We know from (14-31) that the general displacement can be written as a superposition of standing waves for all the possible frequencies. We have also just seen in (15-4) that each of these standing waves can in turn be written in terms of traveling waves and that all these traveling waves move with the same velocity. The consequence of this finding is that any general displacement of the continuous uniform string will travel along the string *with its form unchanged*. The reason, of course, is that each wave which goes into the superposition travels right along with all the others so that they are always "in step," and thus always add up to the same total displacement. This is *not* true of the weighted string, as we shall see shortly.

If the velocity of sinusoidal wave propagation in a medium depends on the frequency (or, equally, on the wavelength), the medium is called *dispersive* and the general phenomenon is known as *dispersion*. (As we have just seen, the uniform string is an example of a non-dispersive medium.) Therefore, in a dispersive medium, an arbitrary wave form which is written as a superposition of sinusoidal waves will *not* travel with its form unchanged. In other words, the general shape of the displacement will alter as it moves along because the various components of its superposition will travel at different velocities, will become relatively "out of step," and will generally add up differently as the wave form moves along.

A simple example of a dispersive medium is the weighted string. As we see from (13-7), (13-9), and (14-3), it is possible to write a solution in the form

$$u_j = \bar{A}e^{i(jk-\omega t)} = \bar{A}e^{i[(k/d)x-\omega t]} = \bar{A}e^{i(k/d)[x-(\omega d/k)t]} \qquad (15\text{-}8)$$

and by comparing it with (15-2) we see that this equation has the form of a wave whose velocity is given by the coefficient of t as

$$v = \frac{\omega d}{k} = \left[\frac{2T d(1 - \cos k)}{mk^2}\right]^{1/2} \qquad (15\text{-}9)$$

when we use (13-10) to obtain the relation between ω and k. Thus we see that v does depend on ω (or, equally, on k), so that the weighted string is dispersive. We recall from (13-10) that k can vary from 0 to π in order to cover the whole range of frequencies.

For low frequencies, $\cos k \simeq 1$ and k is small, so that, if we also use (14-2), we can approximate (15-9) as

$$v \simeq \left[\frac{2Td}{m}\frac{(\frac{1}{2}k^2)}{k^2}\right]^{1/2} = \sqrt{\frac{Td}{m}} = \sqrt{\frac{T}{\mu}} \qquad (15\text{-}10)$$

Thus, for low frequencies, the velocity is independent of frequency and equal to that for a continuous string of the same ratio of tension to equivalent linear density μ. The maximum frequency is obtained when $k = \pi$, and the corresponding velocity is found from (15-9) to be

$$v(\omega_{\max}) = \frac{2}{\pi}\sqrt{\frac{Td}{m}} < v(\text{low freq}) \qquad (15\text{-}11)$$

and we see that the velocity decreases as k (and ω) increases.

We can also write the first two terms of (15-9) as

$$v_p = (\omega/k)\,d = d\tan\alpha \qquad (15\text{-}12)$$

where α is shown on the ω vs. k curve of Fig. 15-2, which is like that of Fig. 14-1; we note that $\tan\alpha$ is a function of ω or k. In other words, (15-12) says that the velocity for a given frequency is proportional to the slope of the line drawn from the origin of the ω vs. k curve to the corresponding point on the curve. If the velocity is the same for all frequencies, the slope of this line is constant and the ω vs. k curve is a straight line. The velocity v_p is called the *phase velocity*. This name is given to it because it is the velocity

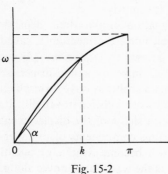

Fig. 15-2

with which a certain characteristic or "phase" of the wave is propagated along.

The slope of the ω vs. k curve of Fig. 15-2 can also be given a physical interpretation; thus we want to consider

$$v_g = \left(\frac{d\omega}{dk}\right) d = \text{group velocity} \qquad (15\text{-}13)$$

We see from Fig. 15-2 that $v_g < v_p$ for the weighted string, since the slope of the curve is less than the slope of the chord. The name arises from the fact, which we shall show at once, that if we superimpose two waves of *almost* the same frequency the resultant pattern travels with the group velocity v_g, while the individual components of the superposition travel along with their own phase velocity.

Let us choose the particular superposition to be the sum of two traveling waves of unit amplitude and of nearly the same values of k and ω; thus, if we use (15-8), we can write the superposition as

$$e^{i[(k+\delta k)(x/d)-(\omega+\delta\omega)t]} + e^{i[(k-\delta k)(x/d)-(\omega-\delta\omega)t]}$$

$$= e^{i[(kx/d)-\omega t]}\left\{e^{i[\delta k(x/d)-\delta\omega t]} + e^{-i[\delta k(x/d)-\delta\omega t]}\right\}$$

$$= e^{i(k/d)[x-(\omega d/k)t]} \cdot 2\cos\left\{\frac{\delta k}{d}\left[x - \left(\frac{\delta\omega}{\delta k}\right)dt\right]\right\}$$

$$= e^{i(k/d)[x-v_p t]} \cdot 2\cos\left[\frac{\delta k}{d}(x - v_g t)\right] \qquad (15\text{-}14)$$

with the use of (15-12) and (15-13); v_p is the average phase velocity of the two waves. The real part of (15-14) is

$$2\cos\left[\frac{\delta k}{d}(x - v_g t)\right]\cos\left[\frac{k}{d}(x - v_p t)\right] \qquad (15\text{-}15)$$

whose second factor is a wave with the average wavelength and velocity of the superimposed waves, while the first factor is a wave traveling with the group velocity since $\delta\omega$ and δk are small. This modulation of the amplitude given by the first factor travels more slowly because the group velocity is less than the phase velocity; this result is an example of the more general phenomenon known as *beats*. The resultant displacement represented by (15-15) is shown at a given time in Fig. 15-3; this figure does not show the individual waves which are added to give this result.

In (13-16), we found that $\omega_{max} = 2\sqrt{T/md}$ and corresponded to $\cos k = -1$ or $k = \pi$, and we said at that time that this meant that no mode or wave was possible for a higher frequency. Of course, we could easily imagine the actual possibility of shaking one end of the weighted string

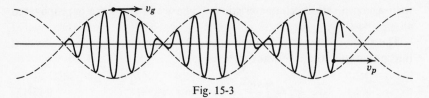

Fig. 15-3

at a frequency greater than ω_{max}, and we would then like to know what would occur; therefore we want to look into the whole question a little more deeply than before.

We assert first of all that in order to get $\omega > \omega_{max}$, with ω given by (13-10), it is necessary that

$$k = \pi + ik' \tag{15-16}$$

where k' is real; that is, k must be complex. As proof, we see that then

$$\cos k = \cos(\pi + ik') = -\cos(ik') = -\tfrac{1}{2}(e^{-k'} + e^{k'}) = -\cosh k'$$

so that (13-10) becomes

$$\omega = \left[\frac{2T}{md}(1 + \cosh k')\right]^{\frac{1}{2}} \geqslant \omega_{\text{max}} \tag{15-17}$$

since $\cosh k' \geqslant 1$. Now let us see how a complex k affects our solution. If we substitute (15-16) into (15-8), it becomes

$$u_j = \bar{A}e^{ij(\pi+ik')-i\omega t} = \bar{A}e^{ij\pi-jk'-i\omega t} = \bar{A}(-1)^j e^{-jk'-i\omega t}$$

and the real part is

$$u_j = \bar{A}(-1)^j e^{-jk'} \cos \omega t \tag{15-18}$$

This is not a wave, but it describes a situation where the displacement decreases exponentially and changes sign as one goes from one particle to the next along the weighted string. This gives us a picture *at a fixed time* like that shown in Fig. 15-4. In other words, for frequencies greater than

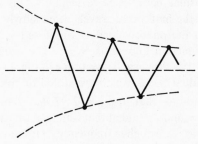

Fig. 15-4

the maximum frequency, we do not get wave propagation along the weighted string, but the displacement can be described as an attenuated "disturbance" instead. Thus the weighted string cuts off higher frequencies in the sense that, if the string were long enough, no disturbance would be observed at the other end because of the exponential decrease in the displacement; the weighted string, therefore, is an example of a "low-pass" filter.

16 The string of variable tension and density

If we assume the linear density of the string to be independent of the time, the general differential equation (14-19) for the string becomes

$$\frac{\partial}{\partial x}\left(T\frac{\partial u}{\partial x}\right) = \mu\frac{\partial^2 u}{\partial t^2} \qquad (16\text{-}1)$$

We are interested in problems in which the tension and density can both vary with position; that is, we have $T = T(x)$ and $\mu = \mu(x)$. In spite of this complication, we can still look for normal modes. In order to do this, we assume a solution of the form

$$u(x, t) = \bar{u}(x)e^{-i\omega t} \qquad (16\text{-}2)$$

so that $\partial^2 u/\partial t^2 = -\omega^2 \bar{u} e^{-i\omega t}$, and (16-1) becomes

$$\frac{d}{dx}\left(T\frac{d\bar{u}}{dx}\right) + \omega^2\mu\bar{u} = 0 \qquad (16\text{-}3)$$

This is a second order differential equation with variable coefficients for which there are no general methods of solution. At most, one can hope to be able to solve special cases, or to use various approximate methods which have been developed, such as expansion in power series.

16-1 Exponential string

As an example, let us consider a case in which the tension and density both vary exponentially in the same way along the string; that is, we assume

$$T = T_0 e^{\alpha x}, \quad \mu = \mu_0 e^{\alpha x} \qquad (16\text{-}4)$$

where T_0, μ_0, and α are constants. The principal importance of the exponential string is that we can solve (16-3) exactly for this string and are thereby able to see the general effect of a variation in T and μ.

Let us try an exponential form for $\bar{u}$ and assume that

$$\bar{u}(x) = \bar{u}_0 e^{i\gamma x} \qquad (16\text{-}5)$$

When (16-5) is substituted into (16-3), the latter becomes,

$$\frac{d}{dx}[T_0 \bar{u}_0 i\gamma e^{(\alpha+i\gamma)x}] + \omega^2 \mu_0 \bar{u}_0 e^{(\alpha+i\gamma)x} = 0$$

from which we find that

$$-\gamma^2 + i\gamma\alpha + \omega^2 \frac{\mu_0}{T_0} = 0 \qquad (16\text{-}6)$$

which can be solved for γ, with the result that

$$\gamma = \frac{i\alpha}{2} \pm \left[\frac{\omega^2 \mu_0}{T_0} - \left(\frac{\alpha}{2}\right)^2\right]^{\frac{1}{2}} \qquad (16\text{-}7)$$

Since there are two possible values of γ, the general expression for $\bar{u}$ obtained from (16-5) will be a sum of terms:

$$\bar{u}(x) = e^{-\frac{1}{2}\alpha x}\{\bar{u}_{0+} e^{i[(\omega/v_0)^2 - (\alpha/2)^2]^{\frac{1}{2}}x} + \bar{u}_{0-} e^{-i[(\omega/v_0)^2 - (\alpha/2)^2]^{\frac{1}{2}}x}\} \qquad (16\text{-}8)$$

where $\bar{u}_{0+}$ and $\bar{u}_{0-}$ are constants and

$$v_0 = \sqrt{T_0/\mu_0} \qquad (16\text{-}9)$$

When we substitute (16-8) into (16-2), we see that we shall have "waves" again, and we now want to look at these solutions more closely.

As a check, we can let $\alpha = 0$, and then (16-8) and (16-2) give us

$$u(x, t) = \bar{u}_{0+} e^{i(\omega/v_0)(x-v_0 t)} + \bar{u}_{0-} e^{-i(\omega/v_0)(x+v_0 t)} \qquad (16\text{-}10)$$

which is exactly of the proper form for waves on the uniform string for which the velocity is given by (16-9).

If $\alpha \neq 0$, we notice first that the amplitude of $\bar{u}$ in (16-8) is proportional to $e^{-\frac{1}{2}\alpha x}$. Thus the amplitude is small where the tension and density are large, and vice versa, as seems reasonable in view of the larger inertia and constraining force. The velocity of propagation is also affected. We can find the velocity easily if we look at (15-4) and note that the coefficient of ix in the exponential can be set equal to ω/v; therefore, from (16-8), we can say that

$$\frac{\omega}{v} = \left[\frac{\omega^2}{v_0^2} - \left(\frac{\alpha}{2}\right)^2\right]^{\frac{1}{2}}$$

so that

$$v = \frac{v_0}{[1 - (\alpha v_0/2\omega)^2]^{\frac{1}{2}}} \qquad (16\text{-}11)$$

We see that the phase velocity given in (16-11) depends on frequency; hence the exponential string is also a dispersive medium.

Suppose that the square root appearing in (16-8) is zero; that is,

$$\left[\left(\frac{\omega}{v_0}\right)^2 - \left(\frac{\alpha}{2}\right)^2\right]^{1/2} = 0 \tag{16-12}$$

Then we see that (16-8) becomes simply

$$\bar{u} = \bar{u}_0 e^{-\frac{1}{2}\alpha x} \tag{16-13}$$

where $\bar{u}_0 = \bar{u}_{0+} + \bar{u}_{0-}$. Therefore we have only an exponentially damped displacement and no wave propagation. For a given value of α and v_0, there is always a frequency ω for which (16-12) is possible. For frequencies greater than this frequency, the square root is real and we get wave propagation along the string with a velocity given by (16-11). For frequencies less than this frequency, however, the square root is a pure imaginary and (16-8) describes attenuated displacements, rather than wave propagation. Thus the exponential string acts like a "high-pass" filter in the sense that waves can be propagated along it only if their frequency is greater than a certain critical frequency which, as seen from (16-12), increases as α increases.

16-2 General properties of the normal modes

Now we again assume that the string is rigidly fixed at the ends $x = 0$ and $x = L$. We have seen in the two examples of the weighted string and the continuous uniform string that the existence of these boundary conditions was sufficient to determine the possible frequencies of the normal modes. Hence in this general case, too, we can be sure—without solving the problem explicitly—that the system will have a series of allowed normal frequencies which we simply write as ω_n.

Let $\bar{u}_n(x)$ be the displacement in the normal mode corresponding to ω_n. Since $\bar{u}$ satisfies (16-3), we know that the equations satisfied by any two normal modes, $\bar{u}_n$ and $\bar{u}_m$, of the system are

$$\frac{d}{dx}\left(T\frac{d\bar{u}_n}{dx}\right) + \omega_n^2 \mu \bar{u}_n = 0, \quad \frac{d}{dx}\left(T\frac{d\bar{u}_m}{dx}\right) + \omega_m^2 \mu \bar{u}_m = 0 \tag{16-14}$$

They also satisfy the boundary conditions

$$\bar{u}_n(0) = \bar{u}_m(0) = 0, \quad \bar{u}_n(L) = \bar{u}_m(L) = 0 \tag{16-15}$$

We now want to show that the requirements given in (16-14) and (16-15) are sufficient to make the functions $\bar{u}_n$ and $\bar{u}_m$ orthogonal. We multiply the first equation of (16-14) by $\bar{u}_m$, the second by $\bar{u}_n$, subtract the two resulting equations, integrate the final expression over the length of the string, and simplify part of the result by integrating by parts; in this way, we obtain

$$\int_0^L \left[\bar{u}_m \frac{d}{dx}\left(T \frac{d\bar{u}_n}{dx} \right) - \bar{u}_n \frac{d}{dx}\left(T \frac{d\bar{u}_m}{dx} \right) \right] dx = (\omega_m{}^2 - \omega_n{}^2) \int_0^L \mu \bar{u}_n \bar{u}_m \, dx$$

$$= \left[T \left(\bar{u}_m \frac{d\bar{u}_n}{dx} - \bar{u}_n \frac{d\bar{u}_m}{dx} \right) \right]_0^L - \int_0^L T \left(\frac{d\bar{u}_m}{dx} \frac{d\bar{u}_n}{dx} - \frac{d\bar{u}_n}{dx} \frac{d\bar{u}_m}{dx} \right) dx = 0$$

since the first term vanishes because the functions $\bar{u}_n$ and $\bar{u}_m$ vanish at the ends according to (16-15) and the integrand of the second term is zero. Thus we get the general result

$$(\omega_m{}^2 - \omega_n{}^2) \int_0^L \mu \bar{u}_n \bar{u}_m \, dx = 0 \tag{16-16}$$

If $\omega_m \neq \omega_n$, we see that

$$\int_0^L \mu \bar{u}_n \bar{u}_m \, dx = 0 \tag{16-17}$$

while, if $\omega_m = \omega_n$, we can choose the multiplicative factor which will always appear in $\bar{u}_n$ in a way which is compatible with (16-16) and is convenient for further applications by making

$$\int_0^L \mu \bar{u}_n{}^2 \, dx = 1 \tag{16-18}$$

We finally see then that it is a consequence of the form of the equation of motion (16-3) *and* the boundary conditions that

$$\int_0^L \mu(x) \bar{u}_n(x) \bar{u}_m(x) \, dx = \delta_{nm} \tag{16-19}$$

and $\bar{u}_n$ and $\bar{u}_m$ are then said to be *orthonormal* in the sense that the *weighting function* $\mu(x)$ is a necessary part of the integrand. We see that (16-19) is similar to our previous results, obtained for the coupled system of discrete particles in (12-43) and for the uniform string in (14-10).

The general displacement of the string fixed at the ends $x = 0$ and $x = L$ can now be written as a superposition of the normal modes in a form which follows from (16-2) as

$$u(x, t) = \sum_n (A_n \cos \omega_n t + B_n \sin \omega_n t) \bar{u}_n(x) \tag{16-20}$$

In this equation, we do not know the explicit form of the normal modes $\bar{u}_n(x)$ because we have not solved (16-3) for a particular case, but we do know from (16-19) that the normal modes are orthonormal. The initial conditions are

$$u(x, 0) = u_0(x) = \sum_n A_n \bar{u}_n(x) \tag{16-21a}$$

$$\left(\frac{\partial u}{\partial t}\right)_{t=0} = \dot{u}_0(x) = \sum_n \omega_n B_n \bar{u}_n(x) \tag{16-21b}$$

In order to find the coefficients, we can use (16-19) in the now familiar way:

$$\int_0^L \mu \bar{u}_m u_0 \, dx = \sum_n A_n \int_0^L \mu \bar{u}_m \bar{u}_n \, dx = \sum_n A_n \, \delta_{nm} = A_m \tag{16-22}$$

and, similarly,

$$B_m = \frac{1}{\omega_m} \int_0^L \mu \bar{u}_m \dot{u}_0 \, dx \tag{16-23}$$

We can see now that our method of obtaining our previous results for the uniform string in which the displacement was expanded in a series of sines is simply a special case of the general method of expansion of arbitrary functions in series of *orthogonal functions*. This general concept is of great importance in theoretical physics generally and is particularly useful in the formulation of quantum theory. In our next section, we consider an important approximation method in which the expansion of a function in a series of orthogonal functions plays an essential role.

16-3   Perturbation theory

This method is useful when the problem is "almost solvable"; that is, the tension and density are only slightly different from the values for a problem which can be solved. We shall illustrate the method by finding approximate expressions for the normal frequencies. In order not to make the situation too involved, let us assume that $T = $ const., so that only the density varies with position.

Let $\mu_0(x)$ be the density for which the problem can be solved exactly. The results of the solution will be the normal frequencies ω_{0n} and the orthonormal functions $\bar{u}_{0n}(x)$ which we can assume to be known. Using (16-3) and (16-19), we can also say that these known functions satisfy the equations

$$T\frac{d^2 \bar{u}_{0n}}{dx^2} + \omega_{0n}^2 \mu_0 \bar{u}_{0n} = 0 \tag{16-24}$$

$$\int_0^L \mu_0 \bar{u}_{0n} \bar{u}_{0m} \, dx = \delta_{nm} \tag{16-25}$$

Let $\mu(x)$ be the density for the actual problem of interest. Although we are not able to solve this problem exactly, we do know that there must exist a set of normal frequencies ω_n and associated normal modes $\bar{u}_n$ which satisfy the equation

$$T\frac{d^2\bar{u}_n}{dx^2} + \omega_n^2\mu\bar{u}_n = 0 \tag{16-26}$$

Our problem is to find the ω_n approximately; in the general case, we would also want to find the $\bar{u}_n$ as well, but for many applications a knowledge of only the frequencies is sufficient.

If we expand the general function $\bar{u}_n(x)$ as a superposition of the known orthonormal set $\bar{u}_{0n}$, we can write

$$\bar{u}_n(x) = \sum_k a_{nk}\bar{u}_{0k}(x) \tag{16-27}$$

where the a_{nk} are constants which, if they were known, would determine the exact form of $\bar{u}_n$. Substituting (16-27) into (16-26), and using (16-24), we get

$$\sum_k a_{nk}\left[T\frac{d^2\bar{u}_{0k}}{dx^2} + \omega_n^2\mu\bar{u}_{0k}\right] = \sum_k a_{nk}(-\omega_{0k}^2\mu_0 + \omega_n^2\mu)\bar{u}_{0k} = 0 \tag{16-28}$$

In order to eliminate the $\bar{u}_{0k}$ in (16-28), we can multiply by $\bar{u}_{0m}$ and use (16-25); in this way we obtain

$$\sum_k a_{nk}\left[\omega_{0k}^2\int_0^L \mu_0\bar{u}_{0m}\bar{u}_{0k}\,dx - \omega_n^2\int_0^L \mu\bar{u}_{0m}\bar{u}_{0k}\,dx\right]$$
$$= \sum_k a_{nk}(\omega_{0k}^2\,\delta_{mk} - \omega_n^2\mu_{mk}) = 0 \tag{16-29}$$

where we have set

$$\mu_{mk} = \int_0^L \mu\bar{u}_{0m}\bar{u}_{0k}\,dx \tag{16-30}$$

Since μ is known from the statement of the problem, and the $\bar{u}_{0m}$ are assumed to be already known, the μ_{mk} defined in (16-30) can be found in principle. Since $\mu \simeq \mu_0$, by hypothesis, the integral (16-30) is almost the same as that in (16-25); hence $\mu_{mk} \simeq \delta_{mk}$.

For a given n, the equations in (16-29) are an infinite set for the unknown constants a_{nk} because we obtain one equation for each possible value of m and m can be 1, 2, 3, ... The general procedure is then similar to what we did in finding the normal frequencies in Sec. 12-2, and the frequencies would be determined in principle from the requirement that the determinant of the coefficients of the a_{nk} in (16-29) be equal to zero. We shall not do this, however, but proceed differently.

Up to this point, all our results have been exact, and now we shall begin to make approximations. If μ does not differ very much from μ_0, we must expect that $\bar{u}_n$ will not differ very much from $\bar{u}_{0n}$, i.e., $\bar{u}_n \simeq \bar{u}_{0n}$. Then we see from (16-27) that as a *first approximation* we can take

$$a_{nn} \simeq 1, \quad a_{nk} \simeq 0 \quad \text{if} \quad k \neq n \tag{16-31}$$

and (16-29) becomes simply

$$a_{nn}(\omega_{0n}^2 \delta_{mn} - \omega_n^2 \mu_{mn}) = 0$$

Since $\mu_{mn} \simeq \delta_{mn}$, the only one of these equations which will give us any information about ω_n^2 is that for which $m = n$. Then we obtain $a_{nn}(\omega_{0n}^2 - \omega_n^2 \mu_{nn}) = 0$, or

$$\omega_n^2 = \frac{\omega_{0n}^2}{\mu_{nn}} \tag{16-32}$$

which is our desired approximate result. It can be put into a more convenient form by introducing the difference, μ', of the two densities; then we can write

$$\mu = \mu_0 + \mu', \quad \mu' \ll \mu_0 \tag{16-33}$$

If we use (16-30), (16-33), and (16-25), we find that

$$\mu_{nn} = \int_0^L (\mu_0 + \mu')\bar{u}_{0n}^2 \, dx = 1 + \int_0^L \mu' \bar{u}_{0n}^2 \, dx$$

and therefore, if we use the approximation $(1 + x)^{-1} \simeq 1 - x$ for $x \ll 1$, we can write (16-32) in the more useful form

$$\omega_n^2 \simeq \omega_{0n}^2 \left[1 - \int_0^L \mu' \bar{u}_{0n}^2 \, dx \right] = \omega_{0n}^2 (1 - \Delta_n) \tag{16-34}$$

We see from the last result that if μ' is positive everywhere, so that the total mass of the string is increased, then the frequency is decreased, as we might have expected from the increased inertia of the whole system. If we desire, we can use this approximation for ω_n^2 in (16-29) in order to find a better approximation than δ_{nk} to the a_{nk} and thereby obtain from (16-27) a better approximation to the actual normal mode of the system.

Example. Linearly Varying Density. Suppose the density is given by $\mu = \mu_0 + \epsilon(x/L)$, where μ_0 and ϵ are constants and $\epsilon \ll \mu_0$. Clearly,

$$\mu' = \epsilon(x/L) \tag{16-35}$$

Since $\mu_0 = \text{const.}$, the $\bar{u}_{0n}$ and ω_{0n} we want are the normal modes and frequencies of the uniform string as given by (14-5) and (14-6); in our present notation, therefore, we have,

$$\omega_{0n}^2 = \left(\frac{n\pi}{L}\right)^2 \frac{T}{\mu_0}, \quad \bar{u}_{0n} = \sqrt{\frac{2}{\mu_0 L}} \sin\left(\frac{n\pi x}{L}\right) \tag{16-36}$$

The integral needed in (16-34) then is

$$\Delta_n = \int_0^L \mu' \bar{u}_{0n}{}^2 \, dx = \int_0^L \frac{2\epsilon x}{\mu_0 L^2} \sin^2 \left(\frac{n\pi x}{L} \right) dx$$

If we let $z = (n\pi x/L)$, this equation becomes

$$\Delta_n = \frac{2\epsilon}{\mu_0 (n\pi)^2} \int_0^{n\pi} z \sin^2 z \, dz$$

$$= \frac{2\epsilon}{\mu_0 (n\pi)^2} \left[\frac{z^2}{4} - \frac{z \sin 2z}{4} - \frac{\cos 2z}{8} \right]_0^{n\pi} = \frac{\epsilon}{2\mu_0}$$

and, when this is substituted into (16-34), and (16-36) is used, the frequencies are found to be given by

$$\omega_n{}^2 \simeq \left(\frac{n\pi}{L} \right)^2 \frac{T}{\mu_0} \left(1 - \frac{\epsilon}{2\mu_0} \right) \qquad (16\text{-}37)$$

In this particular example, the correction term turned out to be independent of n, although this does not generally occur.

Exercises

16-1. An exponential string of length L is held rigidly fixed at the ends. Show that the normal frequencies are given by

$$\omega_n = \frac{n\pi}{L} \left\{ \frac{T_0}{\mu_0} \left[1 + \left(\frac{\alpha L}{2n\pi} \right)^2 \right] \right\}$$

Also show by direct integration that the corresponding normal modes satisfy the orthogonality relation (16-17).

16-2. A *very* small mass m is fastened to a string of constant tension and density at the point $x = a$. Show that the new normal frequencies are given approximately by

$$\omega_n{}^2 \simeq \left(\frac{n\pi}{L} \right)^2 \frac{T}{\mu} \left[1 - \frac{2m}{\mu L} \sin^2 \left(\frac{n\pi a}{L} \right) \right]$$

Explain the significance of the result obtained if $a = \tfrac{1}{2}L$.

17 The membrane

We now want to discuss briefly some of the complications which can arise when our vibrating system has more than the one dimension characteristic of the string. We shall consider our system to have a two-dimensional plane surface; that is, it is a membrane such as a drumhead. If we let the surface of the membrane lie in the xy plane, we can define a displacement which is at right angles to the equilibrium plane; we again represent the displacement by u, and now it is a function of three variables and we can write $u = u(x, y, t)$.

From what we have learned from our study of the string, we can now expect that, after we have found the equation of motion of the membrane and found the solution, we shall find that the possible frequencies of vibration of this system as a whole will be determined by the boundary conditions. Our string had relatively simple boundary conditions in that it was rigidly fixed at the ends. We shall consider only analogous boundary conditions for the membrane, in that we shall assume that it is held rigidly around its perimeter. However, we can have so many different possible shapes for a two-dimensional membrane that the boundary conditions can become analytically quite complicated, and, in fact, it is only for very simple shapes that we can get explicit solutions at all.

17-1 Equation of motion and normal modes

First of all, we want to put $F = ma$ into a form suitable to the membrane. If we let μ be the mass per unit area, which we assume to be constant, the mass of a small element of the membrane bounded by dx and dy is $\mu \, dx \, dy$ and the mass of this element times the acceleration normal to the plane is

$$\mu \, dx \, dy \, \frac{\partial^2 u}{\partial t^2} \tag{17-1}$$

We let T be the tension per unit length; by this we mean that, if we imagine the membrane cut along a distance ds, the total force normal to the cut is $T \, ds$, as illustrated in Fig. 17-1a. We assume that T is constant over the whole surface.

The calculation of the net force acting on an element $dx \, dy$ of the membrane is very similar to our calculation for the string, and it is illustrated in Fig. 17-1b. We assume small displacements so that we can make the same type of approximation as in (14-18). Then the force along the u direction at $x + dx$ due to the force perpendicular to dy is seen to be

$$(T \, dy)\left(\frac{\partial u}{\partial x}\right)_{x+dx} \tag{17-2}$$

Similarly, the force along the u direction at x is

$$-(T \, dy)\left(\frac{\partial u}{\partial x}\right)_{x} \tag{17-3}$$

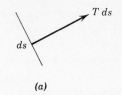

(a)

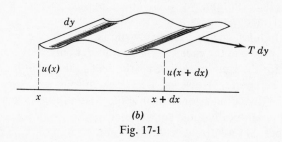

(b)

Fig. 17-1

Hence, when (17-2) and (17-3) are added, we find that the net transverse force due to the membrane forces perpendicular to dy is

$$(T\,dy)\left[\left(\frac{\partial u}{\partial x}\right)_{x+dx} - \left(\frac{\partial u}{\partial x}\right)_{x}\right] = T\left(\frac{\partial^2 u}{\partial x^2}\right)\,dx\,dy \qquad (17\text{-}4)$$

In the same way, the net transverse force on $dx\,dy$ due to the membrane forces perpendicular to the side dx is found to be

$$T\left(\frac{\partial^2 u}{\partial y^2}\right)\,dy\,dx \qquad (17\text{-}5)$$

If we add (17-4) and (17-5), we obtain the total transverse force on the element $dx\,dy$ of the membrane; we can then equate this to (17-1), cancel out the common factor $dx\,dy$, and finally get

$$\frac{\partial^2 u}{\partial x^2} + \frac{\partial^2 u}{\partial y^2} = \frac{1}{v^2}\frac{\partial^2 u}{\partial t^2} \qquad (17\text{-}6)$$

where

$$v^2 = \frac{T}{\mu} \qquad (17\text{-}7)$$

This result (17-6) is called the *wave equation in two dimensions*.

Rather than directly looking for the normal mode type of solutions of (17-6), we shall illustrate a method of solving partial differential equations known as *separation of variables*. We try to find a solution of the form

$$u(x,\,y,\,t) = w(x,\,y)\theta(t) \qquad (17\text{-}8)$$

so that

$$\frac{\partial^2 u}{\partial x^2} = \frac{\partial^2 w}{\partial x^2}\,\theta, \quad \frac{\partial^2 u}{\partial y^2} = \frac{\partial^2 w}{\partial y^2}\,\theta, \quad \frac{\partial^2 u}{\partial t^2} = w\,\frac{d^2\theta}{dt^2} \tag{17-9}$$

If we substitute (17-9) into (17-6) and divide by the product $w\theta$, we obtain

$$\frac{1}{w}\left(\frac{\partial^2 w}{\partial x^2} + \frac{\partial^2 w}{\partial y^2}\right) = \frac{1}{v^2\theta}\frac{d^2\theta}{dt^2} \tag{17-10}$$

On the left side of this equation we now have a function only of x and y, while on the right side we have a function only of t. These two functions of different variables cannot generally be equal unless they are equal to the same *constant*, which we shall write as $-k^2$. Then, from (17-10), we get the *two* equations

$$\frac{1}{w}\left(\frac{\partial^2 w}{\partial x^2} + \frac{\partial^2 w}{\partial y^2}\right) = -k^2 \quad \text{and} \quad \frac{1}{v^2\theta}\frac{d^2\theta}{dt^2} = -k^2 \tag{17-11}$$

The last equation involves only the time, which has thus been "separated" by this process. The first equation of (17-11) can also be written

$$\frac{\partial^2 w}{\partial x^2} + \frac{\partial^2 w}{\partial y^2} + k^2 w = 0 \tag{17-12}$$

which is known as the *wave equation without the time*. The second equation of (17-11) can be written

$$\frac{d^2\theta}{dt^2} + \omega^2\theta = 0 \tag{17-13}$$

where

$$k^2 = \omega^2/v^2 \tag{17-14}$$

A solution of (17-13) is

$$\theta = \theta_0 e^{-i\omega t} \tag{17-15}$$

which thus automatically gives us a normal mode type of expression for u.

We can also solve (17-12) by separation of variables by writing

$$w(x, y) = X(x)\,Y(y) \tag{17-16}$$

If we substitute (17-16) into (17-12) and divide the result by the product XY, we find that

$$\frac{1}{X}\frac{d^2 X}{dx^2} = -k^2 - \frac{1}{Y}\frac{d^2 Y}{dy^2} = \text{const.} = -k_x^2 \tag{17-17}$$

after we again use the fact that a function only of x cannot always be equal to a function only of y unless they both equal the same constant. We now obtain the two equations

$$\frac{d^2 X}{dx^2} + k_x^2 X = 0, \quad \frac{d^2 Y}{dy^2} + k_y^2 Y = 0 \tag{17-18}$$

where

$$k^2 = k_x^2 + k_y^2 \tag{17-19}$$

These equations have the solutions

$$X(x) = \sin k_x x \quad or \quad \cos k_x x \tag{17-20a}$$

$$Y(y) = \sin k_y y \quad or \quad \cos k_y y \tag{17-20b}$$

Combining (17-20) with (17-16), (17-15), and (17-8), we find that there are *four* possible expressions for u which are obtained from all the combinations we can make from the sines and cosines of (17-20) by multiplying them together in pairs; we can write these expressions schematically as

$$u = u(x, y, t) = \alpha \begin{Bmatrix} \sin k_x x \\ \cos k_x x \end{Bmatrix} \begin{Bmatrix} \sin k_y y \\ \cos k_y y \end{Bmatrix} e^{-i\omega t} \tag{17-21}$$

where $\alpha =$ const. Of course, an arbitrary sum of these solutions will also be a solution of (17-6).

17-2   Rectangular membrane

As an example let us consider a rectangular membrane whose sides have lengths a and b and which is oriented as shown in Fig. 17-2. The boundary conditions are that the displacement is zero along the edges, or that

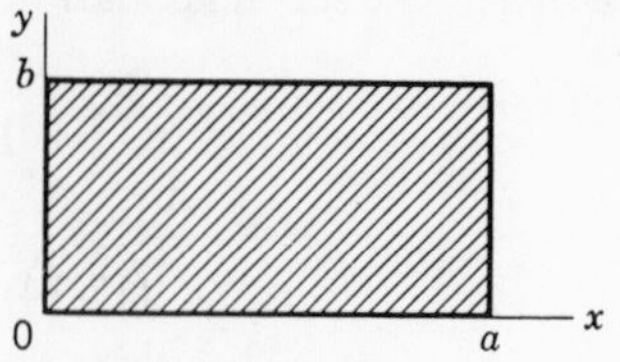

$$u = 0 \quad \text{for} \quad x = 0, \quad x = a,$$

$$y = 0, \quad y = b \tag{17-22}$$

We see at once that any terms in (17-21) which involve the cosines cannot appear because they do not vanish at $x = 0$ and $y = 0$. Therefore the solution is reduced to the possible form of

Fig. 17-2

$$u = \alpha \sin k_x x \sin k_y y \, e^{-i\omega t} \tag{17-23}$$

In order that $u = 0$ for $x = a$, we must have $\sin k_x a = 0$ or $k_x a = m\pi$, or

$$k_x = \frac{m\pi}{a}, \qquad m = 1, 2, 3, \ldots \tag{17-24}$$

Similarly, in order that $u = 0$ for $y = b$, we must have

$$k_y = \frac{n\pi}{b}, \qquad n = 1, 2, 3, \ldots \tag{17-25}$$

These conditions fix the allowed frequencies, for by (17-4) and (17-19) we see that the frequencies are given by $\omega = vk$ or

$$\omega_{mn} = \pi v \left[\left(\frac{m}{a}\right)^2 + \left(\frac{n}{b}\right)^2 \right]^{1/2} \tag{17-26}$$

where m and n independently take on the values $1, 2, 3, \ldots$. In contrast to the string, where the higher frequencies (overtones) were all integral multiples of the lowest (fundamental), we see that the various possible frequencies of the rectangular membrane are determined by a more complicated formula.

The general solution for the displacement will be given by a sum of terms like (17-23) with one term for each possible normal frequency; thus

$$u = \sum_m \sum_n \alpha_{mn} \sin\left(\frac{m\pi x}{a}\right) \sin\left(\frac{n\pi y}{b}\right) e^{-i\omega_{mn}t}$$

If the real part of this is taken, we obtain

$$u(x, y, t) = \sum_m \sum_n (A_{mn} \cos \omega_{mn} t + B_{mn} \sin \omega_{mn} t) \sin\left(\frac{m\pi x}{a}\right) \sin\left(\frac{n\pi y}{b}\right)$$

(17-27)

which is the general solution for the rectangular membrane which satisfies both the equation of motion and the boundary conditions and involves a set of constants of integration which can be evaluated from a knowledge of the initial displacement and velocity of each point of the membrane.

Just as we did for the string, we could now prove that these normal modes of the membrane satisfy orthonormal relations; thus we could obtain explicit formulas for the expansion coefficients A_{mn} and B_{mn} by using these orthonormal properties.

It is of interest to see what shape the membrane has in some of the normal modes. As examples, we consider three modes in which the displacements are proportional to

$$m = n = 1 \qquad \sin\left(\frac{\pi x}{a}\right) \sin\left(\frac{\pi y}{b}\right)$$

$$m = 2, n = 1 \qquad \sin\left(\frac{2\pi x}{a}\right) \sin\left(\frac{\pi y}{b}\right)$$

$$m = 3, n = 2 \qquad \sin\left(\frac{3\pi x}{a}\right) \sin\left(\frac{2\pi y}{b}\right)$$

These functions are plotted as parts (*a*), (*b*), (*c*), respectively, of Fig. 17-3. For the one-dimensional string we had nodal points, but we see here that we have *nodal lines* in this two-dimensional case, that is, lines on which the displacement is always zero. These nodal lines are parallel to the edges of the rectangle; we also see that the number of nodal lines normal to a given axis is always one less than the index for that direction, as, for example, when $m = 3$, there are two nodal lines at $x = \frac{1}{3}a$ and $\frac{2}{3}a$.

Another complicating property of the membrane, which did not exist for the string, is that of *degeneracy*, by which we mean that different

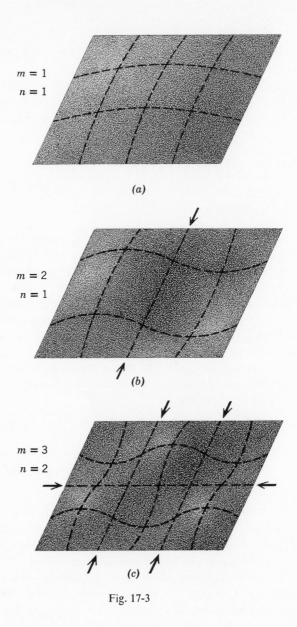

$m = 1$
$n = 1$

(a)

$m = 2$
$n = 1$

(b)

$m = 3$
$n = 2$

(c)

Fig. 17-3

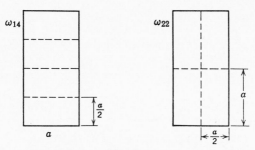

Fig. 17-4

normal modes have the same frequency. Degeneracy generally occurs when the dimensions are simply related. For example, if the membrane is square and therefore $a = b$, (17-26) becomes $\omega_{mn} = (\pi v/a)\sqrt{m^2 + n^2}$ and all modes which have the same value of $m^2 + n^2$ will have the same frequency; thus $\omega_{12} = \omega_{21}$, $\omega_{17} = \omega_{55}$, etc. As another example, if $b = 2a$, then $\omega_{mn} = (\pi v/a)[m^2 + (\frac{1}{2}n)^2]^{1/2}$ and $\omega_{14} = \omega_{22}$, $\omega_{26} = \omega_{34}$, etc. The normal modes for ω_{14} and ω_{22} are illustrated in Fig. 17-4 which shows only the dashed nodal lines. We can get a clue to why these frequencies might be the same when we note that in both modes the membrane vibrates in four equal parts which are the same individual size although they are differently arranged.

Discussions similar to what we have just given for the rectangular membrane can also be given for other shapes of the bounding surface, e.g., circular. The mathematical details are a little more complicated, but the basic ideas and results remain exactly the same.

Exercises

17-1. Explain why the integers m and n of (17-24) and (17-25) do *not* take on the values $0, -1, -2, -3, \ldots$.

17-2. Verify the normal mode structure shown in Fig. 17-4.

17-3. Derive the orthonormal relation satisfied by the normal modes of the membrane, and then obtain explicit formulas for the expansion coefficients A_{mn} and B_{mn} in terms of the initial displacement and velocity of each point of the membrane.

18 Ideal fluids

As a final example of a continuous mechanical system, we shall briefly consider some of the results which can be obtained for an ideal fluid. Many of the concepts and mathematical methods which we shall use in this chapter will be of great importance in our subsequent discussion of electromagnetism, and it is useful to be able to become acquainted with these ideas in connection with a system with tangible properties. As we shall see, many aspects of the study of fluids have close analogies in electromagnetism and these have been of importance in the development of the theories.

By an ideal fluid we mean a system which offers no resistance to a shearing stress, that is, to a force which is tangent to the surface bounding that fluid element of immediate interest. Thus we are assuming that there are no internal forces which offer resistance to flow and hence the only internal force we have to consider is the *pressure*, that is, the force per unit area normal to the surface bounding the fluid element. Another way of describing this is to say that we are assuming that the fluid has no *viscosity*. By treating the fluid as continuous, we are assuming that when we consider differential volume elements they are small compared to macroscopic dimensions but still large enough to contain so very many molecules that the basic molecular structure of the fluid is not evident.

18-1 Kinematics

If we let **v** be the velocity of a small element of the fluid which is located at the point $P(x, y, z)$ at the time t, the fluid velocity at a nearby point $Q(x + dx, y + dy, z + dz)$ at a slightly different time $t + dt$ can be written $\mathbf{v} + d\mathbf{v}$. If we regard the velocity as a function of position and time so that we can write $\mathbf{v} = \mathbf{v}(x, y, z, t)$, we have

$$d\mathbf{v} = \frac{\partial \mathbf{v}}{\partial t} dt + \frac{\partial \mathbf{v}}{\partial x} dx + \frac{\partial \mathbf{v}}{\partial y} dy + \frac{\partial \mathbf{v}}{\partial z} dz$$

$$= \frac{\partial \mathbf{v}}{\partial t} dt + (d\mathbf{r} \cdot \mathrm{grad})\mathbf{v} \tag{18-1}$$

where

$$d\mathbf{r} = dx\hat{\mathbf{i}} + dy\hat{\mathbf{j}} + dz\hat{\mathbf{k}} \tag{18-2}$$

is the position vector of Q with respect to P, and

$$d\mathbf{r} \cdot \text{grad} = dx \frac{\partial}{\partial x} + dy \frac{\partial}{\partial y} + dz \frac{\partial}{\partial z} \qquad (18\text{-}3)$$

So far, we have assumed no necessary relation between Q and P. If, however, we now assume that

$$d\mathbf{r} = \mathbf{v}\, dt \qquad (18\text{-}4)$$

the fluid which is at Q at $t + dt$ is the same element of fluid which was located at P at t, and we are now talking about a particular fluid element. If we substitute (18-4) into (18-1) in order to find the total change in velocity, and then divide by dt, we find the acceleration of this particular fluid element to be

$$\mathbf{a} = \frac{d\mathbf{v}}{dt} = \frac{\partial \mathbf{v}}{\partial t} + (\mathbf{v} \cdot \text{grad})\mathbf{v} \qquad (18\text{-}5)$$

We want now to investigate the average rotational motion of the fluid particles which are in the immediate neighborhood of a given point P at a given time t. We consider first the fluid particles in a small ring of radius r which is normal to the z axis and at a distance dz from P so that the ring's z coordinate is $z + dz$; this situation is illustrated in Fig. 18-1. If we calculate the line integral of $\mathbf{v}$ for this ring, use (1-40) and (1-7), we obtain

$$\oint \mathbf{v} \cdot d\mathbf{s} = \int \text{curl } \mathbf{v} \cdot d\mathbf{a} = [(\text{curl } \mathbf{v})_z]_{z+dz} \cdot \pi r^2$$

$$= \left\{ [(\text{curl } \mathbf{v})_z]_z + \left[\frac{\partial}{\partial z} (\text{curl } \mathbf{v})_z \right]_z dz \right\} \pi r^2 \qquad (18\text{-}6)$$

The average tangential component of $\mathbf{v}$ for the particles on this ring is

$$\bar{v}_{\text{tang}} = \frac{1}{2\pi r} \oint \mathbf{v} \cdot d\mathbf{s} \qquad (18\text{-}7)$$

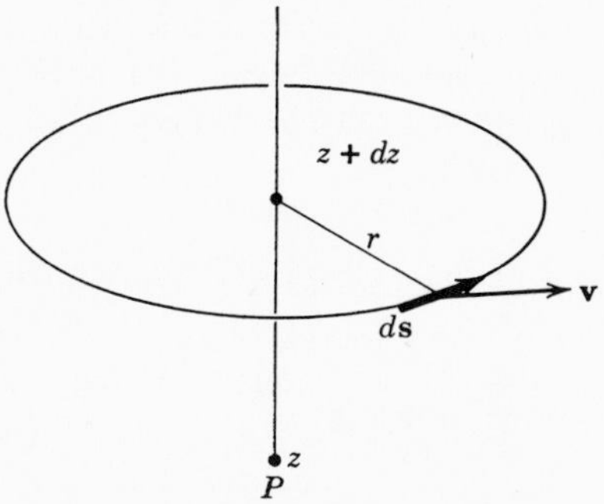

Fig. 18-1

and their *average angular velocity* about the z axis as obtained from (9-2) is

$$\omega_z = \frac{\bar{v}_{\text{tang}}}{r} \tag{18-8}$$

Combining (18-6), (18-7), and (18-8), we get

$$2\omega_z = [(\text{curl } \mathbf{v})_z]_z + \left[\frac{\partial}{\partial z}(\text{curl } \mathbf{v})_z\right]_z dz \tag{18-9}$$

In order to obtain a result which describes the average for all particles neighboring P, we must average (18-9) over all similar rings about P. For a ring like that shown in Fig. 18-1, there will be a ring of the same size on the opposite side of P but at the distance $-dz$ from P. When we write an expression like (18-9) for the latter ring and add it to (18-9) in order to get the average over the two rings, the terms in dz will cancel because of their opposite signs and we shall be left with $2\omega_z = (\text{curl } \mathbf{v})_z$. Since this result will be obtained for each pair of rings, we can say that the average of ω_z for the complete neighborhood of P will be given by

$$\bar{\omega}_z = \tfrac{1}{2}(\text{curl } \mathbf{v})_z \tag{18-10}$$

We shall obviously obtain similar expressions for the other two components; then we can write the vector equation for the average angular velocity of the fluid particles as

$$\bar{\boldsymbol{\omega}} = \tfrac{1}{2}\,\text{curl } \mathbf{v} \tag{18-11}$$

This result is helpful in clarifying the physical significance of the curl of a vector.

If the average angular velocity of the fluid is zero everywhere, we see from (18-11) that

$$\text{curl } \mathbf{v} = 0 \tag{18-12}$$

everywhere and the flow is said to be *irrotational*. As a result of the general vector theorem that curl grad $u = 0$ where u is any scalar, we see from (18-12) that for irrotational flow we can always write

$$\mathbf{v} = -\text{grad } \Phi \tag{18-13}$$

where Φ is a scalar called the *velocity potential*. An *equipotential surface* is defined as a surface on which Φ is constant. A *streamline* is defined as a curve which at every point has the same direction as the velocity $\mathbf{v}$. We know from Fig. 1-15 that grad Φ is everywhere perpendicular to the surface $\Phi = $ const., and we can conclude that the streamlines are perpendicular to the equipotential surfaces. This result is often helpful in

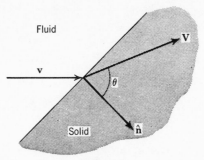

Fig. 18-2

sketching out the flow pattern of the fluid once the shapes of the equi-potentials are known.

Now let us consider a boundary condition at the surface of a solid with which a fluid is in contact. In order that the fluid may remain in contact with the solid, yet not penetrate the solid, the fluid velocity normal to the surface must be the same as that of the solid. Only the normal components enter because the fluid and solid can slip freely past each other tangentially as we have assumed no viscosity. From Fig. 18-2, we see that this boundary condition is

$$\mathbf{v} \cdot \hat{\mathbf{n}} = \mathbf{V} \cdot \hat{\mathbf{n}} = V \cos \theta \qquad (18\text{-}14)$$

where $\mathbf{V}$ is the velocity of the solid and $\hat{\mathbf{n}}$ is the unit vector normal to the bounding surface.

18-2 Equation of continuity

This important kinematical relation, which we want to derive now, expresses the fact of conservation of matter. We define a mass current density $\mathbf{M}$ as the mass of fluid flowing through a unit cross section perpendicular to the flow in unit time. In order to evaluate this in terms of other quantities we make use of Fig. 18-3a. In a time dt, the particles which were

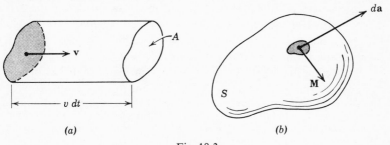

(a)　　　　　　　　　(b)

Fig. 18-3

originally located on the shaded cross section of area A will have traveled a distance $v\,dt$; clearly, the total mass which has passed through this shaded cross section is equal to the mass contained in the volume which has height $v\,dt$ and base area A. Then, from the definition of **M**, we have

$$\text{Mass in volume} = M \cdot A\,dt = (\text{density}) \times (\text{volume}) = \rho(v\,dt\,A)$$

so that $M = \rho v$; since the vectors **M** and **v** are parallel, we have,

$$\mathbf{M} = \rho\mathbf{v} \tag{18-15}$$

We now want to consider an arbitrary volume of fluid bounded by a surface S as shown in Fig. 18-3b. Since the total mass must be conserved, the total rate of flow out through the bounding surface must equal the rate of decrease of mass in the volume, and, since density is mass per unit volume, this statement of conservation of mass becomes

$$\int_S \mathbf{M} \cdot d\mathbf{a} = -\frac{\partial}{\partial t}\int_V \rho\,dv = \int_V \text{div}\,\mathbf{M}\,dv = \int_V \left(-\frac{\partial\rho}{\partial t}\right)dv \tag{18-16}$$

with the use of (1-33) and of the fact that the volume is fixed so that the second integral can change in time only if ρ does. This equation (18-16) must hold for an arbitrary volume, including an arbitrarily small one; this is possible only if the integrands are equal everywhere, so that we obtain

$$\text{div}\,\mathbf{M} + \frac{\partial\rho}{\partial t} = \text{div}\,(\rho\mathbf{v}) + \frac{\partial\rho}{\partial t} = 0 \tag{18-17}$$

which is the *equation of continuity*.

Under appropriate conditions, (18-17) leads to important consequences. If the fluid is *incompressible*, so that $\rho = \text{const.}$, then (18-17) becomes

$$\text{div}\,\mathbf{v} = 0 \tag{18-18}$$

If, in addition, the flow is irrotational, then (18-13) is also applicable and can be combined with (18-18) to give

$$\text{div grad}\,\Phi = \nabla^2\Phi = 0 \tag{18-19}$$

Thus the velocity potential for incompressible flow satisfies this partial differential equation which is known as *Laplace's equation*. As we shall see, if a solution of (18-19) can be found which satisfies the given boundary conditions, the problem is completely solved.

Laplace's equation is extremely important in many branches of theoretical physics, and we shall have many occasions to consider it. If we use (1-32), then (18-19) can be written in terms of rectangular coordinates as

$$\frac{\partial^2\Phi}{\partial x^2} + \frac{\partial^2\Phi}{\partial y^2} + \frac{\partial^2\Phi}{\partial z^2} = 0 \tag{18-20}$$

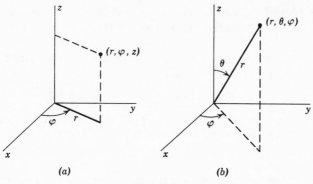

Fig. 18-4

It is often convenient to have explicit expressions for Laplace's equation in other coordinate systems. Although these expressions can be derived for very general systems, we need to consider only the two important cases of cylindrical and spherical coordinates illustrated in parts (*a*) and (*b*), respectively, of Fig. 18-4. It can be shown by a long but straightforward transformation that, for cylindrical coordinates, (18-20) becomes

$$\nabla^2\Phi = \frac{1}{r}\frac{\partial}{\partial r}\left(r\frac{\partial\Phi}{\partial r}\right) + \frac{1}{r^2}\frac{\partial^2\Phi}{\partial\varphi^2} + \frac{\partial^2\Phi}{\partial z^2} = 0 \qquad (18\text{-}21)$$

and it is written

$$\nabla^2\Phi = \frac{1}{r^2}\frac{\partial}{\partial r}\left(r^2\frac{\partial\Phi}{\partial r}\right) + \frac{1}{r^2\sin\theta}\frac{\partial}{\partial\theta}\left(\sin\theta\frac{\partial\Phi}{\partial\theta}\right) + \frac{1}{r^2\sin^2\theta}\frac{\partial^2\Phi}{\partial\varphi^2} = 0 \quad (18\text{-}22)$$

in terms of spherical coordinates.

18-3 Uniqueness of solution of Laplace's equation

Before we go on, let us digress and show that, if we have found a solution of Laplace's equation which satisfies the given boundary conditions (that is, it reduces to the correct preassigned values on all points of the surface surrounding the region), this solution is unique. Let Φ_1 be a solution of (18-19) which satisfies the boundary conditions, and suppose we assume that there is another distinct solution Φ_2 which also satisfies these same boundary conditions. We want to prove that Φ_1 and Φ_2 are identical.

We let $\Phi = \Phi_1 - \Phi_2$. Then $\nabla^2\Phi = \nabla^2\Phi_1 - \nabla^2\Phi_2 = 0$ because of (18-19); therefore Φ is also a solution of Laplace's equation. On the bounding surface S, $\Phi_1 = \Phi_2$ so that

$$\Phi = 0 \quad \text{on boundary} \qquad (18\text{-}23)$$

Now we see that

$$\frac{\partial}{\partial x}\left(\Phi\frac{\partial\Phi}{\partial x}\right) = \Phi\frac{\partial^2\Phi}{\partial x^2} + \left(\frac{\partial\Phi}{\partial x}\right)^2 \tag{18-24}$$

and, if we write the two similar equations for y and z, add them, use (1-29), (1-25), and (1-11), we obtain

$$\text{div}\,(\Phi\,\text{grad}\,\Phi) = \Phi\,\nabla^2\Phi + (\text{grad}\,\Phi)^2 \tag{18-25}$$

which is a general result for any function Φ. We now integrate (18-25) over the volume V in which Φ satisfies (18-19); therefore, if we also use (1-33), we get

$$\int_V (\text{grad}\,\Phi)^2\,dv = \int_V \text{div}\,(\Phi\,\text{grad}\,\Phi)\,dv = \int_S \Phi\,\text{grad}\,\Phi \cdot d\mathbf{a} = 0 \tag{18-26}$$

since $\Phi = 0$ on S, according to (18-23). As the integrand in the first integral of (18-26) is a sum of squares, and thereby intrinsically positive, the integral can be zero only if the integrand is zero everywhere; therefore

$$(\text{grad}\,\Phi)^2 = \left(\frac{\partial\Phi}{\partial x}\right)^2 + \left(\frac{\partial\Phi}{\partial y}\right)^2 + \left(\frac{\partial\Phi}{\partial z}\right)^2 = 0 \tag{18-27}$$

The quantity in (18-27) is again a sum of squares, and therefore the individual terms must be zero, or

$$\frac{\partial\Phi}{\partial x} = \frac{\partial\Phi}{\partial y} = \frac{\partial\Phi}{\partial z} = 0$$

so that $\Phi = \text{const}$. But, since Φ is zero on the boundary and is constant, we see that $\Phi = 0$ everywhere, and therefore

$$\Phi_1 = \Phi_2 \quad \text{everywhere} \tag{18-28}$$

which was what we were to prove.

The significance of this result from a practical point of view is that, once we find a solution of Laplace's equation, by any means whatsoever, which satisfies the given boundary conditions, we know that it is the only solution and we do not need to consider the possibility that there are others.

18-4   Equation of motion

Let us consider the rectangular parallelopiped of volume $dx\,dy\,dz$ which is fixed relative to our xyz axes as shown in Fig. 18-5. If p is the fluid pressure on side A, the pressure on A' is

$$p' = p + \left(\frac{\partial p}{\partial x}\right)dx \tag{18-29}$$

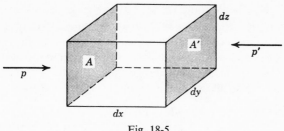

Fig. 18-5

Since pressure is normal force per unit area by definition, we see that the net force in the positive x direction on the fluid inside the volume, which is due to the pressure on the faces perpendicular to the x axis, is

$$pA - p'A' = p\,dy\,dz - \left(p + \frac{\partial p}{\partial x}\,dx\right)dy\,dz = -\frac{\partial p}{\partial x}\,dx\,dy\,dz \quad (18\text{-}30)$$

This is actually the total force in the x direction since there are no tangential forces. Similar expressions hold for the y and z directions; therefore, if we add these three forces and divide by the volume $dx\,dy\,dz$, we find the net force *per unit volume* due to pressure to be

$$-\frac{\partial p}{\partial x}\,\hat{\imath} - \frac{\partial p}{\partial y}\,\hat{\jmath} - \frac{\partial p}{\partial z}\,\hat{k} = -\text{grad}\ p \quad (18\text{-}31)$$

There may also be external forces acting on the fluid such as that due to gravity; it is customary to write these forces in terms of

$$\mathbf{F} = \text{external force per unit mass} \quad (18\text{-}32)$$

so that the external force per unit volume is $\rho\mathbf{F}$. If we add the last result to (18-31), we get the total force per unit volume, which in turn is equal to the mass per unit volume (density) times the acceleration of the fluid; hence, if we also use (18-5), we find the equation of motion to be

$$\rho\mathbf{F} - \text{grad}\ p = \rho\mathbf{a} = \rho\left[\frac{\partial \mathbf{v}}{\partial t} + (\mathbf{v}\cdot\text{grad})\mathbf{v}\right] \quad (18\text{-}33)$$

This is usually written in the form

$$\frac{\partial \mathbf{v}}{\partial t} + (\mathbf{v}\cdot\text{grad})\mathbf{v} = \mathbf{F} - \frac{\text{grad}\ p}{\rho} \quad (18\text{-}34)$$

which is a fundamental equation describing the motion of an ideal fluid; its components are called Euler's equations. The x component of (18-34) is

$$\frac{\partial v_x}{\partial t} + v_x\frac{\partial v_x}{\partial x} + v_y\frac{\partial v_x}{\partial y} + v_z\frac{\partial v_x}{\partial z} = F_x - \frac{1}{\rho}\frac{\partial p}{\partial x} \quad (18\text{-}35)$$

and we see that it involves products of the velocity components with gradients of the velocity components. Thus the equations are *not* linear and we cannot use all of the nice methods of superimposing special solutions to get the general solution which we found so useful in preceding chapters. This non-linearity is the basic source of much of the difficulty of solving problems in the mechanics of fluids.

For the *static* case in which the fluid is at rest and $\mathbf{v} = 0$, (18-34) becomes simply

$$\rho\mathbf{F} = \operatorname{grad} p \tag{18-36}$$

As an example, consider the fluid in a tank; the fluid surface coincides with the value $z = 0$ of the vertical coordinate. The external force of gravity per unit mass has only a z component given by (7-44) to be

$$F_z = -g \tag{18-36'}$$

so that (18-36) becomes

$$\rho F_z = -\rho g = \frac{\partial p}{\partial z} = \frac{dp}{dz}$$

This equation can be integrated to give

$$p = -\rho g z + \text{const.} = \rho g(\text{depth}) + p_{\text{atm}} \tag{18-37}$$

since the depth below the surface is $-z$, and the pressure at the surface is the atmospheric pressure p_{atm}. Thus we see that the static pressure increases linearly with depth; this is a familiar result for an incompressible fluid.

To turn to non-static cases, we consider only the fairly common one in which the external force (18-32) is derivable from a potential energy per unit mass Ω; hence

$$\mathbf{F} = -\operatorname{grad} \Omega \tag{18-38}$$

and (18-34) becomes

$$\frac{\partial \mathbf{v}}{\partial t} + (\mathbf{v} \cdot \operatorname{grad})\mathbf{v} = -\operatorname{grad} \Omega - \frac{\operatorname{grad} p}{\rho} \tag{18-39}$$

We now want to show that, if, in addition, the flow is irrotational and the density is at most a function of pressure only, we can integrate (18-39) exactly. If the flow is irrotational, $\mathbf{v}$ is given by (18-13), and we can say that

$$(\mathbf{v} \cdot \operatorname{grad})v_x = -(\mathbf{v} \cdot \operatorname{grad})\frac{\partial \Phi}{\partial x} = -\left[v_x \frac{\partial^2 \Phi}{\partial x^2} + v_y \frac{\partial^2 \Phi}{\partial y\, \partial x} + v_z \frac{\partial^2 \Phi}{\partial z\, \partial x} \right]$$

$$= \frac{\partial \Phi}{\partial x}\frac{\partial^2 \Phi}{\partial x^2} + \frac{\partial \Phi}{\partial y}\frac{\partial^2 \Phi}{\partial x\, \partial y} + \frac{\partial \Phi}{\partial z}\frac{\partial^2 \Phi}{\partial x\, \partial z}$$

$$= \frac{1}{2}\frac{\partial}{\partial x}\left[\left(\frac{\partial \Phi}{\partial x}\right)^2 + \left(\frac{\partial \Phi}{\partial y}\right)^2 + \left(\frac{\partial \Phi}{\partial z}\right)^2 \right]$$

$$= \frac{1}{2}\frac{\partial}{\partial x}(v_x{}^2 + v_y{}^2 + v_z{}^2) = \frac{\partial}{\partial x}(\tfrac{1}{2}v^2) \tag{18-40}$$

Because similar equations hold for the y and z components, in general we have

$$(\mathbf{v} \cdot \mathrm{grad})\mathbf{v} = \mathrm{grad}\ (\tfrac{1}{2}v^2) \tag{18-41}$$

Since we also have

$$\frac{\partial \mathbf{v}}{\partial t} = -\frac{\partial}{\partial t}\ \mathrm{grad}\ \Phi = -\mathrm{grad}\ \frac{\partial \Phi}{\partial t}$$

(18-39) becomes

$$\mathrm{grad}\left[-\frac{\partial \Phi}{\partial t} + \Omega + \tfrac{1}{2}v^2\right] + \frac{\mathrm{grad}\ p}{\rho} = 0 \tag{18-42}$$

Let us now use our assumption that $\rho = \rho(p)$ and define a function $P(p)$ by

$$P(p) = \int_0^p \frac{dp'}{\rho(p')} \tag{18-43}$$

so that

$$\mathrm{grad}\ P = \frac{dP}{dp}\ \mathrm{grad}\ p = \frac{\mathrm{grad}\ p}{\rho} \tag{18-44}$$

and (18-42) can now be written

$$\mathrm{grad}\left[-\frac{\partial \Phi}{\partial t} + \Omega + \tfrac{1}{2}v^2 + \int_0^p \frac{dp'}{\rho(p')}\right] = 0$$

The quantity in brackets is constant as far as differentiation with respect to the coordinates is concerned and can be set equal to a possible function of t, $G(t)$:

$$\int_0^p \frac{dp'}{\rho(p')} + \tfrac{1}{2}v^2 + \Omega = \frac{\partial \Phi}{\partial t} + G(t) \tag{18-45}$$

For *steady flow* in which the flow pattern does not change in time, we must have Φ and $\mathbf{v}$ both independent of the time; therefore $G(t) = \mathrm{const.}$, and (18-45) becomes

$$\int_0^p \frac{dp'}{\rho(p')} + \tfrac{1}{2}v^2 + \Omega = \mathrm{const.} \tag{18-46}$$

This equation is known as *Bernoulli's equation*. It takes a more familiar form for an incompressible fluid for which $\rho = \mathrm{const.}$ and (18-46) becomes

$$\frac{p}{\rho} + \tfrac{1}{2}v^2 + \Omega = \mathrm{const.} \tag{18-47}$$

Example. Flow in a Smooth Horizontal Trough. Here Ω is due to gravitational forces and, since the fluid is always at the same height, $\Omega = \mathrm{const.}$ and (18-47) becomes $p + \tfrac{1}{2}\rho v^2 = \mathrm{const.}$ This tells us that the pressure is lowest where the flow velocity is highest, and vice versa.

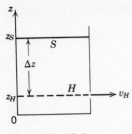

Fig. 18-6

Example. Velocity of Efflux. The fluid is contained in a large tank in which there is a hole near the bottom at H as illustrated in Fig. 18-6; we want to find the velocity v_H with which the fluid leaves the container. At the open surface S, the fluid is very nearly at rest and $v_S = 0$. The pressure is equal to the atmospheric pressure p_a at both S and H, so that $p_S = p_H = p_a$. As we saw in (18-36'), the gravitational force per unit mass is $-g$, and $\Omega = gz$ from (18-38). Therefore, since (18-47) has the same value at S and H, we obtain

$$\frac{p_a}{\rho} + gz_S = \frac{p_a}{\rho} + \tfrac{1}{2}v_H{}^2 + gz_H$$

Therefore

$$v_H = \sqrt{2g(z_S - z_H)} = \sqrt{2g\,\Delta z} \qquad (18\text{-}48)$$

This familiar simple result is known as *Torricelli's law.*

18-5 Kelvin's circulation theorem

One might wonder why so much emphasis has been put on irrotational flow so far, since it may seem like such a special case that it would not persist long enough to be of practical interest. The answer to this question is provided by the theorem which we shall prove below and which essentially says that, if a flow is initially irrotational, it will always be irrotational.

Let us consider a closed curve L which we imagine drawn in the fluid at some specified instant. This curve is shown in Fig. 18-7, which also

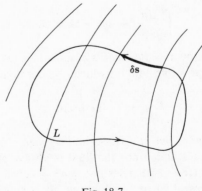

Fig. 18-7

includes some of the streamlines. We define the *circulation* of the fluid about this curve as the line integral

$$K = \oint \mathbf{v} \cdot \delta\mathbf{s} \tag{18-49}$$

taken around this closed curve. We are using $\delta\mathbf{s}$ as the element of displacement in the integral, as we want $d\mathbf{s}$ to refer to the actual displacement of the fluid as it flows along the stream-line, and (18-49) involves displacements in which we move at a given time from one streamline to another. We already know from (1-40) that a vector will be irrotational, that is, have a zero curl, if its line integral about any closed path is zero. Hence another way of saying that the flow is irrotational is to say that the circulation vanishes everywhere. We

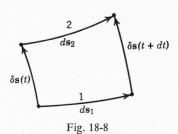

Fig. 18-8

now want to consider how the circulation changes in time, and in order to do this we have to see how segments of the curve L are altered as L goes along with the fluid particles whose locations define it, so that we will always be calculating the circulation for the same elements of the fluid.

If the external force can be derived from a potential, (18-39) and (18-5) give us

$$\frac{d\mathbf{v}}{dt} = -\operatorname{grad}\Omega - \frac{\operatorname{grad} p}{\rho} \tag{18-50}$$

Also

$$\frac{d}{dt}(\mathbf{v} \cdot \delta\mathbf{s}) = \frac{d\mathbf{v}}{dt} \cdot \delta\mathbf{s} + \mathbf{v} \cdot \frac{d}{dt}(\delta\mathbf{s}) \tag{18-51}$$

where the last term involves the change in the separation between two streamlines as the fluid particles move along; we can calculate this factor with the help of Fig. 18-8. In the figure, curves 1 and 2 are streamlines; the separation between two given particles initially is $\delta\mathbf{s}(t)$, and it is $\delta\mathbf{s}(t + dt)$ a time dt later. We see from the figure that

$$\delta\mathbf{s}(t) + d\mathbf{s}_2 = d\mathbf{s}_1 + \delta\mathbf{s}(t + dt)$$

so that

$$\frac{d}{dt}\delta\mathbf{s} = \frac{\delta\mathbf{s}(t + dt) - \delta\mathbf{s}(t)}{dt} = \frac{d\mathbf{s}_2}{dt} - \frac{d\mathbf{s}_1}{dt} = \delta\left(\frac{d\mathbf{s}}{dt}\right) = \delta\mathbf{v} \tag{18-52}$$

where $\delta\mathbf{v}$ is the difference between the fluid velocities on the two streamlines.

If we substitute (18-50) and (18-52) into (18-51) and use (1-26), we obtain

$$\frac{d}{dt}(\mathbf{v} \cdot \delta\mathbf{s}) = -\text{grad } \Omega \cdot \delta\mathbf{s} - \frac{\text{grad } p \cdot \delta\mathbf{s}}{\rho} + \mathbf{v} \cdot \delta\mathbf{v}$$

$$= -\delta\Omega - \frac{\delta p}{\rho} + \delta(\tfrac{1}{2}v^2) \tag{18-53}$$

where $\delta\Omega$ is the difference in Ω between the two streamlines, etc. If we integrate (18-53) over the closed path L at a given time t, we get

$$\frac{d}{dt}\oint \mathbf{v} \cdot \delta\mathbf{s} = \frac{dK}{dt} = -\oint \delta\Omega - \oint \frac{\delta p}{\rho} + \oint \delta(\tfrac{1}{2}v^2) \tag{18-54}$$

Now consider the first of the integrals on the right; its value is found as

$$\oint \delta\Omega = \Omega \text{ (final point)} - \Omega \text{ (initial point)} = 0 \tag{18-55}$$

since the path is closed and hence the final and initial points are identical. The last integral of (18-54) vanishes in the same way. If ρ is constant, or is a function of the pressure only, the middle integrand is also an exact differential, that is, the differential of a definite function of position, and it will also vanish, for the same reason as in (18-55). Therefore all the integrals on the right of (18-54) will vanish under these conditions; thus

$$\frac{dK}{dt} = 0 \quad \text{or} \quad K = \oint \mathbf{v} \cdot \delta\mathbf{s} = \text{const.} \tag{18-56}$$

and the circulation about any closed curve carried along by the fluid is constant; this is the theorem we desired to prove.

Therefore, if the circulation is initially zero everywhere, it will always remain zero; if irrotational motion has once begun, it will persist indefinitely, since zero circulation is equivalent to irrotational flow. Similarly, an initial circulation will never decrease. However, if the external force cannot be derived from a potential or if there is friction between the fluid and the walls of the container, it may happen that a circulation may be produced in an initially irrotational flow, leading to the formation of eddies and turbulence.

18-6   Uniformly moving sphere in an incompressible fluid

As an example of the solution of a problem in the dynamics of ideal fluids, we consider a sphere of radius a moving with constant speed V in the z direction as shown in Fig. 18-9. The sphere is immersed in an incompressible fluid of infinite extent, and we want to find the velocity of the fluid at every point P.

Since the fluid is of infinite extent, we can assume that the portions of the fluid at very large distances from the sphere are at rest; we shall neglect external forces such as gravity. We shall assume the flow to be irrotational, and therefore the basic equation to be solved is (18-19). The origin is chosen to be at the center of the sphere, and we shall use spherical coordinates. As a result of the symmetry illustrated in Fig. 18-9, the velocity potential Φ cannot depend on the azimuthal angle φ, but only on r and θ; then $\partial\Phi/\partial\varphi = 0$ and (18-22) becomes

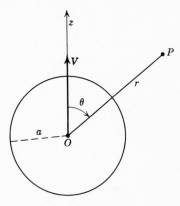

$$\frac{\partial}{\partial r}\left(r^2 \frac{\partial\Phi}{\partial r}\right) + \frac{1}{\sin\theta}\frac{\partial}{\partial\theta}\left(\sin\theta \frac{\partial\Phi}{\partial\theta}\right) = 0$$

(18-57)

Fig. 18-9

We can get an idea about how to proceed in solving this equation by considering the form of the boundary conditions. If v_r is the component of **v** in the direction of increasing r, for which the increment of distance is dr, then from (18-13) we obtain

$$v_r = -\frac{\partial\Phi}{\partial r}$$

(18-58)

The boundary condition at the surface of the sphere as given by (18-14) is

$$v_{r,\text{sphere}} = -\left(\frac{\partial\Phi}{\partial r}\right)_{r=a} = V\cos\theta$$

(18-59)

while at infinity where the fluid is at rest we have

$$v_{r,\infty} = -\left(\frac{\partial\Phi}{\partial r}\right)_{r=\infty} = 0$$

(18-60)

Since we shall eventually have to make our solution reduce to (18-59), it seems reasonable to try to include this particular dependence on angle from the very outset, with the hope that this will make the satisfying of the boundary condition easier; we also know that the solution we obtain will be unique, regardless of the method we use to obtain it. Accordingly, we try a solution of the form

$$\Phi(r, \theta) = R(r)\cos\theta$$

(18-61)

When (18-61) is substituted into (18-57), we get

$$\cos\theta \frac{d}{dr}\left(r^2 \frac{dR}{dr}\right) + \frac{R}{\sin\theta}\frac{d}{d\theta}(-\sin^2\theta) = 0$$

which, after we cancel out the $\cos\theta$, gives us the following equation for R:

$$r^2 \frac{d^2R}{dr^2} + 2r\frac{dR}{dr} - 2R = 0 \qquad (18\text{-}62)$$

Now let us try to solve (18-62) with the form

$$R(r) = kr^n \qquad (18\text{-}63)$$

where k is a constant and n is to be found; when (18-63) is substituted into (18-62), we obtain

$$k[n(n-1) + 2n - 2]r^n = 0$$

and therefore $n^2 + n - 2 = 0$, which has the solutions $n = 1, -2$. Thus there are two possible forms (18-63), but, since (18-62) is a linear differential equation, the most general form for R is an arbitrary sum of the two, or

$$R(r) = Ar + \frac{B}{r^2} \qquad (18\text{-}64)$$

where A and B are constants. Substituting (18-64) into (18-61), we find the velocity potential to be

$$\Phi = \left(Ar + \frac{B}{r^2}\right)\cos\theta \qquad (18\text{-}65)$$

Our remaining task is to determine A and B so that the boundary conditions (18-59) and (18-60) are satisfied. Now

$$\frac{\partial\Phi}{\partial r} = \left(A - \frac{2B}{r^3}\right)\cos\theta$$

and (18-60) becomes

$$\left(\frac{\partial\Phi}{\partial r}\right)_{r=\infty} = A\cos\theta = 0$$

and therefore $A = 0$. We now find that (18-59) gives us

$$-\left(\frac{\partial\Phi}{\partial r}\right)_{r=a} = \frac{2B}{a^3}\cos\theta = V\cos\theta$$

so that $B = \frac{1}{2}Va^3$, and therefore the complete solution to our problem is given by

$$\Phi = \frac{Va^3}{2r^2}\cos\theta \qquad (18\text{-}66)$$

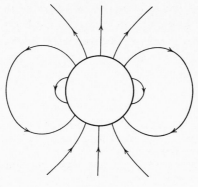

Fig. 18-10

The components of the fluid velocity in the directions of increasing r and θ are found to be

$$v_r = -\frac{\partial \Phi}{\partial r} = V\left(\frac{a}{r}\right)^3 \cos \theta \qquad (18\text{-}67a)$$

$$v_\theta = -\frac{1}{r}\frac{\partial \Phi}{\partial \theta} = \frac{V}{2}\left(\frac{a}{r}\right)^3 \sin \theta \qquad (18\text{-}67b)$$

[The latter expression can be seen to be correct by referring to Fig. 18-4b, where it is seen that the increment of distance in the direction of increasing θ is $r\,d\theta$.] The streamlines obtained from (18-67) are shown in Fig. 18-10. Let us calculate the total kinetic energy of the fluid. Using (18-67) and

$$v^2 = v_r{}^2 + v_\theta{}^2 = \left(\frac{Va^3}{r^3}\right)^2 (\cos^2 \theta + \tfrac{1}{4}\sin^2 \theta)$$

we find that

$$T_f = \int_0^\pi \int_a^\infty \tfrac{1}{2}\rho v^2 \cdot 2\pi r^2 \sin \theta \, dr \, d\theta$$

$$= \pi\rho V^2 a^6 \int_a^\infty \frac{dr}{r^4} \int_0^\pi (\cos^2 \theta + \tfrac{1}{4}\sin^2 \theta) \sin \theta \, d\theta = \tfrac{1}{4}m_f V^2 \quad (18\text{-}68)$$

where $m_f = \tfrac{4}{3}\pi a^3 \rho$ is the mass of the fluid displaced by the sphere. If the mass of the sphere is m, the total kinetic energy of the whole system of sphere plus fluid is

$$T_t = T_s + T_f = \tfrac{1}{2}mV^2 + \tfrac{1}{4}m_f V^2 = \tfrac{1}{2}(m + \tfrac{1}{2}m_f)V^2 \qquad (18\text{-}69)$$

This result shows us that, as far as the kinetic energy is concerned, the total effect of the fluid is equivalent to adding one half of the mass of the displaced fluid to the mass of the sphere; thus we can speak of an "effective" mass of $m + \tfrac{1}{2}m_f$. The essential reason for this is that, when we apply a force to the sphere, we have to do work on the fluid as well as on the sphere in order to increase the velocity (and hence the kinetic energy) of the system so that the total effective inertia is greater than that of the sphere alone.

Exercises

18-1. How would (18-16) and (18-17) be modified if there were a source of fluid which produced P kilograms of fluid per (meter)^3 per second? To what sort of situation would this apply?

18-2. Verify (18-21) and (18-22) by direct transformation of Laplace's equation in rectangular coordinates.

18-3. Using the static equation (18-36), prove Archimedes' principle, which says that if a body is submerged in a fluid there is an upward buoyant force on it equal to the weight of the fluid displaced by the volume of the body.

18-4. Calculate the total momentum of the fluid for the problem discussed in Sec. 18-6 and interpret the result. Is it reasonable?

18-5. Starting with the general equations of motion and the equation of continuity and assuming that: (1) $\mathbf{F} = 0$, (2) all velocity components and their rates of change are small, (3) $p = p(\rho)$, and (4) $\rho = \rho_0(1 + \sigma)$ where $\sigma \ll 1$ and ρ_0 is a constant, show that the excess density σ approximately satisfies the three-dimensional wave equation

$$\nabla^2 \sigma = \frac{1}{c^2} \frac{\partial^2 \sigma}{\partial t^2}$$

where

$$c^2 = \left(\frac{\partial p}{\partial \rho} \right)_{\rho_0}$$

Part Two

Electromagnetic Fields

19 Maxwell's equations

Electromagnetism is most conveniently summarized in a set of partial differential equations known as Maxwell's equations which describe the properties of the electromagnetic field vectors. Our primary purpose in this chapter is to derive these equations from a small number of basic experimental results and concepts. The remainder of our study of electromagnetism will then be devoted to looking at the solutions of these fundamental equations for certain special conditions and classes of problems. These subdivisions have been given such names as electrostatics, electromagnetic waves, diffraction. A convenient starting point for us is the concept of electric charge.

19-1 Electric charge

The idea of electric charge was introduced to help describe phenomena such as those associated with electrification by friction. Electric charge can be given a precise definition in terms of forces and distances. An excellent description of this lengthy procedure can be found in *American Journal of Physics* **18**, 1 (1950), but we shall start by accepting the idea of electric charge as well known and proceed from there, noting, however, that charge differs from mass in that it can be assigned both negative and positive values.

We use the notation that charge is represented by q, while charge density = charge/volume = ρ.

From long experience, it has been concluded that electric charge satisfies a conservation law similar to that for mass and energy; thus we say that the total charge in the universe is constant or (net) charge cannot be created or destroyed. The mathematical statement of this principle is the *equation of continuity* which we have already discussed in Sec. 18-2. To state it here, we introduce the important concept of current density = $\mathbf{J}$ = charge passing through unit area normal to the flow per unit time. If the velocity of the charges is $\mathbf{v}$, we have, as before, that $\mathbf{J} = \rho\mathbf{v}$, where ρ is the moving charge density and the equation of continuity becomes

$$\operatorname{div}\mathbf{J} + \frac{\partial\rho}{\partial t} = \operatorname{div}(\rho\mathbf{v}) + \frac{\partial\rho}{\partial t} = 0 \qquad (19\text{-}1)$$

19-2 Coulomb's law

The experimental law which we take as our starting point is due to Coulomb, and it expresses the facts that like charges repel each other while unlike charges attract and that the force between these charges at rest varies inversely as the square of the distance between them:

$$\mathbf{F}_{q'} = \frac{\gamma q q' \mathbf{r}}{r^3} \tag{19-2}$$

In this equation, $\mathbf{F}_{q'}$ is the force on q' due to q and γ is a constant which depends on the units used. Also, q and q' are assumed to be *point* charges; that is, the dimensions of the charge distributions associated with q and q' are so small compared to the other distances of interest that we can neglect any influences arising from a finite size of q and q'. The direction of $\mathbf{r}$ is toward the charge for which the force is being calculated, as shown in Fig. 19-1.

We shall use exclusively the rationalized mks system of units. Thus the unit of length is a meter, that of mass is a kilogram, and the unit of time is a second. The unit of force ($=$ mass times acceleration) is therefore one kilogram meter/(second)^2; this unit is given the name one newton. The unit of work and energy is one newton-meter $=$ one joule.

Electric charge is measured in coulombs; for the moment, we can define a coulomb in terms of the fundamental charge of the electron; thus the magnitude of the electronic charge is 1.60×10^{-19} coulomb. Then the unit of ρ is coulomb/(meter)^3, and that of $\mathbf{J}$ is coulomb/(meter)^2 second $=$ ampere/(meter)^2.

Once the units have been decided upon in this way, the constant γ in Coulomb's law (19-2) can no longer be given an arbitrary value but must be found by *experiment*. The result is usually written in the form

$$\mathbf{F}_{q'} = \frac{q q' \mathbf{r}}{4\pi \epsilon_0 r^3} \tag{19-3}$$

where $\epsilon_0 = 8.85 \times 10^{-12}$ farad/meter. It is useful to note that $(4\pi\epsilon_0)^{-1} = 9 \times 10^9$, approximately.

Suppose now that there are a lot of point charges q_i at positions $\mathbf{r}_i$ with

$$q \qquad\qquad\qquad\qquad \mathbf{r} \qquad\qquad\qquad\qquad q'$$

Fig. 19-1

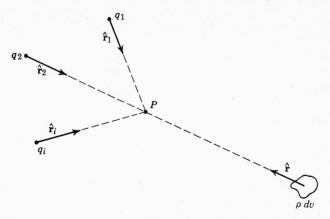

Fig. 19-2

respect to q'; that is, $\mathbf{r}_i$ is the radius vector from q_i to q'. Then, when we add the forces vectorially, the total force on q' is

$$\mathbf{F}_{q'} = \sum_i \frac{q_i q' \mathbf{r}_i}{4\pi\epsilon_0 r_i^3} = q' \sum_i \frac{q_i \mathbf{r}_i}{4\pi\epsilon_0 r_i^3} \qquad (19\text{-}4)$$

Thus the force is a product of the charge q' and a vector which depends only on the distribution of the other charges. As a result, it is useful to define the *electric field* $\mathbf{E}$ as the ratio of the force on the point charge to the charge itself; that is, we write

$$\mathbf{F}_{q'} = q'\mathbf{E} \qquad (19\text{-}5)$$

and therefore we see that the electric field resulting from a given distribution of point charges can be easily calculated, for from (19-4) and (19-5) we obtain

$$\mathbf{E} = \frac{1}{4\pi\epsilon_0} \sum_i \frac{q_i \mathbf{r}_i}{r_i^3} = \frac{1}{4\pi\epsilon_0} \sum_i \frac{q_i \hat{\mathbf{r}}_i}{r_i^2} \qquad (19\text{-}6)$$

where $\hat{\mathbf{r}}_i$ is a unit vector drawn from the point charge q_i to the point P at which we wish to calculate the field $\mathbf{E}$, as illustrated in Fig. 19-2.

If the charges are distributed continuously with a total density ρ_t, we can regard the charge $\rho_t\,dv$ in the small volume dv as a point charge and write

$$\mathbf{E} = \frac{1}{4\pi\epsilon_0} \int \frac{\rho_t \hat{\mathbf{r}}\,dv}{r^2} \qquad (19\text{-}7)$$

19-3 Gauss' theorem

We want to show that

$$\int_S \mathbf{E} \cdot d\mathbf{a} = \frac{Q}{\epsilon_0} = \frac{1}{\epsilon_0} \sum_i q_i \qquad (19\text{-}8)$$

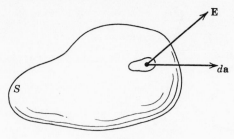

Fig. 19-3

where $Q = \sum_i q_i =$ net charge contained *within* the volume enclosed by the arbitrary surface S, as illustrated in Fig. 19-3.

Now, from (19-6),

$$\int_S \mathbf{E} \cdot d\mathbf{a} = \frac{1}{4\pi\epsilon_0} \sum_i q_i \int_S \frac{\hat{\mathbf{r}}_i \cdot d\mathbf{a}}{r_i^{\,2}} \tag{19-9}$$

There are two cases to consider.

1. q_i is inside S (Fig. 19-4). Now

$$\frac{\hat{\mathbf{r}}_i \cdot d\mathbf{a}}{r_i^{\,2}} = \frac{da \cos \alpha}{r_i^{\,2}} = \frac{\text{area} \perp \text{to } \hat{\mathbf{r}}_i}{r_i^{\,2}} = d\omega$$

= element of solid angle subtended at q_i by the area da

Therefore, in this case,

$$\int_S \frac{\hat{\mathbf{r}}_i \cdot d\mathbf{a}}{r_i^{\,2}} = \int_S d\omega = 4\pi \tag{19-10}$$

2. q_i is outside S (Fig. 19-5). Consider the two elements of area $d\mathbf{a}_1$

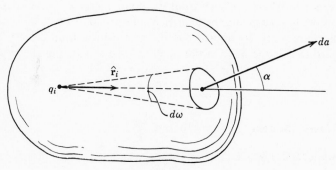

Fig. 19-4

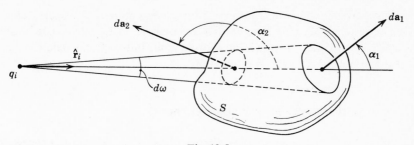

Fig. 19-5

and da_2 cut out by the same solid angle $d\omega$ but on opposite sides of S. Since $\alpha_2 > \pi/2$, $\cos \alpha_2 < 0$, and therefore

$$\frac{d\mathbf{a}_1 \cdot \hat{\mathbf{r}}_i}{r_i^2} = d\omega = -\frac{d\mathbf{a}_2 \cdot \hat{\mathbf{r}}_i}{r_i^2} \tag{19-11}$$

Hence as we integrate over the surface these two will cancel each other out. Since all the elements of area on the surface can be paired off in this way, their contributions to the integral mutually cancel and we obtain

$$\int_S \frac{\hat{\mathbf{r}}_i \cdot d\mathbf{a}}{r_i^2} = 0 \tag{19-12}$$

Therefore, from (19-9), (19-10), and (19-12),

$$\int_S \mathbf{E} \cdot d\mathbf{a} = \frac{1}{4\pi\epsilon_0} \sum_{\text{inside}} q_i \int_S \frac{\hat{\mathbf{r}}_i \cdot d\mathbf{a}}{r_i^2} = \frac{1}{\epsilon_0} \sum_{\text{inside}} q_i = \frac{Q}{\epsilon_0} \tag{19-13}$$

Thus we have proved Gauss' theorem as stated above.

We can write

$$Q = \int_V \rho_t \, dv,$$

where V is the volume enclosed by S, and by the divergence theorem we can also write (19-13) in the form

$$\int_S \mathbf{E} \cdot d\mathbf{a} = \int_V \text{div } \mathbf{E} \, dv = \frac{1}{\epsilon_0} \int_V \rho_t \, dv \tag{19-14}$$

Since this result holds for an arbitrary volume V, it will hold for an infinitesimal volume, and we can equate the integrands. In this way, we obtain the important result

$$\text{div } \mathbf{E} = \frac{\rho_t}{\epsilon_0} \tag{19-15}$$

which is to be remembered as another way of stating Coulomb's law for the force between point charges.

This particular equation, however, is inconvenient in some respects, and we want to put it into a somewhat different form to take account of essentially two ways in which the charges contributing to the field can be classified for convenience in calculation.

19-4   Electric polarization and displacement

One type of charge we want to discuss is the "free" (or "true") charge, by which we mean, in a crude sense, the charges which we can distribute around in space at will on conductors or on the surfaces of insulators. The others are the so-called "bound" (or "polarization") charges which are the constituent charges of matter—protons and electrons—and over whose distribution we generally do not have much control. In this connection, we should note that the charge density in a material fluctuates very widely as we pass from proton to electron in an atom, but ordinary electrical measuring instruments are unable to measure these fluctuations because they occur in so short a distance. The measurements which we make and which are to be described by the theory we are developing here have rather to do with *mean* values of the charge densities averaged over regions containing many thousands of atoms yet still small on the macroscopic scale. Then, of course, we shall mean by electric field the smooth field resulting from this smoothed-out distribution of charge.

In general, the normal density of bound charge is zero, since each atom and each molecule contain equal quantities of positive and negative charge. Now let us consider what happens, for example, in the presence of an externally applied electric field: The forces on the positive and negative atomic charges are oppositely directed, and thus they tend to be displaced in opposite directions. As a result, these bound charges are displaced until the forces due to the external fields are balanced by internal forces— leaving the previously "coincident" positive and negative charge distributions slightly displaced with respect to each other. This indicates that it will be useful to consider the properties of the simple arrangement of charges shown in Fig. 19-6. Such a configuration is called an electric dipole, and we define $\mathbf{p} = q\mathbf{d}$ = electric dipole moment. Our preceding considerations then lead us to the idea of replacing the actual matter by an assemblage of electric dipoles for the purpose of describing its electrical properties.

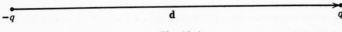

$-q$ \hspace{4cm} $\mathbf{d}$ \hspace{4cm} q

Fig. 19-6

The dipoles we spoke of above are called "induced" dipoles because they are produced by the action of the electric field on atomic and molecular charges. It sometimes happens that the structure of a molecule is such that the positive and negative charges are separated even in the absence of a field; such dipoles are called permanent dipoles. We therefore have to consider both types of dipoles when evaluating the effect of a field on the material.

We can now define a quantity characteristic of the electrical state—again averaged over a region large compared to the size of an atom but small compared to the usual macroscopic dimensions. It is

Polarization $= \mathbf{P} =$ average electric dipole moment per unit volume.

$$(19\text{-}16)$$

Example. Suppose there are N molecules in a volume V and the dipole moment of each is $\mathbf{p}$; then $\mathbf{P} = (N\mathbf{p})/V$.

Now, of course, if $\mathbf{P}$ is uniform throughout the material, the average density of positive and negative charges will be numerically equal and the net density of bound charge will be zero. However, if $\mathbf{P}$ is not uniform, it is possible that the positive and negative bound, but displaced, charges will not cancel each other out, thus resulting in a net charge density due to the displacement of the charges.

We now want to make these general considerations more quantitative. Let $\rho_P =$ density of "bound" (or "polarized") charge, and let $\rho =$ density of "free" charge. Then the total charge density is given by

$$\rho_t = \rho + \rho_P \qquad (19\text{-}17)$$

and our previous equation (19-15) can be written

$$\text{div } (\epsilon_0 \mathbf{E}) = \rho + \rho_P \qquad (19\text{-}18)$$

There is a relation between $\mathbf{P}$ and ρ_P which we now wish to find.

When a material is not polarized, there are no induced dipoles and the contribution from any permanent dipoles which may be present is zero. The latter effect arises because the permanent dipoles are randomly oriented; hence there are as many with their axes in one direction as another and they cancel out on the average. Therefore the positive and negative charges within a given volume cancel; thus the net bound charge is zero for the unpolarized state. When the matter is polarized, bound charge will be displaced; this displacement may arise from the separation of positive and negative charges when induced dipoles are formed, or from the rotation of permanent dipoles. In any event, charges will pass through the surfaces bounding a given volume and the result may be the appearance

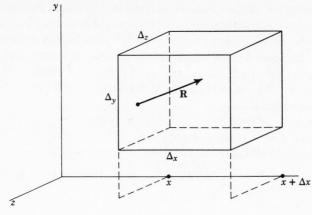

Fig. 19-7

of a net bound charge within the volume. We now proceed to calculate this effect.

Let ρ_+ = positive charge of the dipoles per unit volume, and $\mathbf{R}$ = mean displacement of this positive charge when the material is polarized. From Fig. 19-7, we see that the positive charge which passes into the volume through the left-hand face perpendicular to the x axis when the matter is polarized equals the charge in the volume $R_x \, \Delta y \, \Delta z = \rho_+ R_x \, \Delta y \, \Delta z$.

Similarly, the positive charge passing out through the right-hand face is

$$\left[\rho_+ R_x + \frac{\partial}{\partial x} (\rho_+ R_x) \, \Delta x \right] \Delta y \, \Delta z$$

Therefore the net gain of charge due to the motion of positive charge is

$$- \frac{\partial}{\partial x} (\rho_+ R_x) \, \Delta x \, \Delta y \, \Delta z$$

Let $\mathbf{R}'$ = mean displacement of the negative charge of the dipoles per unit volume $(-\rho_+)$. The net gain of charge due to motion of negative charge is

$$- \frac{\partial}{\partial x} (-\rho_+ R_x') \, \Delta x \, \Delta y \, \Delta z$$

Therefore the net gain from both sources is

$$- \frac{\partial}{\partial x} [\rho_+ (R_x - R_x')] \, \Delta x \, \Delta y \, \Delta z = - \frac{\partial P_x}{\partial x} \, \Delta x \, \Delta y \, \Delta z$$

since $\rho_+ (\mathbf{R} - \mathbf{R}') = \rho_+ \mathbf{d}$ = mean electric dipole moment per unit volume = $\mathbf{P}$.

Proceeding similarly for the other faces, we find that the net gain in charge from all the faces is

$$-\left(\frac{\partial P_x}{\partial x} + \frac{\partial P_y}{\partial y} + \frac{\partial P_z}{\partial z}\right) \Delta x\,\Delta y\,\Delta z = \rho_P\,\Delta x\,\Delta y\,\Delta z$$

from the definition of ρ_P, and therefore

$$\rho_P = -\operatorname{div} \mathbf{P} \tag{19-19}$$

is our desired relation.

Combining this with (19-18), we obtain

$$\operatorname{div}(\epsilon_0 \mathbf{E}) = \rho - \operatorname{div} \mathbf{P}$$

or

$$\operatorname{div}(\epsilon_0 \mathbf{E} + \mathbf{P}) = \rho$$

(Remember: ρ is the density of *free* charge.)

It is convenient to define

$$\mathbf{D} = \text{electric displacement} = \epsilon_0 \mathbf{E} + \mathbf{P} \tag{19-20}$$

so that

$$\operatorname{div} \mathbf{D} = \rho \tag{19-21}$$

The unit of $\mathbf{D}$ is coulomb/(meter)^2.

Equation (19-21) is one of the fundamental equations of electromagnetic theory, and it is one of Maxwell's equations. We recall that it summarizes Coulomb's law of force between charges plus the effect of bound charges in matter.

There is another consequence of Coulomb's law which we wish to point out now. Consider the line integral of $\mathbf{E}$ along the path shown in Fig. 19-8:

$$\int_1^2 \mathbf{E} \cdot d\mathbf{s} = \frac{1}{4\pi\epsilon_0} \sum_i q_i \int_1^2 \frac{\hat{\mathbf{r}}_i \cdot d\mathbf{s}}{r_i^{\,2}} = \frac{1}{4\pi\epsilon_0} \sum_i q_i \int_1^2 \frac{dr_i}{r_i^{\,2}}$$

$$= -\frac{1}{4\pi\epsilon_0} \sum_i q_i \left(\frac{1}{r_{i2}} - \frac{1}{r_{i1}}\right) \tag{19-22}$$

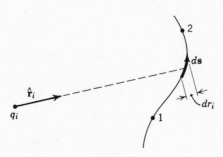

Fig. 19-8

We see that this integral is independent of the path since it depends only on the coordinates of the end points. If we now consider this integral to be taken over a closed path, so that $r_{i1} = r_{i2}$, we get

$$\oint \mathbf{E} \cdot d\mathbf{s} = 0 = \int \text{curl } \mathbf{E} \cdot d\mathbf{a}$$

and, since this holds for a path of any size, it holds for a closed path enclosing an infinitesimal area; therefore

$$\text{curl } \mathbf{E} = 0 \tag{19-23}$$

and thus the electric field as given by Coulomb's law is a conservative field.

Because of (19-23), we can write

$$\mathbf{E} = -\text{grad } \phi \tag{19-24}$$

where ϕ is called the scalar potential. Now

$$\int_1^2 \mathbf{E} \cdot d\mathbf{s} = -\int_1^2 \text{grad } \phi \cdot d\mathbf{s} = -\int_1^2 d\phi = -(\phi_2 - \phi_1)$$

Comparing this with (19-22), we see that we can write for the scalar potential

$$\phi = \sum_i \frac{q_i}{4\pi\epsilon_0 r_i} \tag{19-25}$$

Hence we can calculate the scalar potential from the given charge distribution and then find $\mathbf{E}$ from (19-24). This is often much easier than trying to calculate $\mathbf{E}$ directly from (19-6). If the charges are distributed with total density ρ_t, we have

$$\phi = \frac{1}{4\pi\epsilon_0} \int \frac{\rho_t \, dv}{r} \tag{19-25'}$$

Fig. 19-9

As usual, any scalar constant can be added to (19-25) or (19-25') without changing the physical situation, i.e., the value of $\mathbf{E}$ as calculated from (19-24).

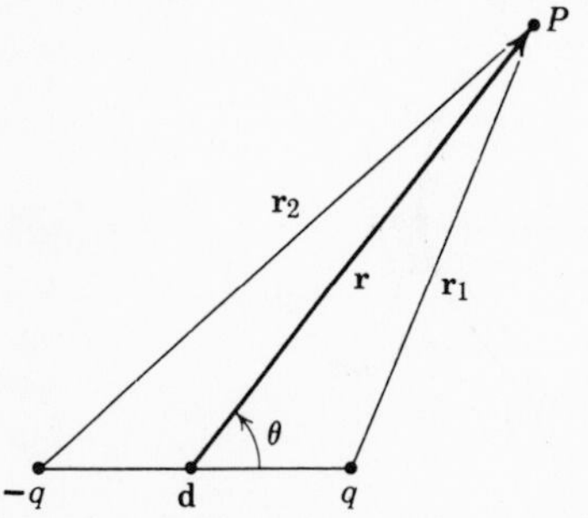

Example. Potential of a Dipole. We want to calculate the potential due to the dipole at a point P whose distance from the dipole is large compared to the separation between the charges, i.e., for $d \ll r$. Now from (19-25) and Fig. 19-9

$$4\pi\epsilon_0\phi = q\left(\frac{1}{r_1} - \frac{1}{r_2}\right)$$

$$= q\left[\frac{1}{(r^2 + (d^2/4) - dr\cos\theta)^{\frac{1}{2}}} - \frac{1}{(r^2 + (d^2/4) + dr\cos\theta)^{\frac{1}{2}}}\right]$$

$$= \frac{q}{r}\left\{\frac{1}{[1 + (d/2r)^2 - (d/r)\cos\theta]^{\frac{1}{2}}} - \frac{1}{[1 + (d/2r)^2 + (d/r)\cos\theta]^{\frac{1}{2}}}\right\}$$

$$\simeq \frac{q}{r}\left(1 + \frac{d\cos\theta}{2r} - 1 + \frac{d\cos\theta}{2r} + \cdots\right) = \frac{qd\cos\theta}{r^2} = \frac{p\cos\theta}{r^2}$$

Therefore

$$\phi_{\text{dipole}} = \frac{p\cos\theta}{4\pi\epsilon_0 r^2} = \frac{\mathbf{p} \cdot \mathbf{r}}{4\pi\epsilon_0 r^3} \tag{19-26}$$

Now we want to go on to the study of the forces between currents and the magnetic analog of Coulomb's law.

19-5   Ampère's law

Ampère studied the forces between closed loops of wires carrying currents and by a remarkable analysis was able to deduce the law of force between *infinitesimal* current elements. Rather than go through this procedure, we shall simply accept his final result, which is

$$d\mathbf{F}_1 = \frac{\mu_0}{4\pi} i_1 i_2 \frac{[d\mathbf{s}_1 \times (d\mathbf{s}_2 \times \mathbf{r})]}{r^3} \tag{19-27}$$

where $d\mathbf{F}_1$ is the force on current element $i_1 \, d\mathbf{s}_1$ due to the element $i_2 \, d\mathbf{s}_2$. [Equation (19-27) is the magnetic equivalent to Coulomb's law, and it describes the situation illustrated in Fig. 19-10.]

By *definition*,

$$\mu_0 = 4\pi \times 10^{-7} \text{ henry/meter} \tag{19-28}$$

At this point, we can see that (19-27) and (19-28) together give us our ultimate definition of the unit of charge, for, once μ_0 is defined, (19-27) can be used to determine the ampere experimentally in terms of the forces and distances involved. Since an ampere is defined as one coulomb/second, we can obtain an experimental value for the coulomb which of course agrees with the value we first gave in terms of the electronic charge.

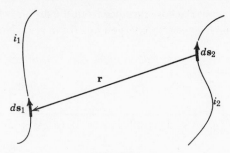

Fig. 19-10

The total force on element $i_1 \, d\mathbf{s}_1$ due to all other current elements is then given by

$$\mathbf{F}_1 = i_1 \, d\mathbf{s}_1 \times \int \frac{\mu_0}{4\pi} \frac{i \, d\mathbf{s} \times \mathbf{r}}{r^3} \qquad (19\text{-}29)$$

We define the *magnetic induction* **B** so that

$$\mathbf{F}_1 = i_1 \, d\mathbf{s}_1 \times \mathbf{B} \qquad (19\text{-}30)$$

and therefore

$$\mathbf{B} = \frac{\mu_0}{4\pi} \int \frac{i \, d\mathbf{s} \times \mathbf{r}}{r^3} \qquad (19\text{-}31)$$

where the integral is taken over the complete circuit for which we wish to find the induction produced by it at the point P. This is illustrated in Fig. 19-11. In (19-31), **B** is measured in units of webers/(meter)^2.

Before we go on to consider the properties of **B**, let us look a little more closely at the expression $i \, d\mathbf{s}$. Suppose we had, instead of a current element, a charge q moving with velocity **v**. We feel that this is in some way equivalent to a current element and we wish to find the precise relationship. To do this, let us assume that the charge has an average charge density ρ and a cross section A. Then, in a time dt, the charge having flowed across

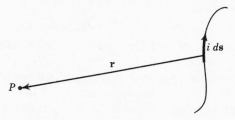

Fig. 19-11

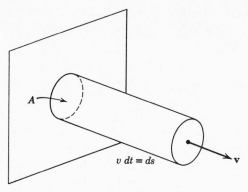

Fig. 19-12

the surface shown in Fig. 19-12 will be that contained in the volume shown; this charge is $\rho Av\, dt = i\, dt$, and, if we multiply by v, we get

$$(\rho Av)\, ds = i\, ds = (\rho A\, ds)v = qv$$

and, since $d\mathbf{s}$ and $\mathbf{v}$ are parallel,

$$i\, d\mathbf{s} = q\mathbf{v} \qquad (19\text{-}32)$$

Combining this with (19-30), we get for the magnetic force on a moving charge

$$\mathbf{F}_m = q\mathbf{v} \times \mathbf{B} \qquad (19\text{-}33)$$

and, if we add this to the force due to the electric field given by (19-5), we get the important expression for the total force on a charge:

$$\mathbf{F} = q(\mathbf{E} + \mathbf{v} \times \mathbf{B}) \qquad (19\text{-}34)$$

Now we return to discussing the properties of **B**. We begin by calculating its divergence. From (19-31), we can write

$$\text{div } \mathbf{B} = \frac{\mu_0}{4\pi} \int i \, \text{div} \left(\frac{d\mathbf{s} \times \mathbf{r}}{r^3} \right) \qquad (19\text{-}35)$$

We can show that

$$\text{div } (\mathbf{F} \times \mathbf{G}) = \mathbf{G} \cdot \text{curl } \mathbf{F} - \mathbf{F} \cdot \text{curl } \mathbf{G} \qquad (19\text{-}36)$$

At the field point where we wish to calculate div **B**, $d\mathbf{s}$ is independent of the coordinates of the point P in Fig. 19-11, and therefore curl $d\mathbf{s}$ in (19-35) is zero. Using this and (19-36), we can write (19-35) as

$$\text{div } \mathbf{B} = -\frac{\mu_0}{4\pi} \int i \, d\mathbf{s} \cdot \text{curl} \left(\frac{\mathbf{r}}{r^3} \right) \qquad (19\text{-}37)$$

Rather than evaluate this directly, we can recall that the electric field due to a point charge is $\mathbf{E} = q\mathbf{r}/4\pi\epsilon_0 r^3$ and, since curl $\mathbf{E} = 0$, we see that curl $(\mathbf{r}/r^3) = 0$, and therefore

$$\operatorname{div} \mathbf{B} = 0 \tag{19-38}$$

We now proceed to evaluate the curl of **B**. We shall do this somewhat indirectly with the aid of Fig. 19-13.

Consider a closed loop of current giving rise to an induction **B** at P. Let Ω be the solid angle subtended at P by the loop. Suppose we displace the point P by the amount $d\boldsymbol{\sigma}$. Let $d\Omega$ = change in solid angle subtended by the loop *at P* resulting from the displacement *of P*. But we can also get the same change in solid angle $d\Omega$ by keeping P fixed and giving every point of the loop the same, but opposite, displacement $-d\boldsymbol{\sigma}$. Then, from Fig. 19-13, we see that $d\Omega$ equals the sum of solid angles subtended by each of the parallelograms bounded by $d\mathbf{s}$ and $-d\boldsymbol{\sigma}$ and therefore equals the sum of projections of these areas along **r** with each divided by r^2; thus we have

$$d\Omega = \sum \frac{(-d\boldsymbol{\sigma} \times d\mathbf{s}) \cdot (\mathbf{r}/r)}{r^2} = -d\boldsymbol{\sigma} \cdot \int \frac{d\mathbf{s} \times \mathbf{r}}{r^3} = \operatorname{grad} \Omega \cdot d\boldsymbol{\sigma}$$

(Note: grad Ω is evaluated *at* the field point P.)

We can now see that

$$\operatorname{grad} \Omega = -\int \frac{d\mathbf{s} \times \mathbf{r}}{r^3}$$

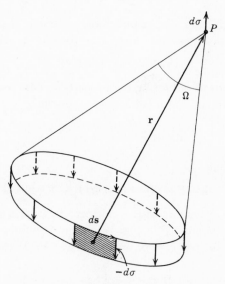

Fig. 19-13

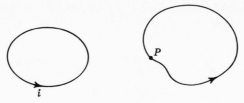

Fig. 19-14

and, using this in (19-31), we have

$$\mathbf{B} = -\mu_0 \, \text{grad} \left(\frac{i\Omega}{4\pi} \right) = -\mu_0 \, \text{grad} \, \phi_m \qquad (19\text{-}39)$$

Thus we see that *this* induction can be written as the negative gradient of a scalar quantity. The quantity $\phi_m = (i\Omega/4\pi) =$ magnetic scalar potential. In this case, therefore, curl $\mathbf{B} = 0$. The last result does not generally hold, however, and we shall have to go back to Stokes' theorem to calculate the more general value of the curl. Using (19-39), we can write

$$\oint \mathbf{B} \cdot d\mathbf{s} = -\frac{\mu_0 i}{4\pi} \oint \text{grad} \, \Omega \cdot d\mathbf{s} = -\frac{\mu_0 i}{4\pi} \int d\Omega$$

$$= -\frac{\mu_0 i}{4\pi} \Delta\Omega \qquad (19\text{-}40)$$

where $\Delta\Omega$ is the total change in solid angle observed as we integrate $\mathbf{B}$ over the closed path.

Suppose our path of integration is like that shown in Fig. 19-14. For this path, when we come back to the initial position, Ω has the same value as before, and

$$\Delta\Omega = 0$$

$$\oint \mathbf{B} \cdot d\mathbf{s} = 0 = \int \text{curl} \, \mathbf{B} \cdot d\mathbf{a}$$

and, therefore,

$$\text{curl} \, \mathbf{B} = 0$$

as we know.

Now suppose our path of integration encloses the current, as shown in Fig. 19-15. Note the sense of the normal and how it is determined from the direction of the current by using the right-hand rule. For simplicity, let us imagine starting at A and ending at B. At A, $\Omega = 2\pi$; at B, $\Omega = -2\pi$; hence

$$\Delta\Omega = (-2\pi) - 2\pi = -4\pi$$

and therefore

$$\oint \mathbf{B} \cdot d\mathbf{s} = \mu_0 i = \mu_0 \, (\text{current enclosed by the path of integration}) \quad (19\text{-}41)$$

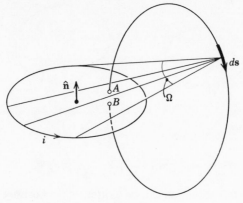

Fig. 19-15

[Note "similarity" to Gauss' theorem (19-8).]

Now, if $\mathbf{J}_t$ = total current density,

$$i = \int \mathbf{J}_t \cdot d\mathbf{a}$$

where the integral is taken over the surface spanning the path around which we calculated the line integral of $\mathbf{B}$. Hence we can write (19-41) as

$$\oint \mathbf{B} \cdot d\mathbf{s} = \mu_0 \int \mathbf{J}_t \cdot d\mathbf{a} = \int \operatorname{curl} \mathbf{B} \cdot d\mathbf{a}$$

Since this result holds for any contour and any surface spanning it, we obtain

$$\operatorname{curl} \mathbf{B} = \mu_0 \mathbf{J}_t \tag{19-42}$$

This is another way of stating Ampère's law. In contrast to $\mathbf{E}$, we see that curl $\mathbf{B} = 0$ only in regions where there are no currents—and we cannot always define a scalar potential from which to calculate $\mathbf{B}$ as we were able to do for $\mathbf{E}$. The magnetic scalar potential has the additional disadvantage that it is not single-valued. Nevertheless, we now want to calculate the potential for a special case.

Example. Potential of a Current Whirl. Suppose we have a current i around a small area S (Fig. 19-16). We want to calculate the magnetic scalar potential of this "whirl" at a point P whose distance from the whirl is large compared to its dimensions, i.e., when $r \gg \sqrt{S}$. From above,

$$\phi_m = \frac{i\Omega}{4\pi} = \frac{i}{4\pi}\left(\frac{S \cos \theta}{r^2}\right) = \frac{(i\mathbf{S}) \cdot \mathbf{r}}{4\pi r^3} \tag{19-43}$$

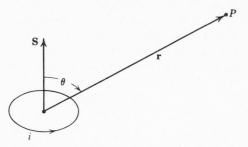

Fig. 19-16

Comparing this equation with (19-26), which gives the potential of an electric dipole, we see that (19-43) is very similar in that it has the same dependence on r and θ and differs only in numerical factors. Hence it is appropriate to speak of this small current whirl as a *magnetic dipole* and to define

$$\mathbf{m} = \text{magnetic dipole moment} = i\mathbf{S} \qquad (19\text{-}44)$$

and therefore

$$\phi_{m,\text{mag dipole}} = \frac{\mathbf{m} \cdot \mathbf{r}}{4\pi r^3} \qquad (19\text{-}45)$$

Now we can discuss the magnetic properties of matter in a way similar to that which we used when we replaced the material by a collection of electric dipoles.

19-6 Magnetization and magnetic field

When we considered electric polarization, we used essentially the model in which it is assumed that matter is composed of molecules which in turn are composed of positive and negative charges such that the whole material is electrically neutral. Another feature of this model is that the charges are not at rest but are assumed to be in continuous motion. We have seen in (19-32) that a moving charge is equivalent in many ways to a current; presumably these charges will be moving in essentially closed paths and, since macroscopic distances are large compared to atomic dimensions, this gives us the idea that they will appear to us to be current whirls or magnetic dipoles. Thus we arrive at the concept of regarding a material, with respect to its *macroscopic* magnetic effects, as being equivalent to a *collection of magnetic dipoles.*

These dipoles can arise in essentially two ways. First, it is possible that, when $\mathbf{B} = 0$, the charges are circulating in such a manner that the net current whirl is zero; that is, the dipole moments of the individual charges add vectorially to zero. Now suppose that somehow things are arranged— by external currents, for example— so that $\mathbf{B} \neq 0$. This will give rise to a force $q\mathbf{v} \times \mathbf{B}$ on each of the charges. It is conceivable that these additional forces will change the paths of the charges enough so that the resulting configuration will give rise to a magnetic dipole moment which is different

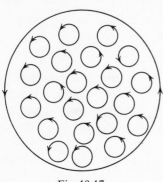

from zero. This moment can properly be spoken of as being "induced" by the field. Second, it can happen that an atom or molecule in the absence of $\mathbf{B}$ has associated with it a structure that results in a permanently circulating current so that the molecule has a permanent dipole moment. Then the application of a $\mathbf{B}$ will give rise to new forces on these currents which can change the alignment of the dipole moment. These permanently circulating currents are often called "Ampèrian

Fig. 19-17

currents" after Ampère who first postulated them to account for the magnetic properties of matter. Their presence and magnitude cannot be accounted for classically; however, it is not part of our task here to account for them, but merely to accept their presence, try to describe them macroscopically, and include them in our equations.

Thus, as far as magnetic effects are concerned, we are replacing matter by a collection of magnetic dipoles. Now, in the same way in which we introduced a polarization vector $\mathbf{P}$ which we defined as the average electric dipole moment per unit volume, we can define a quantity:

Magnetization $= \mathbf{M} =$ average magnetic dipole

moment per unit volume   (19-46)

In general, we can expect to find some relation existing between $\mathbf{M}$ and $\mathbf{B}$, but we leave this to later discussion.

Consider a piece of material composed of magnetic dipoles, which, for simplicity, we assume to be aligned. Suppose for the present that $\mathbf{M}$ is uniform. When we look at Fig. 19-17, showing an end-on view of all the current whirls, we see that, in the interior, the current due to one whirl in one direction is cancelled by the opposite current of the adjacent whirls. Hence, in the interior of a uniformly magnetized material, the "bound" current is zero. But at the surface there are no adjacent dipoles to cancel, and, since the currents in the whirls are all in the same sense, the net result is the appearance of a current circulating on the surface of the material.

Thus we conclude that the existence of a magnetization within a medium implies the existence of surface currents. Now we want to find the quantitative relation.

The definition of surface current density is:

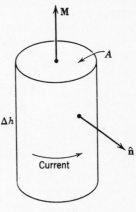

K = current passing across unit length
normal to the flow   (19-47)

If the cross-sectional area of the small uniformly magnetized figure shown in Fig. 19-18 is A and the height is Δh, the volume is $A \Delta h$, so that from (19-46)

Total dipole moment $= M(A \Delta h)$
$$= (M \Delta h)A \quad (19\text{-}48)$$

This is the same dipole moment that would be obtained by a current $M \Delta h$ circulating about the area A in the sense shown. Hence, from (19-47), we can say that the numerical value

Fig. 19-18

of the surface current density is M. Looking at the figure again, we also see that the direction as well as the magnitude of this magnetic surface current density is given by

$$\mathbf{K}_m = \mathbf{M} \times \hat{\mathbf{n}} \quad (19\text{-}49)$$

where $\hat{\mathbf{n}}$ is the *outer* normal to the surface. This is a general result since it does not depend on the shape of the figure we used.

We can also use this result to find the effective surface current density at the surface of discontinuity between two regions of magnetization $\mathbf{M}_1$ and $\mathbf{M}_2$ shown in Fig. 19-19. The respective densities are $\mathbf{K}_1 = \mathbf{M}_1 \times \hat{\mathbf{n}}$ and $\mathbf{K}_2 = \mathbf{M}_2 \times \hat{\mathbf{n}}'$. Therefore the total surface current density is $\mathbf{K}_m = \mathbf{K}_1 + \mathbf{K}_2 = \mathbf{M}_1 \times \hat{\mathbf{n}} + \mathbf{M}_2 \times \hat{\mathbf{n}}'$. But, since the normals are defined as outward normals, we have $\hat{\mathbf{n}}' = -\hat{\mathbf{n}}$; hence

$$\mathbf{K}_m = (\mathbf{M}_1 - \mathbf{M}_2) \times \hat{\mathbf{n}} \quad (19\text{-}50)$$

This reduces to our previous result if $\mathbf{M}_2 = 0$, as it would be in the empty space we previously assumed.

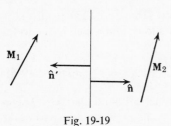

Fig. 19-19

Looking again at our end-on picture, Fig. 19-17, let us now assume that $\mathbf{M}$ is not uniform throughout the material, as could be the case if the currents in each whirl were different. Then we see that there will no longer be complete cancellation of the oppositely

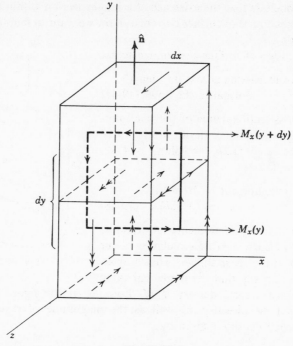

Fig. 19-20

directed currents of the dipoles and there will be a resultant current in the interior. Hence we suspect that there is a relation between the volume density of bound current and a non-uniformity of the magnetization, similar to that found for polarization in (19-19). Our next step is to find this relation. For this purpose, we consider an interior portion of the magnetized material represented by the two adjacent cubes in Fig. 19-20.

The total surface current circulating around the upper cube and resulting from the x component of magnetization is, in magnitude, $M_x(y + dy) \, dx$, while that around the lower cube is $M_x(y) \, dx$. Therefore the net current in the positive z direction through the contour shown and which is due to the x component of the magnetization is

$$M_x(y) \, dx - M_x(y + dy) \, dx = - \frac{\partial M_x}{\partial y} \, dy \, dx = J_{mz}^{(x)} \, dy \, dx \quad (19\text{-}51)$$

where $\mathbf{J}_m$ is the equivalent current density due to bound charges. Therefore the contribution to the z component of the current density from the x component of magnetization is

$$J_{mz}^{(x)} = - \frac{\partial M_x}{\partial y} \quad (19\text{-}52)$$

From Fig. 19-21, we see that the y component of **M** will also contribute to the current in the z direction. By going through the same type of argument as above, we find that its contribution is

$$J_{mz}^{(y)} = \frac{\partial M_y}{\partial x} \tag{19-53}$$

Therefore the total z component of $\mathbf{J}_m$ is the sum of (19-52) and (19-53), or

$$J_{mz} = \frac{\partial M_y}{\partial x} - \frac{\partial M_x}{\partial y} = (\text{curl } \mathbf{M})_z \tag{19-54}$$

and, since we could have chosen any component of $\mathbf{J}_m$, we can say that

$$\mathbf{J}_m = \text{curl } \mathbf{M} \tag{19-55}$$

This verifies our idea that a variation in **M** gives rise to an effective current density.

Now, as we did for charges, we can divide our total current into two types and let $\mathbf{J}$ = real (or true) current density, $\mathbf{J}_m$ = magnetization current density; then the total current density can be written as

$$\mathbf{J}_t = \mathbf{J} + \mathbf{J}_m \tag{19-56}$$

Substituting (19-56) into (19-42), we get

$$\text{curl}\left(\frac{\mathbf{B}}{\mu_0}\right) = \mathbf{J}_t = \mathbf{J} + \mathbf{J}_m = \mathbf{J} + \text{curl } \mathbf{M} \tag{19-57}$$

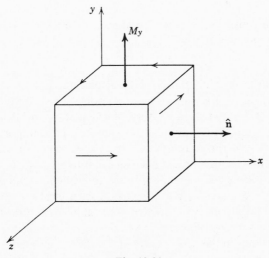

Fig. 19-21

or

$$\text{curl} \left(\frac{\mathbf{B}}{\mu_0} - \mathbf{M} \right) = \mathbf{J} \tag{19-58}$$

This result makes it convenient to define a new quantity:

$$\text{Magnetic field} = \mathbf{H} = \frac{\mathbf{B}}{\mu_0} - \mathbf{M} \tag{19-59}$$

so that

$$\text{curl } \mathbf{H} = \mathbf{J} \tag{19-60}$$

This equation expresses Ampère's law describing the forces between current elements plus the magnetic effects of matter. We note that curl $\mathbf{H}$ is determined only by the real currents and is independent of the medium. In this respect, it is similar to $\mathbf{D}$. The unit of $\mathbf{H}$ is amperes/meter.

There is another way of looking at one of our results which is of some historical interest. We find from (19-38) and (19-59) that

$$\text{div } \mathbf{B} = 0 = \mu_0 \, (\text{div } \mathbf{H} + \text{div } \mathbf{M})$$

so that

$$\text{div } \mathbf{H} = -\text{div } \mathbf{M} \tag{19-61}$$

We recall that, for electric charge, we found that $\rho_P = -\text{div } \mathbf{P}$, where ρ_P is the volume density of bound charge. In the same way, it is sometimes convenient to define an analogous quantity

$$\rho_m = -\text{div } \mathbf{M} \tag{19-62}$$

as the volume density of magnetic charge or volume density of magnetic poles. Then (19-61) becomes

$$\text{div } \mathbf{H} = \rho_m \tag{19-63}$$

which is similar to that found for electric displacement (19-21). This result is essentially the basis for the common older method of introducing magnetic poles into magnetism as a way of calculating the field. But the magnetic case *is* different from the electric case in the important respect that there is no experimental evidence for the existence of free magnetic poles. Their introduction into magnetism according to the present point of view is done merely as a computational convenience without physical justification. As a matter of fact, one can discuss electromagnetic theory very adequately without using isolated poles at all, but instead by dealing only with dipoles. This is what we shall do.

Now we proceed to the formulation of another experimental law which forms an important part of the foundation of electromagnetic theory.

19-7 Faraday's law of induction

Ampère's law expressed a relation between electricity and magnetism, namely, that magnetic fields can be produced by electric charges in motion. The converse production of electric fields by a magnetic system was long suspected and looked for and was finally discovered by Faraday. He did his experiments with circuits and wires, and then his results were assumed to hold in space even if no wires were present to demonstrate the effect. The content of Faraday's law is summed up as the law of electromagnetic induction: The induced emf is equal to the negative of the time rate of change of magnetic flux. Let us define these terms so that we can write Faraday's law in a quantitative form.

$$\text{Magnetic flux} = \Phi_m = \int \mathbf{B} \cdot d\mathbf{a} \tag{19-64}$$

Magnetic flux is measured in webers.

emf = work done per unit charge around a

$$\text{closed path} = \oint \mathbf{E} \cdot d\mathbf{s} \tag{19-65}$$

emf is measured in volts; from the definition we see that 1 volt = 1 joule/coulomb. As a result of (19-65), it is sometimes convenient to use the unit of volt/meter for electric field, as well as our previous unit of newton/coulomb obtained from (19-5).

Thus Faraday's law says that

$$\oint \mathbf{E} \cdot d\mathbf{s} = -\frac{d\Phi_m}{dt} = -\frac{d}{dt} \int \mathbf{B} \cdot d\mathbf{a} \tag{19-66}$$

In (19-66), the surface integral is taken over a surface with the closed path as boundary, as illustrated in Fig. 19-22.

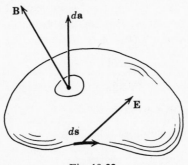

Fig. 19-22

We shall, for the time being, consider only the case in which the path is fixed in space, so that the flux changes in time only because **B** does. Therefore we can write (19-66) as

$$\oint \mathbf{E} \cdot d\mathbf{s} = -\int \frac{\partial \mathbf{B}}{\partial t} \cdot d\mathbf{a} = \int \text{curl } \mathbf{E} \cdot d\mathbf{a} \qquad (19\text{-}67)$$

and we obtain, as usual,

$$\text{curl } \mathbf{E} = -\frac{\partial \mathbf{B}}{\partial t} \qquad (19\text{-}68)$$

which is the desired differential formulation of Faraday's law.

This result shows that our previous equation (19-23) is true only in the static case when the fields are all constant in time.

19-8   Displacement current

Let us pause now and review what we have obtained so far. The fundamental experimental results are summarized in equations (19-21), (19-38), (19-60), and (19-68), together with the relations (19-20) and (19-59).

We also have the equation of continuity (19-1) which describes the law of conservation of charge. It was Maxwell's discovery of the fact that the equations mentioned above are not compatible with the equation of continuity that led him to make his really great contribution to electromagnetic theory—the introduction of the displacement current.

It is a general theorem of vector analysis that div curl **A** = 0, where **A** is any vector. If we calculate the divergence of (19-60) and use (19-1), we get

$$\text{div curl } \mathbf{H} = 0 = \text{div } \mathbf{J} = -\frac{\partial \rho}{\partial t} \neq 0$$

Thus we see that our equations lead us to a contradiction. Because of this, Maxwell assumed that (19-60) was not complete but should have another "current" added to it. If we call this additional current density $\mathbf{J}_d$, we should write, instead of (19-60), the equation

$$\text{curl } \mathbf{H} = \mathbf{J} + \mathbf{J}_d \qquad (19\text{-}69)$$

In order to identify $\mathbf{J}_d$, we calculate the divergence of (19-69) and get

$$\text{div curl } \mathbf{H} = \text{div } \mathbf{J} + \text{div } \mathbf{J}_d = 0$$

Therefore, using (19-1) here, we find that

$$\text{div } \mathbf{J}_d = -\text{div } \mathbf{J} = \frac{\partial \rho}{\partial t}$$

But, if we assume that (19-21) also applies to time-dependent fields, we obtain

$$\frac{\partial \rho}{\partial t} = \text{div} \frac{\partial \mathbf{D}}{\partial t}$$

so that

$$\text{div } \mathbf{J}_d = \text{div} \frac{\partial \mathbf{D}}{\partial t} \qquad (19\text{-}70)$$

Because of this equation, Maxwell *assumed* that one must set

$$\mathbf{J}_d = \frac{\partial \mathbf{D}}{\partial t} \qquad (19\text{-}71)$$

so that (19-69) becomes

$$\text{curl } \mathbf{H} = \mathbf{J} + \frac{\partial \mathbf{D}}{\partial t} \qquad (19\text{-}72)$$

At the time Maxwell did this, there was no direct experimental evidence for the existence of the additional term $\partial \mathbf{D}/\partial t$, and the only arguments available were plausibility ones such as that we gave above. The main evidence for the validity of (19-72) is the agreement of its consequences with experiment. It is extremely well founded, as we shall see.

The expression (19-71) is called the "displacement current." We note that, in the static case, (19-72) becomes (19-60), as it should.

19-9   Maxwell's equations for stationary media

The basic equations of motion of the electromagnetic field are summarized in the following set of equations.

$$\text{div } \mathbf{D} = \rho \qquad (19\text{-}21)$$

$$\text{curl } \mathbf{E} = - \frac{\partial \mathbf{B}}{\partial t} \qquad (19\text{-}68)$$

$$\text{div } \mathbf{B} = 0 \qquad (19\text{-}38)$$

$$\text{curl } \mathbf{H} = \mathbf{J} + \frac{\partial \mathbf{D}}{\partial t} \qquad (19\text{-}72)$$

These are known as Maxwell's equations. With them we need the definitions

$$\mathbf{D} = \epsilon_0 \mathbf{E} + \mathbf{P} \qquad (19\text{-}20)$$

$$\mathbf{H} = \frac{\mathbf{B}}{\mu_0} - \mathbf{M} \qquad (19\text{-}59)$$

which account for the presence of matter as described macroscopically by the vectors $\mathbf{P}$ and $\mathbf{M}$.

In order to use these equations, it is necessary to know how **P** and **M** depend on the fields—this is not discussed or provided by this macroscopic theory, but must be left to determination by experiment or deduced from other theories which discuss the microscopic properties of matter, such as quantum mechanics and statistical mechanics.

Thus a knowledge of the distribution of applied currents, charges, and polarizations enables us in principle to calculate the fields **E**, **B** and **D**, **H**. The connection with experiment is then provided by the force equation

$$\mathbf{F} = q(\mathbf{E} + \mathbf{v} \times \mathbf{B}) \qquad (19\text{-}34)$$

If we know the fields, we obtain the forces on the particles carrying the charges from (19-34), and then by integrating the equations of motion we can find their subsequent motions, which can then be compared with experiment.

Exercises

19-1. A particle of mass m and positive charge q moves in a plane which is perpendicular to a constant induction B. Show that the particle moves in a circle with constant speed, and that the radius of the circle is given by $a = mv/qB$.

19-2. An electric dipole of fixed moment **p** is in a constant field **E**. Show that there is a torque on the dipole given by $\mathbf{p} \times \mathbf{E}$.

19-3. Find the rectangular components of the field produced by a dipole.

20 Boundary conditions

It often happens that one wants to discuss situations in which the physical properties of the matter, in the field, change abruptly across a surface. Such a surface is known as a surface of discontinuity. It is necessary to know how the electromagnetic field vectors change as one goes across this boundary, and we shall now deduce these changes from Maxwell's equations. Since we have assumed in our writing of these equations that the vectors involved are continuous and have continuous derivatives, it is customary to imagine the bounding surface to be replaced by a very thin transition layer in which the material properties change continuously but very rapidly, and then later let the transition layer shrink to zero thickness. We shall see that we can get from each of Maxwell's equations an equation which tells how a component of one of the field vectors changes as one goes across the bounding surface.

We let the values of the vectors in the two media be labeled by subscripts 1 and 2, and let n̂ be the normal to the bounding surface which points from region 1 to region 2. The first situation we want to consider is illustrated in Fig. 20-1.

In the transition layer, we construct a small right cylinder of height h and area ΔS. Let us first consider the surface integral of **B** over this cylinder; using (1-38) and (19-38), we find that

$$\int_{cyl} \mathbf{B} \cdot d\mathbf{a} = \int \operatorname{div} \mathbf{B}\, dv = 0 \tag{20-1}$$

If we choose the area of the base to be small enough, we can assume that **B** is nearly constant over the faces, so that a good approximation to the surface integral can be written:

$$\mathbf{B}_2 \cdot \Delta \mathbf{S}_2 + \mathbf{B}_1 \cdot \Delta \mathbf{S}_1 + W_B = (\mathbf{B}_2 \cdot \hat{\mathbf{n}}_2 + \mathbf{B}_1 \cdot \hat{\mathbf{n}}_1)\, \Delta S + W_B = 0 \tag{20-2}$$

In (20-2), W_B is the contribution to the surface integral from the walls of the cylinder; since the cylinder is so small, W_B will be proportional to h.

As we let the transition layer shrink to zero thickness, so that $h \to 0$, then $W_B \to 0$, and the limiting value of (20-2) becomes

$$(\mathbf{B}_2 \cdot \hat{\mathbf{n}}_2 + \mathbf{B}_1 \cdot \hat{\mathbf{n}}_1)\, \Delta S = 0 \tag{20-3}$$

If we cancel out ΔS and use the relations $\hat{\mathbf{n}}_2 = \hat{\mathbf{n}} = -\hat{\mathbf{n}}_1$ obtained from Fig. 20-1, we find from (20-3) that

$$\hat{\mathbf{n}} \cdot (\mathbf{B}_2 - \mathbf{B}_1) = B_{2n} - B_{1n} = 0 \tag{20-4}$$

This is the first of our boundary conditions; it says that the normal component of **B** is continuous across a surface of discontinuity in the medium.

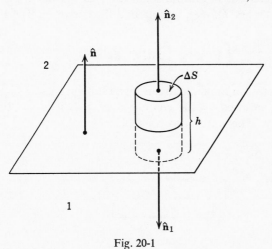

Fig. 20-1

Similarly, using (1-38) and (19-21), we find that

$$\int_{\text{cyl}} \mathbf{D} \cdot d\mathbf{a} = \int \rho \, dv = q = \rho h \, \Delta S \qquad (20\text{-}5)$$

where q is the total free charge contained in the cylinder. As we now let the transition layer shrink to zero thickness, this charge q must be conserved and accordingly can be thought of as a surface charge in the limit as the volume charge density becomes infinite. Then it is convenient to replace the limiting value of ρh by a surface charge density σ where

$$\sigma = \text{charge per unit area} = \lim_{h \to 0} \rho h \qquad (20\text{-}6)$$

Then we can write the total charge $q = \sigma \, \Delta S$, and (20-5) becomes

$$\int_{\text{cyl}} \mathbf{D} \cdot d\mathbf{a} = \sigma \, \Delta S \qquad (20\text{-}7)$$

We can discuss the left-hand side of (20-7) exactly as we did above, replacing $\mathbf{B}$ in (20-3) by $\mathbf{D}$, and 0 by $\sigma \, \Delta S$. The result is

$$\hat{\mathbf{n}} \cdot (\mathbf{D}_2 - \mathbf{D}_1) = D_{2n} - D_{1n} = \sigma \qquad (20\text{-}8)$$

This tells us that the change in the normal component of $\mathbf{D}$ equals the surface density of free charge. These normal components are continuous only if there is no free charge on the surface of discontinuity.

The remaining Maxwell equations involve the curl, and from them we can get information about tangential components. We construct a small rectangular contour in the transition layer as shown in Fig. 20-2.

Using (1-40) and (19-68), we find that the line integral of $\mathbf{E}$ around this contour is

$$\oint \mathbf{E} \cdot d\mathbf{s} = \int \text{curl } \mathbf{E} \cdot d\mathbf{a} = -\int \frac{\partial \mathbf{B}}{\partial t} \cdot d\mathbf{a} \qquad (20\text{-}9)$$

The unit vectors in the direction of integration are $\hat{\boldsymbol{\tau}}_1$ and $\hat{\boldsymbol{\tau}}_2$; the normal to the area enclosed by the contour is $\hat{\mathbf{n}}'$, and it lies in the surface of discontinuity. The vector area is $\hat{\mathbf{n}}' h \, \Delta s$.

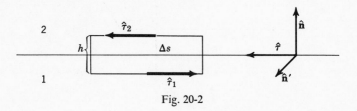

Fig. 20-2

We can approximate the integrals in (20-9) and we obtain

$$(\mathbf{E}_2 \cdot \hat{\boldsymbol{\tau}}_2 + \mathbf{E}_1 \cdot \hat{\boldsymbol{\tau}}_1) \, \Delta s + W_E = - \frac{\partial \mathbf{B}}{\partial t} \cdot \hat{\mathbf{n}}' h \, \Delta s \qquad (20\text{-}10)$$

W_E is the contribution to the line integral from the ends; it will be proportional to h and thus will vanish as $h \to 0$.

If we define the unit tangent vector $\hat{\boldsymbol{\tau}}$ by $\hat{\mathbf{n}}' \times \hat{\mathbf{n}}$, we see from the figure that $\hat{\boldsymbol{\tau}}_2 = \hat{\boldsymbol{\tau}} = -\hat{\boldsymbol{\tau}}_1$. Then, if we also use (1-20), we find that $\hat{\boldsymbol{\tau}}_2 \cdot \mathbf{E}_2 = \hat{\boldsymbol{\tau}} \cdot \mathbf{E}_2 = (\hat{\mathbf{n}}' \times \hat{\mathbf{n}}) \cdot \mathbf{E}_2 = \hat{\mathbf{n}}' \cdot (\hat{\mathbf{n}} \times \mathbf{E}_2)$ and $\hat{\boldsymbol{\tau}}_1 \cdot \mathbf{E}_1 = -\hat{\mathbf{n}}' \cdot (\hat{\mathbf{n}} \times \mathbf{E}_1)$. If we insert these into (20-10) and let the transition layer shrink to zero thickness, we find that

$$\hat{\mathbf{n}}' \cdot \left[\hat{\mathbf{n}} \times (\mathbf{E}_2 - \mathbf{E}_1) + \lim_{h \to 0} \left(h \frac{\partial \mathbf{B}}{\partial t} \right) \right] = 0 \qquad (20\text{-}11)$$

We naturally assume that the field vectors and their derivatives are bounded and hence $\partial \mathbf{B}/\partial t$ is finite. Then

$$\lim_{h \to 0} \left(h \frac{\partial \mathbf{B}}{\partial t} \right) = 0 \qquad (20\text{-}12)$$

Also, since the orientation of our contour is completely arbitrary, the direction of $\hat{\mathbf{n}}'$ is arbitrary and we can obtain from (20-11) and (20-12) our final result that

$$\hat{\mathbf{n}} \times (\mathbf{E}_2 - \mathbf{E}_1) = 0 \qquad (20\text{-}13)$$

Since the normal components of $\mathbf{E}$, which are parallel to $\hat{\mathbf{n}}$, will not contribute to the cross products in (20-13), only the tangential components of $\mathbf{E}$ are involved; thus (20-13) says that the tangential components of $\mathbf{E}$ are continuous across a surface of discontinuity.

Similarly, we find from (19-72) that

$$\oint \mathbf{H} \cdot d\mathbf{s} = \int \left(\mathbf{J} + \frac{\partial \mathbf{D}}{\partial t} \right) \cdot d\mathbf{a} \qquad (20\text{-}14)$$

and therefore that

$$\hat{\mathbf{n}} \times (\mathbf{H}_2 - \mathbf{H}_1) = \lim_{h \to 0} \left[h \left(\mathbf{J} + \frac{\partial \mathbf{D}}{\partial t} \right) \right] = \lim_{h \to 0} h \mathbf{J} \qquad (20\text{-}15)$$

because $\partial \mathbf{D}/\partial t$ is bounded and we can apply an equation like (20-12).

If the total free current passing through the contour is squeezed down into a layer of infinitesimal thickness as the transition layer is shrunk, it is convenient to describe the situation by the surface current density $\mathbf{K}$. Since the total current through the area was originally $i = \mathbf{J} \cdot \hat{\mathbf{n}}' h \, \Delta s$ and would then be written in terms of $\mathbf{K}$ as $i = \mathbf{K} \cdot \hat{\mathbf{n}}' \, \Delta s$, we see that we have

$$\mathbf{K} = \lim_{h \to 0} h \mathbf{J}$$

and (20-15) becomes

$$\hat{n} \times (H_2 - H_1) = K \tag{20-16}$$

The discontinuity in the tangential components of H equals the free surface current density.

We now have found that we can supplement the Maxwell field equations by the four derived relations (20-4), (20-8), (20-13), and (20-16), which determine the transition of the electromagnetic field across a surface of discontinuity of the electromagnetic properties.

Now that we have defined the electromagnetic field vectors, found their equations of motion, and discussed some of their properties, we can discuss electromagnetic theory, which basically consists of the various solutions of Maxwell's equations for varying sets of conditions. After we have done this, we shall take up the question of the interaction between the fields and matter.

21 Electrostatics in vacuum

In the static situation, all derivatives with respect to time are zero and the two relevant Maxwell equations, (19-21) and (19-68), become

$$\text{div } D = \rho \tag{21-1}$$

$$\text{curl } E = 0 \tag{21-2}$$

If, in addition, we have a vacuum, $P = 0$ since there is no matter, and (19-20) becomes $D = \epsilon_0 E$, and (21-1) becomes

$$\text{div } E = \frac{\rho}{\epsilon_0} \tag{21-3}$$

The boundary conditions (20-8) and (20-13) are

$$\hat{n} \cdot (E_2 - E_1) = \frac{\sigma}{\epsilon_0} \tag{21-4}$$

$$\hat{n} \times (E_2 - E_1) = 0 \tag{21-5}$$

Hence we need deal only with the single vector E.

Some problems can be solved by simple, although special, methods if there is sufficient symmetry.

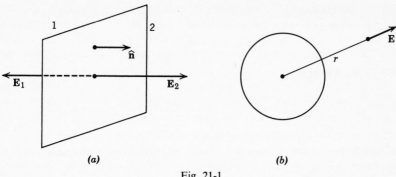

Fig. 21-1

Example. Field of a Charged Plane. Consider an infinite plane which is uniformly charged with the constant surface charge density σ, as shown in Fig. 21-1a. We want to calculate the field $\mathbf{E}$ resulting from it. By symmetry, $\mathbf{E}$ must be normal to the plane and of equal magnitude E on each side. Now $\hat{\mathbf{n}} \cdot \mathbf{E}_2 = E$ and $\hat{\mathbf{n}} \cdot \mathbf{E}_1 = -E$; hence (21-4) becomes $2E = \sigma/\epsilon_0$ and thus

$$E = \frac{\sigma}{2\epsilon_0} \tag{21-6}$$

Example. Field outside a Spherically Symmetric Spherical Charge Distribution. Suppose ρ is independent of angle so that $\rho = \rho(r)$, where r is the distance measured from the center, as shown in Fig. 21-1b. By symmetry, $\mathbf{E}$ must be in the radial direction as shown, and its magnitude E can depend only on r. If we calculate the surface integral of $\mathbf{E}$ on the sphere of radius r where $\mathbf{E}$ is parallel to the element of area $d\mathbf{a}$, we obtain

$$\int \mathbf{E} \cdot d\mathbf{a} = E \int da = 4\pi r^2 E = \int \text{div } \mathbf{E} \, dv = \frac{1}{\epsilon_0} \int \rho \, dv = \frac{Q}{\epsilon_0}$$

where Q is the total charge of the sphere. Therefore

$$E = \frac{Q}{4\pi\epsilon_0 r^2} \tag{21-7}$$

This is precisely the formula for the electric field produced by a point charge Q at the origin. Thus we have proved that a spherically symmetric charge distribution acts as if it were a point charge with its total charge concentrated at the center. This result also holds for the inverse square gravitational field produced by a spherically symmetric mass distribution.

Most problems, of course, do not permit such simple solutions, and we must now turn to more general methods of attack.

21-1   The potential

Since curl $\mathbf{E} = 0$, we know that we can write

$$\mathbf{E} = -\operatorname{grad} \phi \qquad (21\text{-}8)$$

We have already shown how to calculate the potential; the result as given by (19-25′) is

$$\phi(x, y, z) = \frac{1}{4\pi\epsilon_0} \int_{\text{all space}} \frac{\rho\, dv}{r} \qquad (21\text{-}9)$$

We shall prove this again more elegantly later on. The potential is measured in volts because $\mathbf{E}$ can be measured in volts/meter.

A surface on which the potential is constant, as given by the equation $\phi(x, y, z) = \text{const.}$, is called an "equipotential surface." Some possible surfaces are indicated by the solid curves of Fig. 21-2. Since $\mathbf{E} = -\operatorname{grad} \phi$, and since the gradient was shown to be perpendicular to the surfaces of constant ϕ (Sec. 1-8), we see that the directions of the electric field are perpendicular to the equipotentials. Lines which are everywhere tangent to the electric field are called "lines of force"; some are shown dashed in Fig. 21-2. Such concepts as these are often useful in giving one a visualization of the state of the field.

A *conductor* is defined as a region in which charges are free to move about under the influence of an electric field. Now, if an electric field were present in a conductor, the charges would move about, and we would no longer

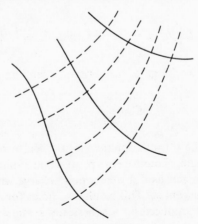

Fig. 21-2

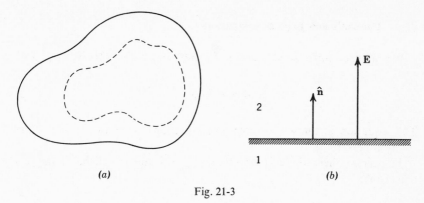

Fig. 21-3

have the *static* situation we are assuming. Hence we see that $\mathbf{E} = 0$ at all points within a conductor. From (21-8), we see that then the potential is constant in the interior of a conductor, so that a conductor forms an equipotential volume. Therefore, at the surface of a conductor, the gradient is perpendicular to the surface at each point, and (21-8) then tells us that the electric field is everywhere perpendicular to the surface of a conductor in a completely static situation.

Let us apply Gauss' theorem (19-8) to an arbitrary surface in the interior of a conductor, such as is shown dashed in Fig. 21-3a. Since $\mathbf{E} = 0$ inside,

$$\int \mathbf{E} \cdot d\mathbf{a} = \frac{Q}{\epsilon_0} = 0 \qquad (21\text{-}10)$$

and $Q = 0 =$ total charge within the surface. Because the surface is completely arbitrary and can be so deformed as to coincide with the bounding surface of the conductor, we can conclude that $Q = 0$ everywhere. In other words, we have found that the net charge in the interior of a conductor is zero; consequently whatever charge is present resides entirely on the surface. This was first shown by Faraday in his famous "ice-pail experiment."

Let us apply our boundary condition to the surface of a conductor, as illustrated in Fig. 21-3b. Since $\mathbf{E}_1 = 0$ and $\mathbf{E}_2 = \mathbf{E}$ is parallel to $\hat{\mathbf{n}}$, so that $\hat{\mathbf{n}} \cdot \mathbf{E}_2 = E$, (21-4) and (21-8) yield

$$\epsilon_0 E = \sigma = -\epsilon_0 \hat{\mathbf{n}} \cdot \text{grad } \phi \qquad (21\text{-}11)$$

Thus, if we somehow know ϕ as a function of position, not only can we find $\mathbf{E}$ everywhere by using (21-8), but also we can calculate the distribution of charge on conducting surfaces by using (21-11). In our next section, we take up the general problem of calculating ϕ.

21-2   Poisson's and Laplace's equations

We can get a differential equation for ϕ by combining (21-3) and (21-8):

$$\text{div grad } \phi = \nabla^2\phi = -\frac{\rho}{\epsilon_0} \qquad (21\text{-}12)$$

This equation is known as Poisson's equation. We already know the solution (21-9).

At points where there is no charge, $\rho = 0$ and ϕ satisfies Laplace's equation:

$$\nabla^2\phi = 0 \qquad (21\text{-}13)$$

As we have already seen, this equation appears in problems other than those of electrostatics.

We see now that the basic problem of electrostatics is that of finding the solution of (21-12) or (21-13) which satisfies the given boundary conditions.

Example. Spherically Symmetric Problem, $\phi = \phi(r)$. Since $\partial\phi/\partial\theta = \partial\phi/\partial\varphi = 0$, (21-13) as now given by (18-22) becomes simply

$$\frac{1}{r^2}\frac{d}{dr}\left(r^2\frac{d\phi}{dr}\right) = 0$$

Therefore

$$r^2\frac{d\phi}{dr} = \text{const.} = -A$$

Then

$$\frac{d\phi}{dr} = -\frac{A}{r^2}$$

so that

$$\phi = \frac{A}{r} + B \qquad (21\text{-}14)$$

where $B = \text{const.}$ This is the complete solution; all that remains is the determination of the constants A and B in terms of the boundary conditions.

Application. Spherical Condenser. Consider the two concentric conducting spheres shown in Fig. 21-4. Let us assume that there is a charge q on the inner sphere, while the outer sphere is kept at a fixed potential ϕ_b. We want to find the potential at all points like P which are in the region between the spheres.

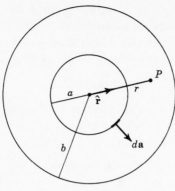

Fig. 21-4

The applicable solution of (21-13) is clearly (21-14). Since ϕ depends only on r, its gradient must be in the radial direction. Thus

$$\text{grad } \phi = \frac{d\phi}{dr}\hat{\mathbf{r}} = -\mathbf{E} = -\frac{A}{r^2}\hat{\mathbf{r}} \tag{21-15}$$

If we now apply (19-8) to the surface of the inner sphere where $r = a$, we find by using (21-15) that

$$\int \mathbf{E} \cdot d\mathbf{a} = \frac{A}{a^2}\int da = \frac{A}{a^2} \cdot 4\pi a^2 = 4\pi A = \frac{q}{\epsilon_0}$$

so that $A = q/4\pi\epsilon_0$, and now

$$\phi = \frac{q}{4\pi\epsilon_0 r} + B \tag{21-16}$$

At $r = b$,

$$\phi = \phi_b = \frac{q}{4\pi\epsilon_0 b} + B$$

Solving this for B, and inserting the result into (21-16), we get as the complete solution to the problem

$$\phi = \frac{q}{4\pi\epsilon_0}\left(\frac{1}{r} - \frac{1}{b}\right) + \phi_b \tag{21-17}$$

We can now use (21-17) to find the potential of the inner sphere, ϕ_a. It is

$$\phi_a = \frac{q}{4\pi\epsilon_0}\left(\frac{1}{a} - \frac{1}{b}\right) + \phi_b \tag{21-18}$$

The capacitance C is defined as the ratio of the magnitude of the (equal) charge of either sphere to the potential difference. From (21-18), we see that the capacitance of this spherical condenser is

$$C = \frac{q}{\phi_a - \phi_b} = \frac{4\pi\epsilon_0 ab}{b - a} \tag{21-19}$$

As $b \to \infty$, $C \to 4\pi\epsilon_0 a$ and this is the formula for the capacitance of an isolated sphere. Since ϵ_0 has the units of farads/meter, we see that capacitance is measured in farads.

Now we want to present a more rigorous derivation of the solution of Poisson's equation given by (21-9). For this we need Green's theorem, (21-21) below.

We previously showed the equivalent of

$$\text{div} \, (\phi \, \text{grad} \, \psi) = \phi \nabla^2 \psi + \text{grad} \, \phi \cdot \text{grad} \, \psi$$

in (18-25) where ϕ and ψ are arbitrary functions. Therefore

$$\int_S \phi \, \text{grad} \, \psi \cdot d\mathbf{a} = \int_V \text{div} \, (\phi \, \text{grad} \, \psi) \, dv$$

$$= \int_V (\phi \nabla^2 \psi + \text{grad} \, \phi \cdot \text{grad} \, \psi) \, dv \tag{21-20}$$

If we interchange ϕ and ψ in (21-20) and subtract the result from (21-20), we find that

$$\int_S (\phi \, \text{grad} \, \psi - \psi \, \text{grad} \, \phi) \cdot d\mathbf{a} = \int_V (\phi \nabla^2 \psi - \psi \nabla^2 \phi) \, dv \tag{21-21}$$

For our application here, we choose $\psi = 1/r$. Since ψ becomes infinite at the origin, which is chosen at the point P in which we are interested, we shall have to exclude this region from the volume of integration. We therefore surround P by a small sphere of radius R (Fig. 21-5) and apply

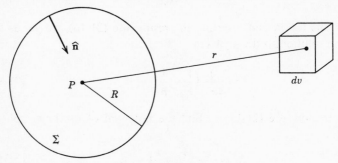

Fig. 21-5

(21-21) to all space *except* this sphere. The outer normal to the bounding surface, n̂, then is directed toward P as shown.

Now $\nabla^2 \psi = \nabla^2(1/r) = 0$; we can prove this directly, or more simply by noting that in (21-14) we have already found this to be a solution of Laplace's equation. We also see that

$$\text{grad } \psi \cdot d\mathbf{a} = \text{grad } \psi \cdot \hat{n} \, da = -\frac{d\psi}{dr} \, da = \frac{da}{r^2} \qquad (21\text{-}22)$$

and

$$\text{grad } \phi \cdot \hat{n} \, da = -\frac{\partial \phi}{\partial r} \, da \qquad (21\text{-}23)$$

Inserting these into (21-21), we find that

$$\int_\Sigma \frac{\phi \, da}{r^2} + \int_\Sigma \left(\frac{\partial \phi}{\partial r}\right)\frac{da}{r} = -\int_V \frac{\nabla^2 \phi \, dv}{r} \qquad (21\text{-}24)$$

where Σ is the surface of the sphere and V includes all space except the sphere.

On the surface of the sphere, $r = R$ and we can write

$$\int_\Sigma \frac{\phi \, da}{r^2} = \frac{1}{R^2}\int_\Sigma \phi \, da = \frac{1}{R^2} \cdot 4\pi R^2 \bar{\phi} = 4\pi \bar{\phi} \qquad (21\text{-}25)$$

where $\bar{\phi}$ is the average value of ϕ on the surface of the sphere. Similarly,

$$\int_\Sigma \left(\frac{\partial \phi}{\partial r}\right)\frac{da}{r} = 4\pi R \overline{\left(\frac{\partial \phi}{\partial r}\right)} \qquad (21\text{-}26)$$

and (21-24) becomes

$$4\pi \bar{\phi} + 4\pi R \overline{\left(\frac{\partial \phi}{\partial r}\right)} = -\int_V \frac{\nabla^2 \phi \, dv}{r} \qquad (21\text{-}27)$$

If we now let the sphere shrink down to the point P, $\bar{\phi}$ approaches the value at the point P; that is, as $R \to 0$, $\bar{\phi} \to \phi_P = \phi$. Also

$$\lim_{R \to 0} 4\pi R \overline{\left(\frac{\partial \phi}{\partial r}\right)} = 0$$

and $V \to$ all space. Therefore, in the limit, (21-17) becomes

$$\phi = -\frac{1}{4\pi} \int_{\text{all space}} \frac{\nabla^2 \phi \, dv}{r} \qquad (21\text{-}28)$$

This result holds for any function ϕ and shows that, if we know the value of $\nabla^2 \phi$ at *all* points in space, we can find the value of ϕ at any point by direct integration.

If we now let ϕ be our potential which satisfies (21-12), we see that here (21-28) becomes exactly (21-9).

21-3   Solution in a bounded region

We have just seen that in principle we can calculate ϕ from a knowledge of the charge density at all points in space. In many problems, however, ρ is known only within a certain finite volume which is surrounded by a surface outside of which we do not know the charge distribution. Nevertheless, we shall now show that, if the potential is known on this bounding surface and the charge density is known within the bounded region, we can still be able to find ϕ.

Going back to Poisson's equation (21-12), we see that we should be able to write the general solution as a sum of a special solution of the inhomogeneous equation (21-12) and the general solution of the homogeneous equation (21-13). Thus the arbitrary boundary conditions can be satisfied with the appropriately chosen general solution of (21-13), while (21-12) will be satisfied because of the inclusion of the particular solution.

We can show this explicitly by again using (21-21). The new situation is illustrated in Fig. 21-6. The surface S' now encloses the volume V throughout which we know ρ, while outside of S' we do not know the charge distribution although we do know the value of ϕ on S'. Again the small sphere around P is temporarily excluded from V. Now on S',

$$\operatorname{grad} \psi = \frac{d\psi}{dr}\hat{\mathbf{r}} = -\frac{\mathbf{r}}{r^3} \qquad (21\text{-}29)$$

and, in (21-21), S consists of Σ plus S'. Proceeding as before, we obtain

$$\int_{\Sigma} \frac{\phi\, da}{r^2} + \int_{\Sigma} \frac{1}{r}\left(\frac{\partial\phi}{\partial r}\right)\, da + \int_{S'}\left(-\frac{\phi\mathbf{r}}{r^3} - \frac{\operatorname{grad}\phi}{r}\right)\cdot d\mathbf{a} = -\int_{V'} \frac{\nabla^2\phi\, dv}{r}$$

$$(21\text{-}30)$$

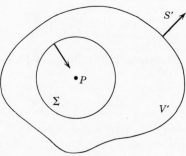

Fig. 21-6

where V' equals V less the volume of the sphere. This will now lead to

$$4\pi\bar{\phi} + 4\pi R\overline{\left(\frac{\partial\phi}{\partial r}\right)} = -\int_{V'} \frac{\nabla^2\phi\, dv}{r} + \int_{S'}\left(\frac{\phi\mathbf{r}}{r^3} + \frac{\text{grad }\phi}{r}\right)\cdot d\mathbf{a} \quad (21\text{-}31)$$

Now, as $R \to 0$, $\phi \to \phi_P = \phi$, $V' \to V$, and $S' \to S$, where S is the total surface surrounding V. If we also use (21-12), (21-31) becomes

$$\phi = \frac{1}{4\pi\epsilon_0}\int_V \frac{\rho\, dv}{r} + \frac{1}{4\pi}\int_S\left(\frac{\phi\mathbf{r}}{r^3} + \frac{\text{grad }\phi}{r}\right)\cdot d\mathbf{a} \quad (21\text{-}32)$$

This result shows that we really are able to calculate the potential within a bounded region provided that we know the charge distribution within the volume as well as ϕ and its gradient on the bounding surface. The surface integral summarizes the effect of the unknown charge distribution *outside* the volume. The volume integral can be considered to be the particular solution of (21-12), while the surface integral is the solution of the homogeneous equation, i.e., Laplace's equation (21-13).

We can obtain our previous result (21-9) from (21-32) by letting V expand to enclose all charges. Once we get far enough away from all the charges involved, they will appear much like a point charge so that, for very large r, $\phi \sim 1/r$ and $|\text{grad }\phi| \sim 1/r^2$. Then, in the surface integral, the integrand $\sim 1/r^3$ while the area $\sim r^2$, so that the whole integral $\sim 1/r$, which approaches zero as $r \to \infty$. Therefore the contribution of the surface integral will vanish and we are left with (21-9).

Although (21-32) enables us in principle to calculate ϕ at any point within V, this is not always a convenient way of solving a given problem. In addition, many problems require us to find the potential within a bounded region when no charge is present in the region. In the latter circumstance, especially, the more appropriate equation to solve is (21-13); because its general solution is needed to solve (21-12), we now want to consider some of the methods of solving (21-13).

21-4   Separation of variables in rectangular coordinates

The equation to be solved is

$$\frac{\partial^2\phi}{\partial x^2} + \frac{\partial^2\phi}{\partial y^2} + \frac{\partial^2\phi}{\partial z^2} = 0 \quad (21\text{-}33)$$

If we assume a solution of the form

$$\phi(x, y, z) = X(x)Y(y)Z(z) \quad (21\text{-}34)$$

then (21-33) becomes

$$YZ \frac{d^2X}{dx^2} + ZX \frac{d^2Y}{dy^2} + XY \frac{d^2Z}{dz^2} = 0$$

and, upon dividing by (21-34), then becomes

$$\frac{1}{X} \frac{d^2X}{dx^2} + \frac{1}{Y} \frac{d^2Y}{dy^2} + \frac{1}{Z} \frac{d^2Z}{dz^2} = 0 \qquad (21\text{-}35)$$

If we use arguments similar to those we have used before (Chapter 17), we see that each of the terms in (21-35) must be equal to a constant. In fact,

$$\frac{1}{X} \frac{d^2X}{dx^2} = \alpha^2, \quad \frac{1}{Y} \frac{d^2Y}{dy^2} = \beta^2, \quad \frac{1}{Z} \frac{d^2Z}{dz^2} = \gamma^2 \qquad (21\text{-}36)$$

where

$$\alpha^2 + \beta^2 + \gamma^2 = 0 \qquad (21\text{-}37)$$

Therefore $d^2X/dx^2 = \alpha^2 X$, so that

$$X(x) = a_1 e^{\alpha x} + a_2 e^{-\alpha x} \qquad (21\text{-}38)$$

Similarly,

$$Y(y) = b_1 e^{\beta y} + b_2 e^{-\beta y}$$

$$Z(z) = c_1 e^{\gamma z} + c_2 e^{-\gamma z} \qquad (21\text{-}39)$$

Because of (21-37), the constants α, β, γ cannot all be real or all imaginary; hence some of the functions X, Y, Z vary sinusoidally with the argument and others vary exponentially.

Since (21-34) is a solution, the most general solution of (21-33) is a sum of products of terms like (21-38) and (21-39); that is,

$$\phi = \sum (a_1 e^{\alpha x} + a_2 e^{-\alpha x})(b_1 e^{\beta y} + b_2 e^{-\beta y})(c_1 e^{\gamma z} + c_2 e^{-\gamma z}) \qquad (21\text{-}40)$$

where the sum is taken over all possible values of α, β, γ which satisfy (21-37). In addition, (21-40) involves all the constants $a_1, a_2, \ldots, c_2$ where there is a different set for each possible α, β, γ. Thus the general solution (21-40) contains an infinite number of arbitrary constants whose values must be determined so that ϕ will satisfy the given boundary conditions.

Example. Semi-infinite Strip. See Fig. 21-7. This is a two-dimensional problem where $\phi = \phi(x, y)$; hence $\gamma = 0$ and (21-37) becomes $\alpha^2 + \beta^2 = 0$. Thus $\alpha = i\beta$, where we shall assume, for definiteness, that $\beta > 0$. Therefore (21-40) becomes

$$\phi = \sum_\beta (A_1 e^{i\beta x} + A_2 e^{-i\beta x})(B_1 e^{\beta y} + B_2 e^{-\beta y}) \qquad (21\text{-}41)$$

where $A_1 = a_1(c_1 + c_2)$, etc.

Let us assume that we are given the four boundary conditions:

at $x = 0$, $\phi(0, y) = 0$ (21-42)

at $x = L$, $\phi(L, y) = 0$ (21-43)

at $y = 0$, $\phi(x, 0) = f(x)$ (21-44)

at $y = \infty$, $\phi(x, \infty) = 0$ (21-45)

where $f(x)$ is some given function, and could be produced by an appropriate distribution of charge outside the strip.

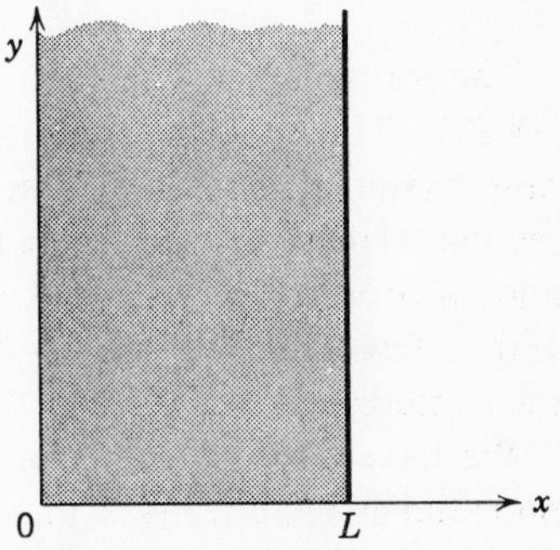

In order to satisfy (21-45), $B_1 = 0$. Let $A_1 B_2 = A_\beta$ and $A_2 B_2 = B_\beta$; at this stage, then, ϕ has the form

$$\phi = \sum_\beta (A_\beta e^{i\beta x} + B_\beta e^{-i\beta x}) e^{-\beta y} \quad (21\text{-}46)$$

Therefore, from (21-42), we find

$$\phi(0, y) = 0 = \sum_\beta (A_\beta + B_\beta) e^{-\beta y} \quad (21\text{-}47)$$

so that $B_\beta = -A_\beta$ and (21-47) becomes

$$\phi = \sum_\beta (2 i A_\beta) \sin (\beta x) e^{-\beta y} \quad (21\text{-}48)$$

With this form, (21-43) yields

Fig. 21-7

$$\phi(L, y) = 0 = \sum_\beta (2 i A_\beta) \sin (\beta L) e^{-\beta y} \quad (21\text{-}49)$$

Then $\beta L = n\pi$ or $\beta = n\pi/L$, where $n = 1, 2, 3, \ldots$ and ϕ now is given by

$$\phi = \sum_n A_n \sin \left(\frac{n\pi x}{L}\right) e^{-n\pi y/L} \quad (21\text{-}50)$$

In order to satisfy the remaining condition (21-44), we must have

$$\phi(x, 0) = f(x) = \sum_n A_n \sin \left(\frac{n\pi x}{L}\right) \quad (21\text{-}51)$$

so that a knowledge of $f(x)$ is sufficient to determine the coefficients A_n. To do this, we use the orthogonality properties of $\sin (n\pi x/L)$:

$$\int_0^L f(x) \sin \left(\frac{m\pi x}{L}\right) dx = \sum_n A_n \int_0^L \sin \left(\frac{m\pi x}{L}\right) \sin \left(\frac{n\pi x}{L}\right) dx$$

$$= \sum_n A_n \cdot \tfrac{1}{2} L \, \delta_{mn} = \tfrac{1}{2} L A_m$$

Then

$$A_m = \frac{2}{L} \int_0^L f(x) \sin \left(\frac{m\pi x}{L}\right) dx \quad (21\text{-}52)$$

Once the coefficients A_m have been determined from (21-52), they can be inserted into (21-50), and we can calculate ϕ at any point of the strip of Fig. 21-7.

Thus we have here an example of determining the constants in the general solution (21-40) by making the general solution reduce to the required values on the boundaries of the region.

21-5   A few solutions in spherical coordinates

The form Laplace's equation takes in spherical coordinates is given by (18-22). The general solution of this equation can also be found by the same systematic method of separation of variables illustrated in the last section. However, the result is much more complicated than is (21-40), and since we do not need it in what follows we shall content ourselves with a few of the simpler solutions in spherical coordinates along with their interpretations.

We have already found and applied one solution—that for which the potential is spherically symmetric and independent of the angles. This is given in (21-14).

The simplest result which does depend on the angle can be shown to be proportional to $\cos \theta$ and independent of φ. Suppose, for example, we consider a constant field along the z axis: $\mathbf{E} = E\hat{\mathbf{k}}$. A potential which describes this is clearly $\phi = -Ez = -Er \cos \theta$. Thus one solution in spherical coordinates can be written $\phi = ar \cos \theta$ where $a = \text{const}$. We now recall the potential of a dipole given by (19-26). This is also proportional to $\cos \theta$, and, since we calculated it directly, we know that it is a solution of Laplace's equation. Thus another solution in spherical coordinates can be written $\phi = (b \cos \theta)/r^2$, where $b = \text{const}$. We saw in Sec. 18-6 that these are the only ones $\sim \cos \theta$, so that the most general solution of Laplace's equation which is $\sim \cos \theta$ can be written as the sum of these, or

$$\phi = \left(ar + \frac{b}{r^2} \right) \cos \theta \qquad (21\text{-}53)$$

There is an interesting application of this result.

Example. Grounded Conducting Sphere in a Previously Uniform Field. See Fig. 21-8. One boundary condition is that at large distances the field is uniform and of magnitude E; that is, as $r \to \infty$, $\phi \to -Ez = -Er \cos \theta$. The other boundary condition is that, at $r = R$, $\phi = \text{const.} = 0$, if the potential of a grounded sphere is taken to be zero.

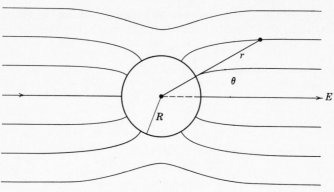

Fig. 21-8

If we let $r \to \infty$, we see from (21-53) that $\phi \to ar \cos \theta$, so that upon comparison with our boundary condition we find that $a = -E$. At $r = R$, (21-53) now gives

$$\phi = 0 = \left(-ER + \frac{b}{R^2}\right) \cos \theta$$

so that $b = ER^3$. Therefore the solution of (21-13) that satisfies the boundary conditions is

$$\phi = \left(-Er + \frac{ER^3}{r^2}\right) \cos \theta \tag{21-54}$$

and from Sec. 18-3 we know that it is the only one.

This result shows that, when a grounded conducting sphere is placed in a uniform field, the resultant potential (21-54) is a superposition of the potential of the uniform field plus the potential of a dipole. By comparison with (19-26), we see that the dipole moment is

$$p = (4\pi\epsilon_0 R^3)E \tag{21-55}$$

Thus the conducting sphere has acquired a dipole moment proportional to the field and has been, in effect, polarized. The ratio of induced moment to applied field is called the polarizability α, and we see from (21-55) that

$$\alpha = \frac{p}{E} = 4\pi\epsilon_0 R^3 = 3\epsilon_0 \text{ (volume)} \tag{21-56}$$

Exercises

21-1. An infinitely long straight conductor of radius a has a charge σ per unit length. Find the potential at a distance r from the axis. [*Hint:* make use of (19-8)].

21-2. A capacitor is made from two large parallel conducting plates, each of area A, which are separated by the small distance d. The potential difference between the plates is $\Delta\phi$. Find the surface charge densities σ and $-\sigma$ on the plates. Show that the capacitance is $C = \epsilon_0 A/d$. Neglect any non-uniformities in the field near the edges of the plates.

21-3. Find the potential ϕ at all points inside a cube of side L. There is no charge within the cube. The potential on the face at $z = 0$ has the constant value ϕ_0, and the potential on all other faces is zero.

21-4. Solve the two-dimensional form of Laplace's equation expressed in plane polar coordinates by separation of variables. Thus show that the general solution can be written as a linear combination of terms like

$$r^n(A_n \cos n\theta + B_n \sin n\theta)$$

where n can be any positive or negative integer.

22 *Electrostatics in matter*

The relevant Maxwell equations are still div $\mathbf{D} = \rho$ and curl $\mathbf{E} = 0$, and we can continue to write $\mathbf{E} = -\text{grad } \phi$. The potential, however, does not necessarily satisfy a simple analog of Poisson's equation (21-12) because now we must use the general relation $\mathbf{D} = \epsilon_0\mathbf{E} + \mathbf{P}$. If we try to find an equation like (21-12) for ϕ by the same method, we obtain the result

$$-\epsilon_0 \nabla^2\phi + \text{div } \mathbf{P} = \rho$$

which can become quite complicated because $\mathbf{P}$ is generally a function of $\mathbf{E}$ and thence of ϕ; that is, $\mathbf{P} = \mathbf{P}(\mathbf{E}) = \mathbf{P}(-\text{grad } \phi)$. Fortunately, it turns out that certain simplifying assumptions can be made which are satisfied quite well by many ordinary materials.

Matter which can be polarized by a field or which can have a permanent polarization is called a *dielectric*.

22-1   Linear dielectrics

In our introduction of the idea of polarizing a dielectric, we considered it as being caused by the field. The simplest assumption which we can make along these lines is that the components of $\mathbf{P}$ are proportional to the first powers of the components of $\mathbf{E}$. The general relation connecting $\mathbf{P}$ and $\mathbf{E}$ would then be written

$$P_x = \epsilon_0(\chi_{xx}E_x + \chi_{xy}E_y + \chi_{xz}E_z)$$
$$P_y = \epsilon_0(\chi_{yx}E_x + \chi_{yy}E_y + \chi_{yz}E_z) \tag{22-1}$$
$$P_z = \epsilon_0(\chi_{zx}E_x + \chi_{zy}E_y + \chi_{zz}E_z)$$

Materials described by (22-1) are called "linear" dielectrics. There are materials, such as some ceramics, which do not obey this law.

We see from (22-1) that, in general, **P** will not be parallel to **E** even in linear dielectrics, and therefore **D** will also not be parallel to **E**. This condition is quite common in crystals, and it accounts for such phenomena as double refraction. The proportionality coefficients χ_{ij} are called the components of the electric susceptibility tensor. In general, the χ_{ij} can vary in magnitude from point to point within the material. Let us now go on to our next simplifying assumption.

22-2 Linear isotropic dielectrics

We now assume, in addition to the linear assumption, that at a given point the electrical properties of the dielectric are independent of the direction of **E**. Such a condition is known as isotropy. Then **P** will necessarily be parallel to **E**, and we can write

$$\mathbf{P} = \chi_e \epsilon_0 \mathbf{E} \tag{22-2}$$

where χ_e = electric susceptibility.

Combining (22-2) with (19-20), we find that

$$\mathbf{D} = (1 + \chi_e)\epsilon_0 \mathbf{E} = \kappa_e \epsilon_0 \mathbf{E} = \epsilon \mathbf{E} \tag{22-3}$$

$$\kappa_e = 1 + \chi_e = \text{dielectric constant} \tag{22-4}$$

$$\epsilon = \kappa_e \epsilon_0 = \text{permittivity} \tag{22-5}$$

We see from (22-3) that **D** is parallel to **E** in this situation.

Using (22-3), we can obtain a differential equation for ϕ: $\operatorname{div} \mathbf{D} = \rho = \operatorname{div}(\epsilon \mathbf{E}) = -\operatorname{div}(\epsilon \operatorname{grad} \phi)$, or

$$\operatorname{div}(\epsilon \operatorname{grad} \phi) = -\rho \tag{22-6}$$

Since we must allow for the possibility that ϵ can vary from point to point within the dielectric, i.e., $\epsilon = \epsilon(x, y, z)$, (22-6) cannot be further simplified. This leads us to our next assumption.

22-3 Linear isotropic homogeneous (l.i.h.) dielectrics

We now assume in addition that the electrical properties are independent of position; such materials are called electrically homogeneous. Generally, gases, liquids, and many solids fall into this category. Thus ϵ is a constant which is characteristic of the material.

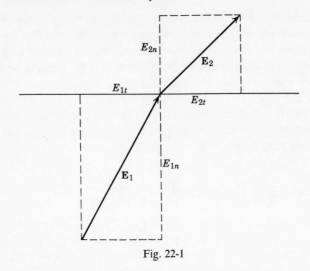

Fig. 22-1

Then (22-6) becomes

$$\text{div grad } \phi = \nabla^2 \phi = - \frac{\rho}{\epsilon} \tag{22-7}$$

which is Poisson's equation with ϵ_0 replaced by ϵ. This means that, for l.i.h. dielectrics, we can take over bodily solutions found for Poisson's equation for the vacuum case and simply replace ϵ_0 by ϵ.

If we use (22-3), the boundary conditions (20-8) and (20-13) can be expressed completely in terms of $\mathbf{E}$; they now are

$$\hat{n} \cdot (\epsilon_2 \mathbf{E}_2 - \epsilon_1 \mathbf{E}_1) = \sigma \tag{22-8}$$

$$\hat{n} \times (\mathbf{E}_2 - \mathbf{E}_1) = 0 \tag{22-9}$$

From (22-8), we see that, even if $\sigma = 0$, the normal components of $\mathbf{E}$ will not be equal in general at the boundary separating the two dielectrics, although the tangential components will be equal. Then, as illustrated in Fig. 22-1, $\mathbf{E}_2$ will not be parallel to $\mathbf{E}_1$ and the direction of $\mathbf{E}$ changes at the boundary. In other words, the lines of force will be *refracted* as they cross the boundary.

An interesting case is that in which the boundary separates a dielectric and a vacuum, and, in addition, $\sigma = 0$, so that there is no free surface charge. If we let region 2 be the vacuum, (20-8) becomes

$$\hat{n} \cdot [\epsilon_0 \mathbf{E}_2 - \mathbf{D}_1] = \hat{n} \cdot [\epsilon_0 \mathbf{E}_2 - (\epsilon_0 \mathbf{E}_1 + \mathbf{P}_1)] = 0$$

or

$$\hat{n} \cdot (\mathbf{E}_2 - \mathbf{E}_1) = \hat{n} \cdot \frac{\mathbf{P}_1}{\epsilon_0} \tag{22-10}$$

We now recall that **E** is determined by *all* charges. Then, by analogy with the case for **D**, (20-8), we see that we can interpret (22-10) as saying that the discontinuity in the normal components of **E** arises from and is equal to a *bound* surface charge density given by $\sigma_P/\epsilon_0 = \hat{n} \cdot (\mathbf{P}/\epsilon_0)$, or

$$\sigma_P = \hat{n} \cdot \mathbf{P} = P_n \qquad (22\text{-}11)$$

Hence we can say that a bound surface charge will appear at the interface between a polarized dielectric and a vacuum, and its magnitude will be equal to the normal component of the polarization.

Example. Field of a Point Charge in a l.i.h. Dielectric

Suppose a point charge is embedded in a l.i.h. dielectric as illustrated in Fig. 22-2. The field of this charge will polarize the dielectric. If the dielectric has a finite size, the bound charges induced on the surfaces will also contribute to the field, and the problem of calculating the field at all points could be extremely complicated. The contribution of the surface charges can be neglected only for an infinite dielectric, and only then can we say that the problem will have spherical symmetry. In this case, then, we can take over our previous result (19-6), replace ϵ_0 by ϵ, and say that the field due to the point charge is given by

$$\mathbf{E} = \frac{q\mathbf{r}}{4\pi\epsilon r^3} \qquad (22\text{-}12)$$

The force between two point charges q and q' will be equal to

$$\mathbf{F} = \frac{qq'\mathbf{r}}{4\pi\epsilon r^3} \qquad (22\text{-}13)$$

This, of course, is Coulomb's inverse square law with ϵ replacing ϵ_0.

This result (22-13) is the basis for a common statement that the presence of a dielectric decreases the force between charges by the factor $\epsilon/\epsilon_0 = \kappa_e$.

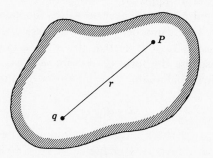

Fig. 22-2

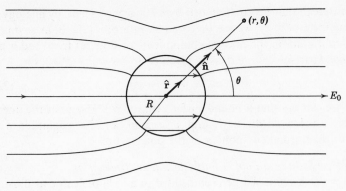

Fig. 22-3

We see now, however, that this is true only for a l.i.h. dielectric of infinite extent, or, as a good approximation, one so large that the polarization charges on the surfaces will not affect the field. In any case, the inverse square law of force between two charges separated by a dielectric does not generally hold; this point is often overlooked in elementary textbooks, and the erroneous impression is given that (22-13) is always correct.

Now we want to turn to an important boundary value problem involving electrostatics and the presence of dielectrics.

Example.   Dielectric Sphere in a Uniform Electric Field.   See Fig. 22-3, which illustrates the directions of the fields. At large distances, the field has constant magnitude E_0 and is in the z direction. Therefore, for the potential outside the sphere, we try the solution (21-53) which reduces to the appropriate form at large r and thus satisfies the boundary condition at infinity:

$$\phi_o = \left(-E_o r + \frac{b}{r^2} \right) \cos \theta \qquad (22\text{-}14)$$

In order to find an appropriate choice for the potential inside the sphere, we recognize that we have to satisfy boundary conditions at the surface of the sphere in order to obtain the result which we know will be unique. It seems reasonable that this will be more easily accomplished if we also use the form (21-53) for ϕ_i. However, we cannot include the term in $1/r^2$ as this diverges at the origin; accordingly we shall use

$$\phi_i = -E_1 r \cos \theta \qquad (22\text{-}15)$$

This also corresponds to a plausible assumption that the field inside the sphere is uniform and of magnitude E_1. We are now left with two constants, b and E_1, which are to be determined by our satisfying the boundary conditions at the surface of the sphere, which is also a surface of discontinuity between a dielectric and a vacuum.

First, we use (22-9), which tells us that the tangential components of **E** are continuous; that is, $E_{o\theta} = E_{i\theta}$. Since **E** = −grad ϕ, this becomes

$$\left(-\frac{1}{r}\frac{\partial \phi_o}{\partial \theta}\right)_{r=R} = \left(-\frac{1}{r}\frac{\partial \phi_i}{\partial \theta}\right)_{r=R} \tag{22-16}$$

Using (22-14) and (22-15), we find that (22-16) leads to

$$-E_o R + \frac{b}{R^2} = -E_1 R \tag{22-17}$$

Second, we use (22-8), which tells us that the normal components of **D** = ϵ**E** are continuous since $\sigma = 0$. From Fig. 22-3, we see that $\hat{\mathbf{n}} = \hat{\mathbf{r}}$, so this becomes $\epsilon_0 E_{or} = \epsilon E_{ir}$, or

$$\left(-\epsilon_0 \frac{\partial \phi_o}{\partial r}\right)_{r=R} = \left(-\epsilon \frac{\partial \phi_i}{\partial r}\right)_{r=R} \tag{22-18}$$

which leads to

$$\epsilon_0 E_o + \frac{2\epsilon_0 b}{R^3} = \epsilon E_1 \tag{22-19}$$

Equations (22-17) and (22-19) can be solved for b and E_1; the results are

$$E_1 = \frac{3\epsilon_0 E_o}{\epsilon + 2\epsilon_0} = \frac{3E_o}{\kappa_e + 2} \tag{22-20}$$

$$b = (E_o - E_1)R^3 = \left(\frac{\kappa_e - 1}{\kappa_e + 2}\right)R^3 E_o \tag{22-21}$$

Since $\kappa_e \geqslant 1$, we see that $E_1 \leqslant E_o$, and the field is less in the sphere than outside of it.

By following the same procedure as in Sec. 21-5, comparing (22-14) and (19-26), and using (22-21), we find that the electric dipole moment of the dielectric sphere is

$$p = 4\pi\epsilon_0 b = \left(\frac{\kappa_e - 1}{\kappa_e + 2}\right)4\pi\epsilon_0 R^3 E_o \tag{22-22}$$

and the (uniform) polarization $P = p/\tfrac{4}{3}\pi R^3$ is

$$P = \left(\frac{\kappa_e - 1}{\kappa_e + 2}\right)3\epsilon_0 E_o \tag{22-23}$$

As a simple check on (22-23), we can calculate P in a more direct way:

$$P = D - \epsilon_0 E_1 = (\epsilon - \epsilon_0)E_1 = (\kappa_e - 1)\epsilon_0 E_1 = \left(\frac{\kappa_e - 1}{\kappa_e + 2}\right)3\epsilon_0 E_o$$

which is the same as above. Thus we see that the external field has uniformly polarized the sphere, giving it a net dipole moment which is parallel to the external field and proportional to it.

Now, by using (22-23), we can rewrite E_1 as given by (22-20) in an interesting and instructive way:

$$E_1 = \frac{3E_o}{\kappa_e + 2} = E_o - \left(\frac{\kappa_e - 1}{\kappa_e + 2}\right)E_o = E_o - \frac{P}{3\epsilon_0} \qquad (22\text{-}24)$$

This shows that the resultant field in the interior equals the sum of the external field and an "internal field" which is proportional to P but

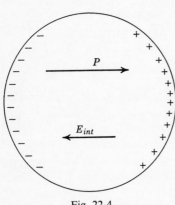

oppositely directed. The source of this internal field is, of course, the bound surface charges appearing on the surface of the sphere, since this is a boundary between a dielectric and a vacuum. These surface charges are given quantitatively by (22-11), and their effect is illustrated qualitatively in Fig. 22-4. When we calculate the field produced by these surface charges, we obtain exactly $-P/3\epsilon_0$ as required by (22-24).

Fig. 22-4

Some special cases of these results are of interest. As $\kappa_e \rightarrow 1$, $\epsilon \rightarrow \epsilon_0$, $E_1 \rightarrow E_o$, and $P \rightarrow 0$. This is what should occur, and it gives us another check on our work. As $\kappa_e \rightarrow \infty$, $\epsilon \rightarrow \infty$, $E_1 \rightarrow 0$, $P \rightarrow 3\epsilon_0 E_o$, and $p \rightarrow 4\pi\epsilon_0 R^3 E_o$. If we compare the last result with (21-55), we see that it is the same as that obtained for a conducting sphere. Thus we see that a conductor acts just like a material of infinite dielectric constant, at least with respect to electrostatic effects.

22-4 Cavity "definitions" of E and D

The two preceding examples have illustrated the important effect that bound charges, arising at the surface between a dielectric and a vacuum, can have in determining the electric field. If we were to consider the problem of calculating the field within a cavity cut out of a dielectric, we would see that it could become quite complicated; the degree of complication would depend on the shape of the cavity. It turns out, however, that for two special shapes the fields inside the cavity are exactly equal to the value of **D** and **E** in the dielectric. Historically, these results were suggested for use in experimental definitions of these vectors, because, as we shall see, they would enable one to determine the vectors in the dielectric by means of measurements made in the cavity.

The first cavity to be considered is shown in Fig. 22-5a. It is a small right cylinder whose height is very small compared to the radius of the base, and which is cut out so that its base is perpendicular to the field in the dielectric. If we consider a point near the center of the cavity, the edges will be too far away to affect the fields, so that D_c (in the cavity) will be parallel to **D** (in the dielectric). Since, by construction, the only components are normal components, which are continuous according to (20-8), we have $\mathbf{D}_c = \mathbf{D}$. Then $\mathbf{E}_c = \mathbf{D}_c/\epsilon_0 = \mathbf{D}/\epsilon_0$. If we now imagine putting a small test charge δq into the cavity, and measuring the force **F** on it, we shall have $\mathbf{F} = \delta q \mathbf{E}_c = \delta q \mathbf{D}/\epsilon_0$, so that $\mathbf{D} = \epsilon_0 \mathbf{F}/\delta q$. Thus we can in principle measure **D** in the dielectric by measuring the force on a small test charge placed within this type of cavity.

Now imagine instead a long needle-shaped cavity cut with its axis parallel to **E** in the dielectric as shown in Fig. 22-5b. Near the center of the cavity, the effects of the ends will be negligible and $\mathbf{E}_c$ (in the cavity) will be parallel to **E** (in the dielectric). Since we have only tangential components by construction, and they are continuous according to (20-13), we have $\mathbf{E}_c = \mathbf{E}$. The measurement of the force on a test charge placed in this cavity will now enable us to write $\mathbf{E} = \mathbf{E}_c = \mathbf{F}/\delta q$. Thus, for this type of cavity, we are able to get a direct determination of **E** in the dielectric.

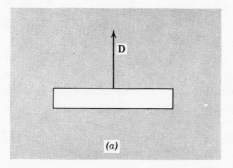

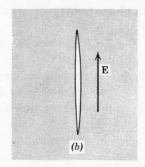

Fig. 22-5

Exercises

22-1. If the fields shown in Fig. 22-1 make the angles θ_1 and θ_2 with the normal to the surface of separation, show that $\kappa_1 \operatorname{ctn} \theta_1 = \kappa_2 \operatorname{ctn} \theta_2$.

22-2. Two large parallel conducting plates are separated by a distance d. The space between is filled with a material of dielectric constant κ_e. If the free surface charge density on one plate is σ, and is $-\sigma$ on the other, find the value of P in the dielectric and the bound charge density on the surface of the dielectric next to the positively charged plate.

22-3. Show that the field produced at the center of the dielectric sphere by the bound surface charges is exactly $-P/3\epsilon_0$ as is shown in (22-24).

22-4. Two point charges q and $-q$ are initially in a vacuum and are separated by a distance a. Then a slab of dielectric of thickness $d < a$ is inserted halfway between them, with the faces of the slab perpendicular to the line connecting the charges. Show qualitatively that the force on q is increased.

22-5. A capacitor is made from two concentric spherical conducting shells of radii a and b. If the region between them has a dielectric constant κ_1 from a to c, and κ_2 from c to b, show that the capacitance is

$$4\pi\epsilon_0\left[\frac{1}{\kappa_1 a} - \frac{1}{\kappa_2 b} + \frac{1}{c}\left(\frac{1}{\kappa_2} - \frac{1}{\kappa_1}\right)\right]^{-1}$$

22-6. Show that, if the free charge density is zero, the bound charge density in a l.i.h. dielectric is always zero.

23 Electrostatic energy

Our objective in this chapter is to calculate the energy required to establish a given configuration of charges. We begin by calculating the work W we would do in moving a charge q_1 from a point a to a point b when q_1 is in the field of another point charge q_2 and therefore experiences a force $\mathbf{F}$ given by (19-3). Using (19-5) and (19-22), we find that

$$W = -\int_a^b \mathbf{F} \cdot d\mathbf{s} = -q_1 \int_a^b \mathbf{E} \cdot d\mathbf{s} = \frac{q_1 q_2}{4\pi\epsilon_0}\left(\frac{1}{r_b} - \frac{1}{r_a}\right) = U_b - U_a \quad (23\text{-}1)$$

where U is the potential energy of the system of two charges, and r_b and r_a are their corresponding separations. Neglecting an additive constant, we can therefore say that the potential energy of the two charges is

$$U_{12} = \frac{q_1 q_2}{4\pi\epsilon_0 r_{12}} \quad (23\text{-}2)$$

where r_{12} is the distance between them.

The total energy U_e of a system of point charges will then be a sum of similar quantities taken over all pairs of charges. We write the energy of a given pair as U_{ij}; if we sum over all values of the indices i and j, we will count all the pairs twice. Therefore, when we find U_e by using (23-2), we must divide by two, so that

$$U_e = \tfrac{1}{2} \sum_{\substack{i,j \\ j \neq i}} U_{ij} = \tfrac{1}{2} \sum_{\substack{i,j \\ j \neq i}} \frac{q_i q_j}{4\pi\epsilon_0 r_{ij}} = \tfrac{1}{2} \sum_i q_i \sum_{j \neq i} \frac{q_j}{4\pi\epsilon_0 r_{ij}}$$

But, according to (19-25), the last sum is ϕ_i, the potential at q_i due to all the other charges, so that the result above can be written

$$U_e = \tfrac{1}{2} \sum_i q_i \phi_i \tag{23-3}$$

If we use our classification of charge into free and bound, we can write (23-3) as a sum of two parts:

$$U_e = U_{e,\text{free}} + U_{e,\text{bound}} = \tfrac{1}{2} \sum_{i(f)} q_{i(f)} \phi_i + \tfrac{1}{2} \sum_{i(b)} q_{i(b)} \phi_i \tag{23-4}$$

where the first sum is over the free charges, and the second over the bound ones. Thus, if we desire, we can divide the energy of the charge distribution into two parts—one associated with the free charge distribution and one associated with the bound charge distribution. We must remember, however, that ϕ_i is the potential at the ith charge resulting from *all* charges.

Let us now consider the energy of the free charges, supposing they are continuously distributed with density ρ. We can then replace the sum over $q_{i(f)}$ by an integral over $\rho \, dv$ so that

$$U_{e,\text{free}} = \tfrac{1}{2} \int_{\text{charges}} \rho \phi \, dv \tag{23-5}$$

This result suggests the point of view in which the energy of the system is regarded as concentrated at the charges. We now proceed to transform this into a form which is more convenient for modern interpretations of the theory.

If we use (19-21), we can write (23-5) as

$$U_{e,\text{free}} = \tfrac{1}{2} \int \phi \operatorname{div} \mathbf{D} \, dv \tag{23-6}$$

Using $\mathbf{E} = -\operatorname{grad} \phi$, we can also write a general theorem of vector analysis in the form

$$\operatorname{div}(\phi \mathbf{D}) = \phi \operatorname{div} \mathbf{D} + \mathbf{D} \cdot \operatorname{grad} \phi = \phi \operatorname{div} \mathbf{D} - \mathbf{D} \cdot \mathbf{E}$$

and (23-6) becomes

$$U_{e,\text{free}} = \tfrac{1}{2}\int \mathbf{D} \cdot \mathbf{E}\, dv + \tfrac{1}{2}\int \text{div}\,(\phi\mathbf{D})\, dv = \tfrac{1}{2}\int \mathbf{D} \cdot \mathbf{E}\, dv + \tfrac{1}{2}\int \phi\mathbf{D} \cdot d\mathbf{a}$$
$$(23\text{-}7)$$

Because we now want these integrals to be evaluated throughout an extremely large volume, the surface integral is taken over the large bounding surface which is a very great distance off. For a finite distribution of charges, when we get a large distance r away,

$$\phi \sim \frac{1}{r}, \quad |\mathbf{D}| \sim \frac{1}{r^2}, \quad \text{Area} \sim r^2$$

so that

$$\int \phi\mathbf{D} \cdot d\mathbf{a} \sim \frac{1}{r} \to 0, \quad \text{as } r \to \infty$$

Then we shall get from (23-7) our final result that

$$U_{e,\text{free}} = \tfrac{1}{2}\int_{\text{all space}} \mathbf{D} \cdot \mathbf{E}\, dv \tag{23-8}$$

The interpretation of (23-8) which is made today, and which is certainly *possible*, is that we can regard the electrostatic energy of the system as being distributed continuously throughout the field, and with an energy per unit volume given by

$$\text{Electrostatic energy density} = u_e = \tfrac{1}{2}\mathbf{D} \cdot \mathbf{E} \tag{23-9}$$

This is a perfectly general result, but, if we are dealing with a case where $\mathbf{D} = \epsilon\mathbf{E}$, (23-9) can also be written

$$u_e = \tfrac{1}{2}\mathbf{D} \cdot \mathbf{E} = \tfrac{1}{2}\epsilon E^2 = \frac{D^2}{2\epsilon} \tag{23-10}$$

Now let us turn to the energy associated with the bound charges, also assuming that they are continuously distributed with density $\rho_P = -\text{div}\,\mathbf{P}$ as given by (19-19). Using the same method of calculation as above, we find that

$$U_{e,\text{bound}} = \tfrac{1}{2}\int \rho_P\phi\, dv = -\tfrac{1}{2}\int \phi\,\text{div}\,\mathbf{P}\, dv = -\tfrac{1}{2}\int_{\text{dielectric}} \mathbf{P} \cdot \mathbf{E}\, dv \tag{23-11}$$

As indicated, we need only evaluate the integral over the dielectric since $\mathbf{P} = 0$ in the absence of polarizable matter. This result can be interpreted in a manner similar to that above: The energy is regarded as being localized in the dielectric, the energy density associated with the polarization being given by

$$-\tfrac{1}{2}\mathbf{P} \cdot \mathbf{E} = -\tfrac{1}{2}\epsilon_0\chi_e E^2 \tag{23-12}$$

The last form follows if (22-2) is also satisfied.

The factor $\frac{1}{2}$ in our expressions above arose because we calculated the total energy of interaction of all the charges which could be grouped by pairs. It is often of interest to consider a somewhat different situation, that of finding the energy of a specific group of charges in the presence of an external field produced by other charges outside of the system of interest. In this case, we do not want to consider the mutual energy of these specific charges, nor that of the external charges. If we review the steps involved in obtaining (23-3), it is clear that the energy expressions involved here will have the forms

$$U'_{e,\text{free}} = \sum_{i(f)} q_{i(f)} \phi_{\text{ext}} = \int \rho \phi_{\text{ext}}\, dv \qquad (23\text{-}13)$$

$$U'_{e,\text{bound}} = \sum_{i(b)} q_{i(b)} \phi_{\text{ext}} = \int \rho_P \phi_{\text{ext}}\, dv = -\int \mathbf{P} \cdot \mathbf{E}_{\text{ext}}\, dv \qquad (23\text{-}14)$$

where ϕ_{ext} and $\mathbf{E}_{\text{ext}}$ are produced by the external charge system.

Example. Energy of a Permanent Dipole in an External Field. If the positive charge q is located at $\mathbf{r} + d\mathbf{r}$, and the negative charge at $\mathbf{r}$, so that the dipole moment is $\mathbf{p} = q\, d\mathbf{r}$, it follows from the first expression in (23-14) and (1-26) that

$$U'_{e,\text{dipole}} = -q\phi_{\text{ext}}(\mathbf{r}) + q\phi_{\text{ext}}(\mathbf{r} + d\mathbf{r})$$
$$= q\, d\mathbf{r} \cdot \text{grad } \phi_{\text{ext}} = -\mathbf{p} \cdot \mathbf{E}_{\text{ext}} \qquad (23\text{-}15)$$

We can also obtain the same result from the last form given in (23-14) if we regard the polarized body as so small in extent that the external field is constant throughout its volume, for then we would also obtain

$$U'_{e,\text{dipole}} = -\int_{\text{dipole}} \mathbf{P} \cdot \mathbf{E}_{\text{ext}}\, dv = -\mathbf{E}_{\text{ext}} \cdot \int_{\text{dipole}} \mathbf{P}\, dv = -\mathbf{p} \cdot \mathbf{E}_{\text{ext}}$$

after using (19-16).

Whenever one speaks of the electrostatic energy of a system, without using any qualifying phrases, one is generally referring to the mutual energy of the free charge distribution. We shall also follow this convention and shall consider the energy density to be that given by (23-9) unless we specifically say otherwise.

Exercises

23-1. Why were we able to extend the range of integration in (23-5) to include all space so as ultimately to get (23-8) without either adding anything to or subtracting from our original expression for $U_{e,\text{free}}$?

23-2. Evaluate (23-8) for the region between the plates of a parallel plate condenser whose difference of potential is $\Delta\phi$, and thus show that the energy can be written $\frac{1}{2}C(\Delta\phi)^2$.

23-3. A conducting sphere of radius R in a vacuum has a charge q uniformly distributed over its surface. Show that the electrostatic energy for this charge distribution is $q^2/8\pi\epsilon_0 R$.

24 Stationary electric fields and currents

Up to this point we have considered only the static case in which all charges are at rest, and, in particular, we found in Sec. 21-1 that it is impossible for an electric field to exist within a conductor in a completely static situation. On the other hand, we are all familiar with the fact that, by applying a difference of potential to a conductor and *by continuously supplying energy to it*, a steady motion of charge can be set up; that is, there is an electric current in the conductor. This motion of the charges implies that there now exist electric fields in the interior of the conductor. The ordinary conservative electric field cannot constantly supply energy to the charges as they circulate throughout a closed circuit; consequently somewhere within the circuit there must be sources of non-conservative electric fields. Perhaps the most familiar of these sources are batteries; they supply energy to the charges through chemical reactions which, although it is not immediately evident, are essentially electromagnetic effects. For simplicity, we shall assume from now on that there are none of these non-conservative electric fields within any of the regions we shall be considering, so that $\mathbf{E}$ can always be written as in (21-8). Such a region would be the interior of a current-carrying wire.

For the time being, we are going to consider only the *stationary* case in which $\mathbf{J} \neq 0$, but $\partial\mathbf{J}/\partial t = 0$ and $\partial\rho/\partial t = 0$. The assumption of constant ρ implies that there is no accumulation of charge in the region. Then, by (19-1),

$$\operatorname{div} \mathbf{J} = 0 \tag{24-1}$$

If we recall that the boundary condition (20-4) was derived from div $\mathbf{B} = 0$, we see that we can at once write a boundary condition for the current density at an interface between two media as

$$\hat{\mathbf{n}} \cdot (\mathbf{J}_2 - \mathbf{J}_1) = 0 \tag{24-2}$$

We can also recall that, from the definition of $\mathbf{J}$, the total current i through an area S is

$$i = \int_S \mathbf{J} \cdot d\mathbf{a} \tag{24-3}$$

The principal experimental law in this field is *Ohm's law*, which holds quite well for metals and solutions of electrolytes but is not a universal relation. It states that

$$i = \frac{|\Delta\phi|}{R} \tag{24-4}$$

where i is the current, $\Delta\phi$ the difference in potential between the points of the conductor in question, and R is a proportionality factor called the resistance. R is measured in ohms and may depend on the temperature, but otherwise it is supposed to be a constant and, in particular, is supposed to be independent of the field. For later use, it is more convenient to put (24-4) in a form involving **J**.

Consider the small cylindrical volume in the conductor shown in Fig. 24-1.

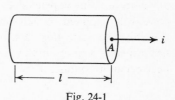

Fig. 24-1

It is found experimentally that R is proportional to the length, and inversely proportional to the cross-sectional area; that is,

$$R = \rho\frac{l}{A} = \frac{l}{\sigma A} \tag{24-5}$$

The proportionality factor ρ is called the resistivity, and σ is the conductivity. (In this context, ρ is *not* the free charge density, nor is σ the free surface charge density; we shall not meet any situations where this standard notation can cause confusion.) Substituting (24-5) into (24-4), using (24-3), (21-8), and (1-26), we find that

$$\frac{i}{A} = \sigma\left(\frac{|\Delta\phi|}{l}\right) = J = \sigma\,|\mathbf{E}| \tag{24-6}$$

where **E** is the electric field in the conductor. If we assume the conductor to be isotropic, **J** will be parallel to **E**, and we can write our differential form of Ohm's law (24-6):

$$\mathbf{J} = \sigma\mathbf{E} \tag{24-7}$$

With the use of (24-7), we can now write (24-2) as

$$\hat{\mathbf{n}} \cdot (\sigma_2\mathbf{E}_2 - \sigma_1\mathbf{E}_1) = 0 \tag{24-8}$$

If we compare (24-8) and (22-8), and note that (22-9) still holds, we see that we have a situation similar to that we had for dielectrics; hence the lines of force are refracted as they cross the boundary.

Also, for a homogeneous conductor, we find that

$$\text{div } \mathbf{J} = 0 = \text{div }(\sigma\,\mathbf{E}) = -\sigma\,\text{div grad }\phi = -\sigma\nabla^2\phi$$

if we combine (24-1), (24-7), and (21-8). Thus the potential for stationary currents satisfies Laplace's equation (21-13). This fact is the basis of an experimental way of solving Laplace's equation by setting up the desired boundary values of ϕ about a conducting region; then if we measure the magnitude and direction of the current, we can determine the electric field throughout the region by the use of (24-7).

The work done *by* the field when a charge q is moved between two points, whose difference of potential is $\Delta\phi$, is given by $W = -q\,\Delta\phi$. For stationary currents, this expended energy appears as heat, and energy must be constantly supplied by external sources to maintain the stationary state. We can also state this relation in differential form. If the work W is performed in a time t in the volume of Fig. 24-1, the rate of production of heat per unit volume, w, is

$$w = \frac{W}{tAl} = -\frac{q\,\Delta\phi}{tAl} = \left(\frac{i}{A}\right)\left(-\frac{\Delta\phi}{l}\right) = JE$$

If we use (24-7), this can also be written

$$w = \mathbf{J} \cdot \mathbf{E} = \sigma E^2 = \frac{\mathbf{J}^2}{\sigma} \tag{24-9}$$

Exercises

24-1. The region between the plates of a parallel plate condenser is filled with a medium of conductivity σ. If the potential difference is kept constant, find the total current between the plates. Show also that the resistance is related to the vacuum value of the capacitance, C_0, as follows: $R = \epsilon_0/\sigma C_0$. (This is actually a very general and useful relation.)

24-2. With the help of (19-1) and (24-7), show that the equation describing the charge density in a conductor is $\partial\rho/\partial t = -\sigma\rho/\epsilon$. Find the time required for a pre-existing charge density within a conductor to decrease to $1/e$ of its initial value. Estimate this time for copper ($\sigma = 6 \times 10^7/\text{ohm-meter}$) and glass (resistivity $= 10^{12}$ ohm-meter). What happens to the charge?

25 *Magnetostatics*

When the fields are constant in time, the two relevant Maxwell equations, (19-38) and (19-72), become

$$\text{div } \mathbf{B} = 0, \quad \text{curl } \mathbf{H} = \mathbf{J} \tag{25-1}$$

If the problem possesses enough symmetry, it can often be solved very simply by using these equations directly. Let us illustrate this for an important practical problem.

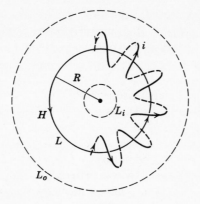

Fig. 25-1

Example.   Field of a Toroidal Solenoid. Suppose we have a current i flowing through a conductor which is wound around a torus of small cross section. In Fig. 25-1 only a few of the turns are shown; the radius of the circle formed by the axis of the torus is R. By symmetry, **H** is directed along the circumference of any circle concentric with the axial circle and must have constant magnitude on this circle.

If we calculate the line integral of **H** around the path labeled L and use (25-1), we find that

$$\oint \mathbf{H} \cdot d\mathbf{s} = H \oint ds = HL = H2\pi R = \int \text{curl } \mathbf{H} \cdot d\mathbf{a} = \int \mathbf{J} \cdot d\mathbf{a} \qquad (25\text{-}2)$$

Now the last integral is the total current passing through the area of integration. For this path L, each of the N turns carries' the current i through the area and the total current is Ni. Thus (25-2) becomes $2\pi R H = Ni$, or

$$H = \frac{Ni}{2\pi R} \qquad (25\text{-}3)$$

If the diameter of the torus is small compared to R, all similar paths through the torus have approximately the same circumference; hence the field given by $HL = Ni$ will be approximately constant over the cross section of the torus.

If we now calculate $\oint \mathbf{H} \cdot d\mathbf{s}$ over the path L_i, we find that $H_i L_i = 0$ since there are no currents enclosed by the path. Therefore $H_i = 0$. Integrating over the path L_o, we also find that $H_o L_o = 0$ and $H_o = 0$, since just as many currents pass through the surface in one direction as in the opposite direction, making a total current of zero. Thus we see that the field of a toroidal solenoid is confined inside the torus.

If there is a vacuum inside the torus, the value of the induction inside is $B = \mu_0 H = \mu_0 Ni/2\pi R$. In a manner similar to that used in Chapter 22, we can define a linear isotropic magnetic material by the equation

$$\mathbf{M} = \chi_m \mathbf{H} \tag{25-4}$$

where χ_m is the magnetic susceptibility. For historical reasons, $\mathbf{M}$ is written as proportional to $\mathbf{H}$, rather than to $\mathbf{B}$ as we would anticipate from our discussion of the origin of the magnetization. We should also note that a material which is linear, isotropic, and homogeneous in its magnetic properties need not be so in its electric properties, and vice versa. The best-known magnetic materials, such as iron, can not be described by (25-4), and they have a much more complicated behavior. The magnetic susceptibility can be negative as well as positive, as we shall see in Chapter 38.

In any event, if (25-4) is satisfied, we have

$$\mathbf{B} = \mu_0(\mathbf{H} + \mathbf{M}) = \mu_0(1 + \chi_m)\mathbf{H} = \kappa_m \mu_0 \mathbf{H} = \mu \mathbf{H} \tag{25-5}$$

$$\kappa_m = 1 + \chi_m = \text{(relative) permeability} \tag{25-6}$$

$$\mu = \text{absolute permeability} \tag{25-7}$$

If the torus is now completely filled with a l.i.h. magnetic material and i is kept constant, we see by (25-3) that H remains constant, while B has the value $\kappa_m \mu_0 H$. The ratio of the two values of B, with and without the material, is κ_m; this result is the basis for one method of measuring the permeability.

25-1   The scalar potential

If $\mathbf{J} = 0$, curl $\mathbf{H} = 0$ and we can write $\mathbf{H} = -\text{grad } \phi_m$. If, in addition, $\mathbf{B} = \mu \mathbf{H}$ and $\mu = \text{const.}$, we also have div $\mathbf{B} = 0 = \mu \text{ div } \mathbf{H} = -\mu \nabla^2 \phi_m$, so that

$$\nabla^2 \phi_m = 0 \tag{25-8}$$

Thus we have found that, in the absence of real currents and in a homogeneous material, $\mathbf{H}$ can be found from a scalar potential which satisfies Laplace's equation. As a result, many magnetostatic problems can be solved by making use of their close analogy to electrostatic problems. The appropriate boundary conditions now are (20-4) and (20-16) with $\mathbf{K} = 0$.

Example.   Field of a Uniformly Magnetized Sphere. The sphere is assumed to have a constant permanent magnetization $\mathbf{M}$, and we want to find the field produced by it. We assume that there is no external field. Using the results obtained for the dielectric sphere in Sec. 22-3, we can write the answer almost immediately.

In the electric problem, there was no free charge, so that div $\mathbf{D} = 0$ and therefore div $(\epsilon_0\mathbf{E}) = -\text{div } \mathbf{P}$. By (22-24), the field *inside* the sphere produced by the polarization is $\epsilon_0\mathbf{E}_i = -\frac{1}{3}\mathbf{P}$. For the magnetic problem, div $\mathbf{B} = 0$, so that div $\mathbf{H} = -\text{div } \mathbf{M}$. Thus we can make the replacement

$$\epsilon_0\mathbf{E} \to \mathbf{H}, \quad \mathbf{P} \to \mathbf{M} \tag{25-9}$$

and the field inside the sphere is

$$\mathbf{H}_i = -\tfrac{1}{3}\mathbf{M} \tag{25-10}$$

Therefore, from (19-59),

$$\mathbf{B}_i = \tfrac{2}{3}\mu_0\mathbf{M} \tag{25-11}$$

We see that $\mathbf{B}$ and $\mathbf{H}$ are oppositely directed in the interior of the magnetized sphere.

In order to find the fields outside the sphere, we can use the fact that the potential will be precisely that arising from the magnetic dipole of moment $m = \frac{4}{3}\pi R^3 M$. If we substitute this into (19-45), we obtain

$$\phi_m = \frac{MR^3 \cos\theta}{3r^2} \tag{25-12}$$

Then the field outside, $\mathbf{H}_o$, can be calculated from (25-12) as $-\text{grad } \phi_m$, and then $\mathbf{B}_o = \mu_0\mathbf{H}_o$.

If we now superimpose a constant external field $\mathbf{H}_c$, we know from (22-14) that we can simply add $\mathbf{H}_c$ and $\mathbf{B}_c = \mu_0\mathbf{H}_c$ to all the fields given above to find the solution to this problem. This assumes that the permanent magnetization is not affected by the extra field.

The directions of the fields produced by this sphere are illustrated in Fig. 25-2, for no external field. We see in the figure that there is a discontinuity in the normal components of $\mathbf{H}$; the reason is that the normal

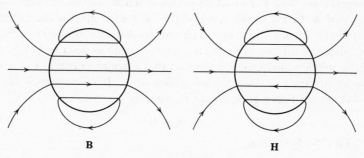

B   H

Fig. 25-2

components of **B** must be continuous and the relation $\mathbf{B} = \mu_0(\mathbf{H} + \mathbf{M})$ must always be satisfied. But the tangential components of **H** are seen to be continuous, as they must be, while those of **B** are not.

The coefficient $\frac{1}{3}$ in (25-10) is called the demagnetizing factor. It can be calculated exactly only for certain special shapes, whereas for other shapes it can be found only approximately. We interpreted the appearance of the same factor for the internal field in the dielectric sphere as resulting from the bound surface charges arising from the discontinuity in **P**. If we recall our discussion about the formal introduction of magnetic charges (poles) in (19-62), we see that we could, if we wanted to, define a surface density of poles by an equation analogous to (22-11) and then ascribe the internal magnetic field (25-10) to these poles. Although this is sometimes done, it is only as a convenient artifice and has no experimental basis.

25-2   Vector potential

Now let us return to the more general case for which $\mathbf{J} \neq 0$; here we must use (25-1). As we know, a scalar potential cannot be easily or satisfactorily introduced. However, we can instead use a *vector potential* **A**. This is based on the vector identity div curl $\mathbf{A} = 0$ and the fact that div $\mathbf{B} = 0$ always. Comparing, we see that we can write

$$\mathbf{B} = \text{curl } \mathbf{A} \qquad (25\text{-}13)$$

Now we have to see how to find **A**.

We shall assume for the present that we are dealing with a situation in which μ in (25-5) is independent of position. Then we have, from (25-1) and (25-13),

$$\mu \text{ curl } \mathbf{H} = \mu\mathbf{J} = \text{curl } \mathbf{B} = \text{curl curl } \mathbf{A} = \text{grad div } \mathbf{A} - \nabla^2\mathbf{A} \quad (25\text{-}14)$$

It can be shown that any vector is completely determined if its curl and divergence are both known at all points in space. All we have defined so far is curl **A**, by the requirement of (25-13) that it give us the correct **B** everywhere. Hence we are free to choose div **A** in any convenient arbitrary way, since this will not affect the physical situation as described by (25-13). This is roughly analogous to the fact that a scalar potential can always have an arbitrary scalar constant added to it. If we now look back at (25-14), we see that a good choice to make is

$$\text{div } \mathbf{A} = 0 \qquad (25\text{-}15)$$

for then (25-14) becomes

$$\nabla^2\mathbf{A} = -\mu\mathbf{J} \qquad (25\text{-}16)$$

In component form, this is $\nabla^2 A_x = -\mu J_x$, etc. Thus we see from (21-12) that each rectangular component of **A** satisfies Poisson's equation. This means that we can use the solution of Poisson's equation (21-12) already given by (21-28) for an infinite region, and, in fact,

$$A_x = \frac{\mu}{4\pi} \int_{\text{all space}} \frac{J_x \, dv}{r} \quad \text{etc.} \tag{25-17}$$

so that

$$\mathbf{A} = \frac{\mu}{4\pi} \int_{\text{all space}} \frac{\mathbf{J} \, dv}{r} \tag{25-18}$$

This result shows us that, if we are given the distribution of currents everywhere, we can find **A** from (25-18), and then we can find the value of **B** everywhere by using (25-13).

As in the electrostatic case, situations may arise in which we know **J** only within a certain bounded region and are ignorant of the current distribution outside this region. We can then proceed in a manner similar to that we discussed at length in Chapter 21, namely, by combining the general solution of Laplace's equation with the special solution of (25-16) so that all the boundary conditions are satisfied and, *in addition*, by making sure that the solution for **A** satisfies the supplementary condition (25-15).

At this stage, it is of interest to see that the solution we obtained for **A** in (25-18) is really equivalent to Ampère's law (19-27) from which we originally started. For simplicity, let us assume a non-magnetic medium where $\mu = \mu_0$ so that (25-18) becomes

$$\mathbf{A} = \frac{\mu_0}{4\pi} \int \frac{\mathbf{J} \, dv}{r} \tag{25-19}$$

We shall deal with the simple situation depicted in Fig. 19-11; as a first step we want to transform the integrand of (25-19). Let the cross-sectional area of the region occupied by the current i be S, and let us consider the small element of length $d\mathbf{s}$. Then $i = JS$, and if we multiply by ds we obtain $i \, ds = J(S \, ds) = J \, dv$, where dv is the volume of this small portion of the flowing charges. Since **J** and $d\mathbf{s}$ are parallel, we can write

$$\mathbf{J} \, dv = i \, d\mathbf{s} \tag{25-20}$$

Inserting this into (25-19), we get

$$\mathbf{A} = \frac{\mu_0 i}{4\pi} \int \frac{d\mathbf{s}}{r} \tag{25-21}$$

Therefore (25-13) yields

$$\mathbf{B} = \frac{\mu_0 i}{4\pi} \operatorname{curl} \int \frac{d\mathbf{s}}{r} \tag{25-22}$$

Since the curl operation involves derivatives with respect to the coordinates x, y, z of the point P of Fig. 19-11 at which we want to find **B**, and since the integration is over the independent set of coordinates x', y', z' of the current element $i\,d\mathbf{s}$, we can interchange the two operations in (25-22). This gives

$$\mathbf{B} = \frac{\mu_0 i}{4\pi} \int \mathrm{curl}\left(\frac{d\mathbf{s}}{r}\right) \tag{25-23}$$

But

$$\mathrm{curl}\left(\frac{d\mathbf{s}}{r}\right) = \frac{\mathrm{curl}\,d\mathbf{s}}{r} + \mathrm{grad}\left(\frac{1}{r}\right) \times d\mathbf{s} = \mathrm{grad}\left(\frac{1}{r}\right) \times d\mathbf{s} \tag{25-24}$$

since $\mathrm{curl}\,d\mathbf{s} = 0$ because $d\mathbf{s}$ is independent of x, y, z. Also

$$\mathrm{grad}\left(\frac{1}{r}\right) = -\frac{\mathrm{grad}\,r}{r^2} \tag{25-25}$$

and

$$\frac{\partial r}{\partial x} = \frac{x - x'}{r} \quad \text{etc.}$$

because $r = [(x - x')^2 + (y - y')^2 + (z - z')^2]^{\frac{1}{2}}$; hence

$$\mathrm{grad}\,r = \frac{\mathbf{r}}{r} \tag{25-26}$$

If we combine (25-24), (25-25), (25-26), and then insert the result into (25-23), we find that

$$\mathbf{B} = \frac{\mu_0 i}{4\pi} \int \left(-\frac{\mathbf{r}}{r^3}\right) \times d\mathbf{s} = \frac{\mu_0 i}{4\pi} \int \frac{d\mathbf{s} \times \mathbf{r}}{r^3}$$

which is exactly (19-31) as obtained originally from Ampère's law.

Exercises

25-1. An infinitely long straight wire of radius a is carrying a constant current i distributed uniformly over the cross section. Show that the directions of **H** form concentric circles perpendicular to the wire and centered at the wire. Show that the magnitude of **H** outside the wire and at a distance r from its axis is $i/2\pi R$. Also, find **H** inside the wire. [How did we obtain (25-3)?]

25-2. An infinitely long cylinder of circular cross section has permeability μ. It is placed in a uniform external magnetic field which is perpendicular to the axis of the cylinder. Find **B** and **H** outside of and inside of the cylinder. Find **M** and then show that the demagnetizing factor is $\frac{1}{2}$.

25-3. An induction is parallel to the z axis and has the constant magnitude B. Find at least two vector potentials which satisfy (25-15) and yield this **B**.

26 *Inductance and magnetic energy*

Our primary aim now is to obtain an expression for the energy in a magnetostatic field; it is much more difficult to find than it was to obtain the one for an electrostatic field. For this reason, we shall have to digress somewhat in order to lay the groundwork for a simplified derivation of our desired result.

26-1 Mutual and self-inductance

We want to apply Faraday's law of induction (19-66) to the following special case. There is a current i_1 in a circuit 1 which produces an induction $\mathbf{B}_1$ everywhere in space. In particular, circuit 1 produces $\mathbf{B}_1$ at all points of another circuit 2. When the current i_1 changes, the value of $\mathbf{B}_1$ also changes. Let us calculate the emf induced in circuit 2 as a result of these changes in 1. Using (19-66), (25-13), (1-40), and (25-21) in succession, we can write

$$\oint \mathbf{E}_2 \cdot d\mathbf{s}_2 = -\frac{\partial}{\partial t} \int \mathbf{B}_1 \cdot d\mathbf{a}_2 = -\frac{\partial}{\partial t} \int \text{curl } \mathbf{A}_1 \cdot d\mathbf{a}_2$$

$$= -\frac{\partial}{\partial t} \oint_2 \mathbf{A}_1 \cdot d\mathbf{s}_2 = -\frac{\partial}{\partial t} \oint_2 \frac{\mu}{4\pi} i_1 \oint_1 \frac{d\mathbf{s}_1 \cdot d\mathbf{s}_2}{r_{12}}$$

$$= -\left[\frac{\mu}{4\pi} \oint_1 \oint_2 \frac{d\mathbf{s}_1 \cdot d\mathbf{s}_2}{r_{12}}\right]\frac{\partial i_1}{\partial t} \tag{26-1}$$

By our use of (25-21), we have now assumed that all space is filled with a material of permeability μ. In other words, we can write (26-1) in the form

$$\text{emf}_2 = \oint \mathbf{E}_2 \cdot d\mathbf{s}_2 = -L_{12}\frac{\partial i_1}{\partial t} \tag{26-2}$$

where

$$L_{12} = \frac{\mu}{4\pi} \oint_1 \oint_2 \frac{d\mathbf{s}_1 \cdot d\mathbf{s}_2}{r_{12}} \tag{26-3}$$

L_{12} is called the mutual inductance between circuits 1 and 2. It is a purely geometrical factor and can be calculated from the configurations of the circuits by means of (26-3). Since both 1 and 2 enter symmetrically in (26-3), we would get exactly the same result for the proportionality factor if we were to calculate the emf induced in 1 by a changing current in 2; that is,

$$L_{21} = L_{12} \tag{26-4}$$

Even if we have only one circuit, the induction produced by currents in it will penetrate the circuit itself. Then a change in the current in the circuit will induce an emf ("back emf") in it, so that we can also write

$$\text{emf}_1 = -L_{11} \frac{\partial i_1}{\partial t} \tag{26-5}$$

L_{11} is called the self-inductance, and from (26-3) it is given by

$$L_{11} = \frac{\mu}{4\pi} \oint \oint \frac{d\mathbf{s}_1 \cdot d\mathbf{s}_1'}{r} \tag{26-6}$$

except that now (26-6) involves a double integration over the same circuit.

As can be imagined, the double integrals in (26-3) and (26-6) are sometimes difficult to evaluate, and then it is often convenient to use another relation involving inductance. Combining (19-66) and (26-2), we obtain

$$\frac{\partial \Phi_{m2}}{\partial t} = L_{12} \frac{\partial i_1}{\partial t} \tag{26-7}$$

If we integrate (26-7) and use the condition that $\Phi_{m2} = 0$ when $i_1 = 0$, we obtain $\Phi_{m2} = L_{12}i_1$, or

$$L_{12} = \frac{\Phi_{m2}}{i_1} \tag{26-8}$$

This result (26-8), which shows that the mutual inductance equals the flux intersecting circuit 2 per unit current in 1, is sometimes easier to use. The same type of relation holds, of course, for the self-inductance L_{11}; that is,

$$L_{11} = \frac{\Phi_{m1}}{i_1} \tag{26-9}$$

We now want to illustrate the use of (26-9).

Example.   Self-Inductance of a Toroidal Solenoid.   By (25-1), we showed that $B = \mu Ni/2\pi R$. We also found that, if the diameter of the cross section is small compared to the radius of the torus, B is approximately constant over the cross section. Therefore, if we use (19-64), we find that the total flux through the N turns, each of cross-sectional area S, is

$$\Phi_m = NBS = \frac{\mu S N^2 i}{2\pi R}$$

Upon comparing this with (26-9), we see that

$$L_{11} = \frac{\mu S N^2}{2\pi R} \tag{26-10}$$

26-2 Magnetostatic energy

We shall use the term magnetostatic energy to refer to the energy of a given distribution of free currents. Let us find the work that has to be done to establish a final current I in a self-inductance L. When the current has the value i, the back emf is $-L(di/dt)$. In a time dt, the charge $i\,dt$ is added to the system; since emf is defined as work done per unit charge, the external source of energy must provide an emf equal to that already existing but of opposite sense. Therefore the work done in the time dt by an external source, and which equals the energy supplied to the self-inductance, is

$$dU_m = L\left(\frac{di}{dt}\right) i\, dt = Li\, di \tag{26-11}$$

Upon integrating (26-11), we find that the total energy necessary to build up the current from 0 to I is

$$U_m = \int_0^I Li\, di = \tfrac{1}{2}LI^2 \tag{26-12}$$

We now put this into a form more suitable for our needs.

Inserting (26-6) into (26-12), using (25-20) and (25-18), we find that

$$U_m = \tfrac{1}{2}I^2 \frac{\mu}{4\pi} \iint \frac{d\mathbf{s}\cdot d\mathbf{s'}}{r} = \tfrac{1}{2}\int I\, d\mathbf{s}\cdot\left\{\frac{\mu}{4\pi}I\int\frac{d\mathbf{s'}}{r}\right\} = \tfrac{1}{2}\int \mathbf{J}\cdot\mathbf{A}\, dv \tag{26-13}$$

This result for the energy of our system of free currents is quite general, in spite of the somewhat special way in which we obtained it. If we compare (26-13) and (23-5), we see that the vector potential plays much the same role in determining the energy of a system of free currents as the scalar potential does for the charges.

We can transform this result so that the energy is expressed in terms of the fields, much as we did to obtain (23-8). If we use (19-36), (25-1), and (25-13), we obtain div $(\mathbf{H} \times \mathbf{A}) = \mathbf{J}\cdot\mathbf{A} - \mathbf{B}\cdot\mathbf{H}$; then (26-13) can be written in the form

$$U_m = \tfrac{1}{2}\int \mathbf{B}\cdot\mathbf{H}\, dv + \tfrac{1}{2}\int \text{div}\,(\mathbf{H} \times \mathbf{A})\, dv$$

$$= \tfrac{1}{2}\int \mathbf{B}\cdot\mathbf{H}\, dv + \tfrac{1}{2}\int (\mathbf{H} \times \mathbf{A})\cdot d\mathbf{a} \tag{26-14}$$

Again we can extend the range of integration to an unbounded region. Then for a finite distribution of currents we see from (25-18) and (25-13) that, as $r \to \infty$, $|\mathbf{A}| \sim 1/r$, $|\mathbf{H}| \sim 1/r^2$, area $\sim r^2$, and

$$\int (\mathbf{H} \times \mathbf{A}) \cdot d\mathbf{a} \sim \frac{1}{r} \to 0$$

Thus the surface integral can be made negligible and (26-14) becomes

$$U_m = \tfrac{1}{2} \int_{\text{all space}} \mathbf{B} \cdot \mathbf{H} \, dv \qquad (26\text{-}15)$$

The interpretation given to (26-15) is similar to that which was used in order to obtain (23-9) from (23-8). The energy is assumed to be distributed continuously throughout space with a density in joules/(meter)^3 given by

$$u_m = \tfrac{1}{2}\mathbf{B} \cdot \mathbf{H} = \tfrac{1}{2}\mu \mathbf{H}^2 = \frac{\mathbf{B}^2}{2\mu} \qquad (26\text{-}16)$$

Exercises

26-1. A small coil of M turns is wound over the toroidal solenoid discussed in the example of Sec. 26-1. Show that the mutual inductance between the two coils is $L_{12} = \mu MNS/2\pi R$.

26-2. Using (26-16), find the magnetic energy produced by a toroidal solenoid carrying a steady current I, and thereby verify directly that it equals $\tfrac{1}{2}LI^2$.

26-3. Show that the work required to establish a current I_1 in a circuit 1 and a current I_2 in a circuit 2 is

$$U_m = \tfrac{1}{2}L_{11}I_1{}^2 + L_{12}I_1I_2 + \tfrac{1}{2}L_{22}I_2{}^2.$$

26-4. If we apply the formula $u_m = \tfrac{1}{2}\mathbf{B} \cdot \mathbf{H}$ to the interior of the uniformly magnetized sphere of Sec. 25-1, we find that u_m is negative because $\mathbf{B}$ and $\mathbf{H}$ are oppositely directed. What is the solution to this apparent difficulty?

27 *Poynting's theorem*

We have seen for *static* fields that the energy of a given linear, isotropic system can be visualized as being spread throughout space with energy densities given by $\tfrac{1}{2}\epsilon \mathbf{E}^2$ and $\tfrac{1}{2}\mu \mathbf{H}^2$. We now want to consider whether these interpretations and relations can continue to be reasonable for the general case in which the fields can vary in time and are interrelated in the manner described by the complete set of Maxwell's equations (19-21), (19-68), (19-38), and (19-72).

We begin by combining (19-36), (19-68), and (19-72). The result is

$$\text{div} (\mathbf{E} \times \mathbf{H}) = -\mathbf{E} \cdot \frac{\partial \mathbf{D}}{\partial t} - \mathbf{H} \cdot \frac{\partial \mathbf{B}}{\partial t} - \mathbf{J} \cdot \mathbf{E} \qquad (27\text{-}1)$$

If, in addition, $\mathbf{D} = \epsilon \mathbf{E}$, then

$$\mathbf{E} \cdot \frac{\partial \mathbf{D}}{\partial t} = \epsilon \mathbf{E} \cdot \frac{\partial \mathbf{E}}{\partial t} = \frac{\partial}{\partial t} (\tfrac{1}{2} \epsilon E^2) \qquad (27\text{-}2)$$

Similarly, if $\mathbf{B} = \mu \mathbf{H}$,

$$\mathbf{H} \cdot \frac{\partial \mathbf{B}}{\partial t} = \frac{\partial}{\partial t} (\tfrac{1}{2} \mu H^2) \qquad (27\text{-}3)$$

With the help of (27-2) and (27-3), we can rewrite (27-1) as

$$-\frac{\partial}{\partial t} (\tfrac{1}{2} \epsilon E^2 + \tfrac{1}{2} \mu H^2) = \mathbf{J} \cdot \mathbf{E} + \text{div} (\mathbf{E} \times \mathbf{H}) \qquad (27\text{-}4)$$

If we integrate (27-4) over a volume V surrounded by the surface S and use

$$\int_V \text{div} (\mathbf{E} \times \mathbf{H}) \, dv = \int_S (\mathbf{E} \times \mathbf{H}) \cdot d\mathbf{a}$$

we obtain

$$-\frac{\partial}{\partial t} \int_V (\tfrac{1}{2} \epsilon E^2 + \tfrac{1}{2} \mu H^2) \, dv = \int_V \mathbf{J} \cdot \mathbf{E} \, dv + \int_S (\mathbf{E} \times \mathbf{H}) \cdot d\mathbf{a} \qquad (27\text{-}5)$$

The last result is called Poynting's theorem.

Recalling our previous discussions of energy as summarized in (23-10), (24-9), and (26-16), we see that we can interpret (27-5) as a statement of conservation of electromagnetic energy: The total decrease of electromagnetic energy in the volume equals the energy dissipated as heat within the volume plus the energy flowing out through the bounding surface. Thus we naturally want to say that the vector $\mathbf{E} \times \mathbf{H}$ is the rate of flow of electromagnetic energy per unit area, or the energy current density.

What we have just stated is, in fact, the accepted interpretation of (27-5), and we define the *Poynting vector* $\mathbf{S}$ by

$$\mathbf{S} = \mathbf{E} \times \mathbf{H} \qquad (27\text{-}6)$$

Since $\mathbf{S}$ is an energy current density, it is measured in joules/(meter)^2-second or watts/(meter)^2. The direction of $\mathbf{S}$ is the direction of energy flow. This whole concept of energy flow, although it was based on the interpretation of the complete integrals in (27-5), is quite plausible, and it will play a very important role in our later discussion of time-dependent solutions of Maxwell's equations.

We can apply these ideas to a simple example involving steady fields in order to show that (27-6) can lead to consistent results. Consider a portion of a long straight cylindrical conductor of length l and radius R as illustrated in Fig. 27-1; the current density $\mathbf{J}$ is constant over the cross section. We want to calculate the value of $\mathbf{S}$ at the surface.

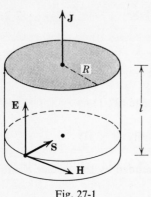

Fig. 27-1

Within the conductor, $\mathbf{J} = \sigma\mathbf{E}$; hence $\mathbf{E} = \mathbf{J}/\sigma$. Since the tangential components are continuous, this is also the value of $\mathbf{E}$ just outside the surface.

Because of the symmetry and (19-31), $\mathbf{H}$ must be tangent to the surface and perpendicular to $\mathbf{J}$ as shown. If we use (19-72), we can easily find $\mathbf{H}$:

$$\oint \mathbf{H} \cdot d\mathbf{s} = 2\pi R H =$$

$$\int \operatorname{curl} \mathbf{H} \cdot d\mathbf{a} = \int \mathbf{J} \cdot d\mathbf{a} = J\pi R^2$$

so that $H = \tfrac{1}{2}JR$.

We see from (27-6) and Fig. 27-1 that $\mathbf{S}$ is normal to the surface and is directed inward, so that there is a steady flow of energy into the volume. Since $\mathbf{E}$ and $\mathbf{H}$ are perpendicular,

$$S = EH = \frac{J^2 R}{2\sigma}$$

Because the vector element of area $d\mathbf{a}$ is directed outward from the surface, and $\mathbf{S}$ is parallel to the ends of the cylinder, the rate at which energy is flowing *into* the volume is given by

$$-\int \mathbf{S} \cdot d\mathbf{a} = S \int da = S(l2\pi R) = \frac{J^2}{\sigma}(\pi R^2 l) = \frac{J^2}{\sigma}\text{(volume)}$$

If we now look at (24-9) again, we see that this result says that the total rate at which energy is flowing into the conductor is exactly equal to the total rate at which energy is being dissipated within the volume. This is, of course, exactly what is required for the steady state situation we have assumed. The ultimate source of this energy is a source, such as a battery, which maintains the potential difference between the ends of the conductor by continuously doing work on the charges as they pass through the complete circuit. Our description here would then picture the energy as being transferred from the source by means of the fields set up throughout space by the charge and current distributions within the source, until the energy flow finally passes through the surface of the conductor to be there transformed into heat.

28 *Plane electromagnetic waves*

In principle, we regard any solution of Maxwell's equations which satisfies any given boundary conditions as a possible electromagnetic field which would be produced by the appropriate distributions of charge and current. In practice, however, one does not go about trying to solve Maxwell's equations indiscriminately, but rather looks for solutions of a desired type, or for those thought to be suitable for the particular situation of interest at the moment. We shall first discuss several examples of the latter procedure, putting off for a while the question of how we would produce these fields if we desired to.

We now assume that the fields can vary with time as well as with position. Let us consider the problem of trying to solve Maxwell's equations in the absence of external charges and currents, and for a uniform material characterized by the constants μ, ϵ, and σ. We shall still have $\mathbf{J} = \sigma\mathbf{E}$, however. Then Maxwell's equations become

$$\operatorname{div} \mathbf{E} = 0 \tag{28-1}$$

$$\operatorname{curl} \mathbf{E} = -\mu \frac{\partial \mathbf{H}}{\partial t} \tag{28-2}$$

$$\operatorname{div} \mathbf{H} = 0 \tag{28-3}$$

$$\operatorname{curl} \mathbf{H} = \sigma\mathbf{E} + \epsilon \frac{\partial \mathbf{E}}{\partial t} \tag{28-4}$$

We can eliminate one of these fields in the following way. If we take the curl of (28-2), use (28-1) and (28-4), we find that

$$\operatorname{curl} \operatorname{curl} \mathbf{E} = \operatorname{grad} \operatorname{div} \mathbf{E} - \nabla^2 \mathbf{E} = -\nabla^2 \mathbf{E} = -\mu \frac{\partial}{\partial t} \operatorname{curl} \mathbf{H}$$

$$= -\mu\sigma \frac{\partial \mathbf{E}}{\partial t} - \mu\epsilon \frac{\partial^2 \mathbf{E}}{\partial t^2}$$

or

$$\nabla^2 \mathbf{E} - \mu\sigma \frac{\partial \mathbf{E}}{\partial t} - \mu\epsilon \frac{\partial^2 \mathbf{E}}{\partial t^2} = 0 \tag{28-5}$$

If we prefer, we can eliminate $\mathbf{E}$ by taking the curl of (28-4) and proceeding similarly. The result is

$$\nabla^2 \mathbf{H} - \mu\sigma \frac{\partial \mathbf{H}}{\partial t} - \mu\epsilon \frac{\partial^2 \mathbf{H}}{\partial t^2} = 0 \tag{28-6}$$

We see that **E** and **H** separately satisfy the same equation. In fact, since (28-5) and (28-6) are vector equations, we really have a total of six equations—one for each component. Because each component satisfies the same equation, if we let $U(x, y, z, t)$ be *any* of the components of **E** or **H**, U satisfies the scalar equation

$$\nabla^2 U - \mu\sigma \frac{\partial U}{\partial t} - \mu\epsilon \frac{\partial^2 U}{\partial t^2} = 0 \qquad (28\text{-}7)$$

28-1   Plane wave in the z direction

Let us look for a solution of (28-7) of the special type $U(z, t)$. In other words, for each value of z, U is constant on the corresponding infinite plane parallel to the xy plane; one such plane is shown in Fig. 28-1. We try a solution of the form

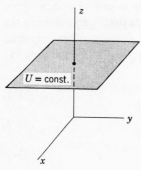

Fig. 28-1

$$U = U_0 e^{i(\gamma z - \omega t)} \qquad (28\text{-}8)$$

where $U_0 = $ const. and γ and a real ω are to be determined so as to satisfy (28-7). Using (28-8), we have

$$\nabla^2 U = \frac{\partial^2 U}{\partial z^2} = -\gamma^2 U,$$

$$\frac{\partial U}{\partial t} = -i\omega U, \quad \frac{\partial^2 U}{\partial t^2} = -\omega^2 U$$

When these are substituted into (28-7), and the common factors are canceled out, we obtain

$$-\gamma^2 + i\omega\mu\sigma + \omega^2\mu\epsilon = 0 \qquad (28\text{-}9)$$

so that

$$\gamma = \pm\omega\left[\mu\left(\epsilon + \frac{i\sigma}{\omega}\right)\right]^{\frac{1}{2}} \qquad (28\text{-}10)$$

Therefore, if ω is given, γ can be found from this equation. We see that in general γ is complex and we can write

$$\gamma = k + i\alpha \qquad (28\text{-}11)$$

where k and α are real.

The graphical procedure of finding the square root of the complex number γ^2 is illustrated in Fig. 28-2. From this figure we see that for the $+$ sign in (28-10), k and α are both positive, while for the $-$ sign k and α are both negative. Thus we can write

$$\gamma = \pm(k + i\alpha) \qquad (28\text{-}12)$$

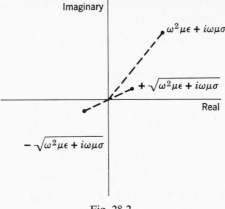

Fig. 28-2

and always take k and α both to be positive. Substituting (28-12) into (28-8), we find that this solution of (28-7) can be written

$$U = U_0 e^{\mp \alpha z} e^{i(\pm kz - \omega t)} \tag{28-13}$$

where we use both upper signs together, or both lower signs together. As usual, we shall have to take the real part of the complex solution (28-13) to be the solution for the component of the real field.

We also see from (28-10) and (28-12) that, if $\sigma = 0$, then $\alpha = 0$, and our solution becomes simply

$$U = U_0 e^{i(\pm kz - \omega t)} \tag{28-14}$$

The form (28-13) represents a "disturbance" which, for a given value of z, varies sinusoidally with a frequency

$$\nu = \frac{\omega}{2\pi} \tag{28-15}$$

If $\alpha = 0$, U also varies sinusoidally with z, the wavelength being given by

$$\lambda = \frac{2\pi}{k} \tag{28-16}$$

Hence the wave velocity is

$$v = \lambda \nu = \frac{\omega}{k} \tag{28-17}$$

If $\alpha \neq 0$, the amplitude decreases as the wave progresses, being lower by the factor $1/e$ after the distance $1/\alpha$.

In summary, then, we have seen that a possible solution of Maxwell's equations is a damped plane wave in a conducting medium, while the plane wave will have constant amplitude in a non-conducting material.

We can find k and α explicitly by squaring (28-10) and (28-12), and then equating real and imaginary parts:

$$\gamma^2 = k^2 - \alpha^2 + 2i\alpha k = \omega^2\mu\epsilon + i\omega\mu\sigma$$

so that

$$k^2 - \alpha^2 = \omega^2\mu\epsilon, \quad 2\alpha k = \omega\mu\sigma$$

and therefore

$$k = \omega\left\{\frac{\mu\epsilon}{2}\left[1 + \sqrt{1 + \left(\frac{\sigma}{\omega\epsilon}\right)^2}\right]\right\}^{\frac{1}{2}} \tag{28-18}$$

$$\alpha = \sigma\sqrt{\frac{\mu}{2\epsilon}}\left[1 + \sqrt{1 + \left(\frac{\sigma}{\omega\epsilon}\right)^2}\right]^{-\frac{1}{2}} \tag{28-19}$$

For a non-conducting medium with $\sigma = 0$, (28-18) becomes $k = \omega\sqrt{\mu\epsilon}$; then from (28-17), (22-5), and (25-5) we find that

$$v = \frac{1}{\sqrt{\mu\epsilon}} = \frac{c}{n} \tag{28-20}$$

where

$$c = \frac{1}{\sqrt{\mu_0\epsilon_0}} \tag{28-21}$$

and

$$\text{Index of refraction} = n = \sqrt{\kappa_e\kappa_m} \tag{28-22}$$

For the special case of free space, $\kappa_e = \kappa_m = 1$, so that $n = 1$ and the velocity of the plane wave is the particular constant c. If we insert the values of ϵ_0 and μ_0 as given after (19-3) and by (19-28), we find that

$$c = 3 \times 10^8 \frac{\text{meters}}{\sqrt{\text{henry-farad}}} = 3 \times 10^8 \frac{\text{meters}}{\text{second}} \tag{28-23}$$

since we know that c must have dimensions of a velocity. It will be left as an exercise to show that $1/\sqrt{\mu_0\epsilon_0}$ actually has the dimensions of length/time.

The speed of plane electromagnetic waves in a vacuum as given by (28-23) is the same as the value found experimentally for the *speed of light* in a vacuum. This result was first obtained by Maxwell and was taken by him, and by others since then, as strong evidence for believing that light waves are actually electromagnetic waves. Since Maxwell's time, much more evidence has been accumulated in support of this idea—so much, in fact, that nowadays it is universally accepted. We shall discuss some of this evidence as we go along.

We have also found that Maxwell's equations relate the index of refraction of a material to its electromagnetic properties as given by (28-22).

This relation turns out to hold quite well for many materials, but water provides us with the standard example to the contrary. If we look up values for water in a table, we find $\kappa_m \simeq 1$, $\kappa_e \simeq 81$, so that $n \simeq 9$. But it is well known that the index of refraction of water for light is very closely given by $\frac{4}{3} = 1.33$. The solution to this apparent difficulty, which we shall take up in detail later, lies in the fact that our macroscopic formulation of electromagnetic theory gives no indication of the values to be expected for κ_e and κ_m but must rely on experiment to obtain them. It turns out that these quantities are not really constant for a given material but usually have a strong dependence on frequency. In the example above, we used the dielectric constant of water for the *static* case, whereas the appropriate one to use is that corresponding to the very high frequency of light waves. The atomic nature of matter is the ultimate reason for this variation with frequency; the atomic charges which are polarized by the fields possess inertia which makes their response to the electromagnetic forces depend on frequency.

28-2 Fields in a general plane wave

Since each of the components of $\mathbf{E}$ and $\mathbf{H}$ have the form (28-8), the fields themselves can be written as

$$\mathbf{E} = \mathbf{E}_0 e^{i(\gamma z - \omega t)}, \quad \mathbf{H} = \mathbf{H}_0 e^{i(\gamma z - \omega t)}$$

where $\mathbf{E}_0$ and $\mathbf{H}_0$ are constant vectors. Although these fields satisfy the independent equations (28-5) and (28-6) which were derived from Maxwell's equations, they do not *necessarily* satisfy (28-1) through (28-4) because these require the fields to be related in a particular way. In other words, $\mathbf{E}_0$ and $\mathbf{H}_0$ are not independent constants. We now want to find their exact relationship. Rather than restricting ourselves to the special plane wave form given above, we shall first consider plane waves from a more general point of view.

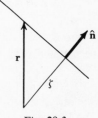

Fig. 28-3

We look now at the case in which all fields are functions only of the time and of the distance ζ of a given plane from the origin; for example, $\mathbf{E} = \mathbf{E}(\zeta, t)$. This is illustrated in Fig. 28-3; the orientation of the plane is given by its normal $\hat{\mathbf{n}}$. Thus the fields have constant values at all points on this plane. We see from the figure that

$$\zeta = \hat{\mathbf{n}} \cdot \mathbf{r} \tag{28-24}$$

where $\mathbf{r}$ is the position vector of any point on the plane.

Since the only spatial change of the vectors occurs in the direction of changing ζ, we can simplify some of our equations. With the use of (28-24), (1-11), and (1-4), the operator ∇ becomes

$$
\nabla = \hat{\imath}\frac{\partial}{\partial x} + \hat{\jmath}\frac{\partial}{\partial y} + \hat{k}\frac{\partial}{\partial z} = \left(\hat{\imath}\frac{\partial \zeta}{\partial x} + \cdots\right)\frac{\partial}{\partial \zeta}
$$

$$
= \left[\hat{\imath}\frac{\partial}{\partial x}(\hat{n}\cdot r) + \cdots\right]\frac{\partial}{\partial \zeta}
$$

$$
= (\hat{\imath}n_x + \hat{\jmath}n_y + \hat{k}n_z)\frac{\partial}{\partial \zeta} = \hat{n}\frac{\partial}{\partial \zeta} \qquad (28\text{-}25)
$$

Therefore, combining (28-25) with (1-29) and (1-30), we can write (28-1) through (28-4) *for plane waves* as

$$
\hat{n}\cdot\frac{\partial E}{\partial \zeta} = 0 \qquad (28\text{-}26)
$$

$$
\hat{n}\times\frac{\partial E}{\partial \zeta} = -\mu\frac{\partial H}{\partial t} \qquad (28\text{-}27)
$$

$$
\hat{n}\cdot\frac{\partial H}{\partial \zeta} = 0 \qquad (28\text{-}28)
$$

$$
\hat{n}\times\frac{\partial H}{\partial \zeta} = \sigma E + \epsilon\frac{\partial E}{\partial t} \qquad (28\text{-}29)
$$

Using (28-29), (1-20), and (1-15), we find that

$$
\hat{n}\cdot\left(\hat{n}\times\frac{\partial H}{\partial \zeta}\right) = 0 = \hat{n}\cdot\left(\sigma + \epsilon\frac{\partial}{\partial t}\right)E = \left(\sigma + \epsilon\frac{\partial}{\partial t}\right)E_n \qquad (28\text{-}30)
$$

where $E_n = \hat{n}\cdot E$ is the longitudinal component of E, i.e., the component perpendicular to the plane of constant ζ. Integrating (28-30), we obtain

$$
E_n = E_{n0}e^{-\sigma t/\epsilon} \qquad (28\text{-}31)
$$

Similarly, (28-26) shows that $\partial E_n/\partial \zeta = 0$; hence E_n is independent of ζ. The last result, together with (28-31), tells us that any longitudinal component of E is constant in space and, if $\sigma = 0$, is also constant in time; whereas, if $\sigma \neq 0$, E_n decays exponentially to zero. In the same way, we find from (28-27) and (28-28) that $\partial H_n/\partial t = 0$ and $\partial H_n/\partial \zeta = 0$, so that H_n is a constant, independent of both ζ and t. Since we are not at present concerned with uniform, static fields, we can conclude that any time-varying solutions of (28-26) through (28-29) must be purely *transverse* fields, i.e., lie entirely in the plane perpendicular to $\hat{n}$. Therefore we can ignore the uniform longitudinal fields and concentrate our attention on the time-dependent transverse fields, which will satisfy the equation

$$\frac{\partial^2 \mathbf{E}}{\partial \zeta^2} - \mu\sigma \frac{\partial \mathbf{E}}{\partial t} - \mu\epsilon \frac{\partial^2 \mathbf{E}}{\partial t^2} = 0 \tag{28-32}$$

which we can obtain by eliminating **H** as we did for (28-5). There will also be another equation which we can get by replacing **E** by **H** in (28-32).

If $\sigma = 0$, we know from the last section that the solution of (28-32) has the form

$$\mathbf{E} = \mathbf{E}_0 e^{i(\pm k\zeta - \omega t)} \tag{28-33}$$

where $\mathbf{E}_0$ is a constant and (28-15), (28-16), (28-17), and (28-20) are still applicable. Using (28-24), we can write $k\zeta = \mathbf{k} \cdot \mathbf{r}$, where the vector **k** is called the propagation vector and is given by

$$\mathbf{k} = k\hat{\mathbf{n}} = \frac{\omega}{v}\hat{\mathbf{n}} = \frac{2\pi}{\lambda}\hat{\mathbf{n}} \tag{28-34}$$

For the upper sign in (28-33), the wave is propagating in the positive ζ direction, which is also the direction of **k**, and (28-33) can be written

$$\mathbf{E} = \mathbf{E}_0 e^{i(\mathbf{k} \cdot \mathbf{r} - \omega t)} \tag{28-35}$$

It is clear that, if the lower sign in (28-33) is used, the solution can also be written as (28-35), by writing **k** as $-k\hat{\mathbf{n}} = k(-\hat{\mathbf{n}})$. But, in this case, the direction of propagation of the wave is the negative ζ direction which is given by $-\hat{\mathbf{n}}$. Therefore we can dispense with the two signs in (28-33) and simply take (28-35) as always representing a plane wave propagating in the direction given by **k**. Then $\hat{\mathbf{n}}$ will be the unit normal to the plane in the direction of propagation; the magnitude of **k** is given by (28-34).

A solution similar to (28-35) can be written for **H**. To see how the fields are related, we turn now to (28-27) which gives

$$\hat{\mathbf{n}} \times \frac{\partial \mathbf{E}}{\partial \zeta} = ik\hat{\mathbf{n}} \times \mathbf{E} = -\mu \frac{\partial \mathbf{H}}{\partial t} = i\omega\mu\mathbf{H}$$

and we find

$$\mathbf{H} = \frac{k}{\omega\mu}\hat{\mathbf{n}} \times \mathbf{E} = \sqrt{\frac{\epsilon}{\mu}}\hat{\mathbf{n}} \times \mathbf{E} \tag{28-36}$$

with the aid of (28-17) and (28-20). Also,

$$\mathbf{B} = \mu\mathbf{H} = \sqrt{\mu\epsilon}\,\hat{\mathbf{n}} \times \mathbf{E} = \frac{\hat{\mathbf{n}} \times \mathbf{E}}{v} \tag{28-37}$$

These results show us that not only are the fields **E** and **H** perpendicular to the direction of propagation, but that they are also *perpendicular to each other*. Thus the vectors **E**, **H** (or **B**),

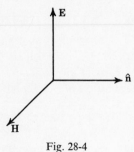

Fig. 28-4

and $\hat{n}$ (or **k**) form a mutually perpendicular set; the exact relation is indicated in Fig. 28-4. We see from the figure that **E** × **H** is in the direction of propagation. But, from (27-6), this is also the direction of the energy flow **S**, so that there is electromagnetic energy being carried along by the wave in the same direction as that in which the wave itself is traveling.

We can easily find the relative magnitudes of the field vectors. From (28-36) and (28-37) we see that

$$\frac{|\mathbf{B}|}{|\mathbf{E}|} = \frac{1}{v}, \quad \frac{|\mathbf{H}|}{|\mathbf{E}|} = \sqrt{\frac{\epsilon}{\mu}} = \frac{1}{Z} \tag{28-38}$$

For a vacuum, these become $1/c$ and $1/Z_0$, respectively, where

$$Z_0 = \sqrt{\frac{\mu_0}{\epsilon_0}} = 376.6 \text{ ohms} \tag{28-39}$$

and is often called the impedance of free space.

28-3   On the use of complex fields

As was amply illustrated above, it is often convenient to obtain solutions in complex form. We must always remember, however, that we must take the *real* part of a complex solution to represent the actual field in question. Since it is often inconvenient to find the real parts, it will be desirable to rewrite some of our previous results so that our complex solutions can be substituted in them directly. However, we shall do this only for fields which have a sinusoidal time dependence, that is, are proportional to $e^{-i\omega t}$.

Let $\mathbf{E}_c$ and $\mathbf{H}_c$ designate our solutions obtained in complex form. Then the physically real fields are

$$\mathbf{E} = \text{Re}\,(\mathbf{E}_c) = \text{Re}\,(\mathbf{E}_0 e^{-i\omega t}) \tag{28-40}$$

$$\mathbf{H} = \text{Re}\,(\mathbf{H}_c) = \text{Re}\,(\mathbf{H}_0 e^{-i\omega t}) \tag{28-41}$$

where $\mathbf{E}_0$ and $\mathbf{H}_0$ are functions only of x, y, and z. If we now write them in terms of their real and imaginary parts, so that

$$\mathbf{E}_0 = \mathbf{E}_r + i\mathbf{E}_i, \quad \mathbf{H}_0 = \mathbf{H}_r + i\mathbf{H}_i$$

where $\mathbf{E}_r$, $\mathbf{E}_i$, $\mathbf{H}_r$, and $\mathbf{H}_i$ are all *real*, then (28-40) and (28-41) become

$$\mathbf{E} = \text{Re}\,[(\mathbf{E}_r + i\mathbf{E}_i)(\cos \omega t - i \sin \omega t)] = \mathbf{E}_r \cos \omega t + \mathbf{E}_i \sin \omega t \quad (28\text{-}42)$$

and

$$\mathbf{H} = \mathbf{H}_r \cos \omega t + \mathbf{H}_i \sin \omega t \qquad (28\text{-}43)$$

Substituting (28-42) and (28-43) into (27-6), we find that the Poynting vector is given by

$$\mathbf{S} = \mathbf{E} \times \mathbf{H} = (\mathbf{E}_r \times \mathbf{H}_r) \cos^2 \omega t + (\mathbf{E}_i \times \mathbf{H}_i) \sin^2 \omega t$$
$$+ \,[(\mathbf{E}_r \times \mathbf{H}_i) + (\mathbf{E}_i \times \mathbf{H}_r)] \sin \omega t \cos \omega t \quad (28\text{-}44)$$

In many problems, we are not particularly interested in the instantaneous value of the energy flow, often because it fluctuates too rapidly to be followed by the measuring instruments. The *time average* of the energy flow is generally of much more significance. We see from (28-44) that the time average of the Poynting vector is

$$\bar{\mathbf{S}} = \overline{\mathbf{E} \times \mathbf{H}} = \tfrac{1}{2}[(\mathbf{E}_r \times \mathbf{H}_r) + (\mathbf{E}_i \times \mathbf{H}_i)] \qquad (28\text{-}45)$$

since $\overline{\cos^2 \omega t} = \overline{\sin^2 \omega t} = \tfrac{1}{2}$ and $\overline{\sin \omega t \cos \omega t} = 0$. This fundamental result can be rewritten in a more convenient form.

Let $\mathbf{H}_c{}^* = $ complex conjugate of $\mathbf{H}_c = \mathbf{H}_c$ with i replaced by $-i =$ $\mathbf{H}_0{}^* e^{i\omega t} = (\mathbf{H}_r - i\mathbf{H}_i)e^{i\omega t}$. Now we consider

$$\mathbf{E}_c \times \mathbf{H}_c{}^* = [(\mathbf{E}_r + i\mathbf{E}_i)e^{-i\omega t}] \times [(\mathbf{H}_r - i\mathbf{H}_i)e^{i\omega t}]$$
$$= [(\mathbf{E}_r \times \mathbf{H}_r) + (\mathbf{E}_i \times \mathbf{H}_i)] + i[(\mathbf{E}_i \times \mathbf{H}_r) - (\mathbf{E}_r \times \mathbf{H}_i)] \quad (28\text{-}46)$$

Comparing (28-45) and (28-46), we see that

$$\bar{\mathbf{S}} = \tfrac{1}{2}\,\text{Re}\,(\mathbf{E}_c \times \mathbf{H}_c{}^*) \qquad (28\text{-}47)$$

Thus we see that we have succeeded in expressing the average value of the Poynting vector entirely in terms of the two complex solutions of Maxwell's equations, so that we can calculate this important quantity directly without the necessity of first finding the real parts.

We can also carry through the same type of calculation for the average energy densities. The results are

$$\bar{u}_e = \overline{\tfrac{1}{2}\epsilon \mathbf{E}^2} = \tfrac{1}{4}\epsilon \mathbf{E}_c \cdot \mathbf{E}_c{}^* \qquad (28\text{-}48)$$

$$\bar{u}_m = \overline{\tfrac{1}{2}\mu \mathbf{H}^2} = \tfrac{1}{4}\mu \mathbf{H}_c \cdot \mathbf{H}_c{}^* \qquad (28\text{-}49)$$

Now that we have obtained these important results, we no longer need to distinguish between real and complex fields. Therefore, in what follows, although we shall continually be dealing with complex solutions of Maxwell's equations, we will not write them as $\mathbf{E}_c$ and $\mathbf{H}_c$ but simply as $\mathbf{E}$ and $\mathbf{H}$. Whenever we need the real parts for specific purposes, we shall point this out explicitly.

28-4   Energy flow in a plane wave

We first consider the case $\sigma = 0$. Substituting (28-36) into (28-47), using (1-21) and the fact that $\hat{\mathbf{n}} \cdot \mathbf{E} = 0$ for the transverse wave, we obtain

$$\bar{\mathbf{S}} = \tfrac{1}{2}\sqrt{\frac{\epsilon}{\mu}}\,\mathrm{Re}\,[\mathbf{E} \times (\hat{\mathbf{n}} \times \mathbf{E}^*)] = \tfrac{1}{2}\sqrt{\frac{\epsilon}{\mu}}\,(\mathbf{E} \cdot \mathbf{E}^*)\hat{\mathbf{n}} \qquad (28\text{-}50)$$

since $\mathbf{E} \cdot \mathbf{E}^*$ is real. If we now use (28-35) and (28-36), (28-50) can be written

$$\bar{\mathbf{S}} = \tfrac{1}{2}\sqrt{\frac{\epsilon}{\mu}}\,|E_0|^2\,\hat{\mathbf{n}} = \tfrac{1}{2}\sqrt{\frac{\mu}{\epsilon}}\,|H_0|^2\,\hat{\mathbf{n}} \qquad (28\text{-}51)$$

We see from (28-51) that not only is the energy flow in the direction of propagation $\hat{\mathbf{n}}$, but also that it is proportional to the square of the amplitude of either $\mathbf{E}$ or $\mathbf{H}$.

Substituting (28-35) and (28-36) into (28-48) and (28-49), we also find that

$$\bar{u}_e = \tfrac{1}{4}\epsilon\mathbf{E} \cdot \mathbf{E}^* = \tfrac{1}{4}|E_0|^2 = \tfrac{1}{4}\mu\,|H_0|^2 = \bar{u}_m \qquad (28\text{-}52)$$

so that the average electric and magnetic energy densities are equal. The total average energy density then becomes

$$\bar{u} = \bar{u}_e + \bar{u}_m = \tfrac{1}{2}\epsilon\,|E_0|^2 = \tfrac{1}{2}\mu\,|H_0|^2 \qquad (28\text{-}53)$$

which enables us to write (28-51) as

$$\bar{\mathbf{S}} = \frac{\bar{u}}{\sqrt{\mu\epsilon}}\,\hat{\mathbf{n}} = \bar{u}v\hat{\mathbf{n}} = \bar{u}\mathbf{v} \qquad (28\text{-}54)$$

with the help of (28-20). Thus we see that (28-54) states the reasonable result that the average energy current equals the average energy density times the velocity of the wave.

In a conducting medium in which $\sigma \neq 0$, the amplitudes are not constant and, according to (28-13), both $\mathbf{E}$ and $\mathbf{H}$ will be proportional to $e^{-\alpha\zeta}$. Then, from (28-51) and (28-53), we see that both the average energy flow and the average energy density will also decrease exponentially with distance; that is,

$$\bar{\mathbf{S}} \sim e^{-2\alpha\zeta}, \quad \bar{u} \sim e^{-2\alpha\zeta} \qquad (28\text{-}55)$$

In a conducting medium, therefore, the intensity of the wave (energy flow) and the energy density are damped or attenuated as the wave progresses. This energy is lost because of the resistive heating of the medium as described by (24-9).

Exercises

28-1. Starting from Coulomb's law and Ampère's law, show that $(\mu_0\epsilon_0)^{-1/2}$ has the dimensions of a velocity. Similarly, show directly that Z_0 is measured in units of ohms.

28-2. Verify (28-48) and (28-49).

28-3. A certain plane wave has a propagation vector $\mathbf{k} = 314\hat{\mathbf{i}} + 314\hat{\mathbf{j}} + 444\hat{\mathbf{k}}$ (meter)$^{-1}$. Find the direction cosines of $\hat{\mathbf{n}}$, the wavelength, and frequency of this wave if it is traveling in a vacuum.

28-4. The solar constant, which is the average rate of incidence of radiation at the surface of the earth from the sun, is 9.2 joules/minute-(centimeter)^2. Assuming that the radiation is a plane wave, find the amplitudes of the electric and magnetic fields.

29 Reflection and refraction of plane waves

We now need to consider what happens when plane electromagnetic waves which are traveling in one medium are incident upon an infinite plane surface separating this medium from another with different electromagnetic properties. The wave will in general be able to pass into the second medium, and we want to see what will occur. Our considerations will be based on the boundary conditions at a surface of discontinuity; we derived them from Maxwell's equations and they are given by (20-4), (20-8), (20-13), and (20-16). If there are no free charges or currents on the surface, they simply say that

normal components of $\mathbf{D}$ and $\mathbf{B}$ are continuous,

tangential components of $\mathbf{E}$ and $\mathbf{H}$ are continuous (29-1)

We can take advantage of the experience of others and begin at once with the knowledge that these conditions can be satisfied only by assuming the existence of three waves: the incident wave, a transmitted wave, and a reflected wave.

29-1 Laws of reflection and refraction

Let us take the surface of separation to be the xy plane ($z = 0$). The semi-infinite medium below this plane has the properties described by ϵ, μ, σ, and those for the medium above are ϵ', μ', σ'. We shall also assume

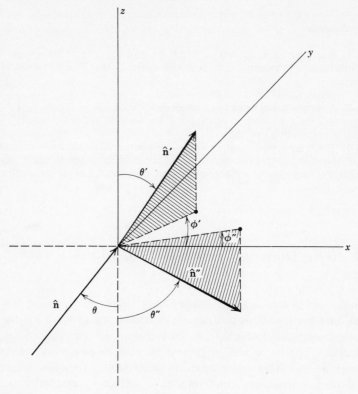

Fig. 29-1

for simplicity that the incident wave is traveling in the medium below the xy plane, and that its direction of propagation lies in the xz plane and is given by $\hat{\mathbf{n}}$. We found in (28-35) that the equation of this plane wave can be written, with the help of (28-34), as

$$U = U_0 e^{i(\mathbf{k} \cdot \mathbf{r} - \omega t)} = U_0 e^{i\omega[(\hat{\mathbf{n}} \cdot \mathbf{r})/v - t]} \tag{29-2}$$

Similar equations can be written for the transmitted wave with direction $\hat{\mathbf{n}}'$, and for the reflected wave with direction $\hat{\mathbf{n}}''$. We need not make any assumptions about the directions $\hat{\mathbf{n}}'$ and $\hat{\mathbf{n}}''$. These propagation directions are all shown in Fig. 29-1.

From the figure, we can write these unit vectors in terms of the angles shown; in rectangular coordinates, they are

$$\hat{\mathbf{n}} = \sin \theta \hat{\mathbf{i}} + \cos \theta \hat{\mathbf{k}} \tag{29-3}$$

$$\hat{\mathbf{n}}' = \sin \theta' \cos \phi' \hat{\mathbf{i}} + \sin \theta' \sin \phi' \hat{\mathbf{j}} + \cos \theta' \hat{\mathbf{k}} \tag{29-4}$$

$$\hat{\mathbf{n}}'' = \sin \theta'' \cos \phi'' \hat{\mathbf{i}} + \sin \theta'' \sin \phi'' \hat{\mathbf{j}} - \cos \theta'' \hat{\mathbf{k}} \tag{29-5}$$

Initially, we cannot say anything definite about the frequencies or relative phases of the waves. If we write the expressions for the electric fields of each of the waves, using the form (29-2) for each component, we get, after substitution of (29-3), (29-4), and (29-5):

$$\mathbf{E} = \mathbf{E}_0 e^{i\omega[(x\sin\theta + z\cos\theta)/v - t]} \tag{29-6}$$

$$\mathbf{E}' = \mathbf{E}_0{}' e^{i\omega'[(x\sin\theta'\cos\phi' + y\sin\theta'\sin\phi' + z\cos\theta')/v' - t]} \tag{29-7}$$

$$\mathbf{E}'' = \mathbf{E}_0{}'' e^{i\omega''[(x\sin\theta''\cos\phi'' + y\sin\theta''\sin\phi'' - z\cos\theta'')/v - t]} \tag{29-8}$$

Since the tangential components of $\mathbf{E}$ are continuous at the surface, we must have

$$E_x + E_x{}'' = E_x{}', \quad E_y + E_y{}'' = E_y{}' \quad \text{(at } z = 0) \tag{29-9}$$

It is clear that these can be correct for *all* t and for *all* values of x and y, only if the exponents of e in (29-6) to (29-8) are all equal; if they are not, we might be able to satisfy (29-9) at some point at a given t, but then (29-9) would not generally be true at other times and places.

We see first of all that this requires that

$$\omega = \omega' = \omega'' \tag{29-10}$$

In other words, no change of frequency is produced by reflection or refraction at this stationary boundary; this is certainly a very reasonable result.

The terms in y which occur in (29-7) and (29-8) would generally prevent us from satisfying (29-9) everywhere since there is no y term in the exponent in (29-6). Therefore these y terms cannot actually be present; hence we must have

$$\phi' = \phi'' = 0 \tag{29-11}$$

This means that the directions of propagation of the three waves *all lie in the same plane.*

We now see from (29-6) and (29-8) that

$$\theta'' = \theta \tag{29-12}$$

This is the well-known optical *law of reflection:* The angle of reflection equals the angle of incidence.

Finally, by equating the remaining terms in (29-6) and (29-7), we obtain $\sin\theta'/v' = \sin\theta/v$, or

$$\frac{\sin\theta'}{\sin\theta} = \frac{v'}{v} = \frac{n}{n'} \tag{29-13}$$

with the use of (28-20). This is most easily remembered in the form

$$n\sin\theta = n'\sin\theta' \tag{29-14}$$

It is the *law of refraction* discovered experimentally by Snell. It relates the angles of incidence and refraction to the indices of refraction of the two media.

Thus we see that these well-known laws of optics are direct consequences of the boundary conditions which must be satisfied by the electromagnetic field vectors, and which were themselves derived from Maxwell's equations.

Now that we have obtained these very simple relations connecting the directions of the waves, we want to find the ratios of the amplitudes of the fields, because they will tell us how the incident energy is divided between the reflected and refracted waves. Before we do this for arbitrary angles of incidence, let us consider a simple case first, as this will clearly illustrate the method we shall use.

29-2   Reflection at normal incidence

Since $\theta = 0$, $\theta' = 0$. Because the direction of propagation is the z axis, the transverse fields $\mathbf{E}$ and $\mathbf{H}$ lie in the xy plane. Thus there will be no normal components of $\mathbf{D}$ and $\mathbf{B}$ to be considered. Let us choose our axes so that $\mathbf{E}$ is along the x axis; then $\mathbf{H}$ must be along the y axis. These relations are shown in Fig. 29-2.

Let us assume real amplitudes for simplicity; then from (28-38) we obtain

$$\frac{|\mathbf{E}|}{|\mathbf{H}|} = \frac{E_x}{H_y} = \sqrt{\frac{\mu}{\epsilon}} = Z, \quad \frac{E_x{}'}{H_y{}'} = \sqrt{\frac{\mu'}{\epsilon'}} = Z' \qquad (29\text{-}15)$$

Since the reflected wave is traveling in the $-\hat{\mathbf{n}}$ direction of Fig. 29-2,

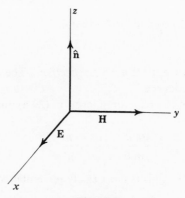

Fig. 29-2

either $\mathbf{E}''$ or $\mathbf{H}''$ must be reversed from the directions shown. In any event, we can write

$$\frac{E_x{}''}{H_y{}''} = -\sqrt{\frac{\mu}{\epsilon}} = -Z \tag{29-16}$$

where Z is called the impedance of the medium.

The boundary conditions (29-1) are simply

$$E_x + E_x{}'' = E_x{}' \tag{29-17}$$

$$H_y + H_y{}'' = H_y{}' \tag{29-18}$$

With the use of (29-15) and (29-16), (29-18) becomes

$$\frac{E_x - E_x{}''}{Z} = \frac{E_x{}'}{Z'} \tag{29-19}$$

We can now find the ratio of the reflected and incident amplitudes by eliminating $E_x{}'$ between (29-17) and (29-19). The result is

$$\frac{E_x{}''}{E_x} = \frac{Z' - Z}{Z' + Z} = \frac{\sqrt{\epsilon/\mu} - \sqrt{\epsilon'/\mu'}}{\sqrt{\epsilon/\mu} + \sqrt{\epsilon'/\mu'}} \tag{29-20}$$

Since one of the H's is reversed in sign, we also get

$$\frac{H_y{}''}{H_y} = -\frac{E_x{}''}{E_x} = -\frac{Z' - Z}{Z' + Z} \tag{29-21}$$

The power flow is given by the Poynting vector (27-6), and, by Fig. 29-2 and (29-16), $|S| = E_x H_y$ and $|S''| = -E_x{}'' H_y{}''$. We can define a reflection coefficient for power, R, as the ratio of the magnitude of the reflected power to the magnitude of the incident power. Then, by using (29-20) and (29-21), we have

$$R = \left| \frac{S''}{S} \right| = -\left(\frac{E_x{}''}{E_x} \right) \left(\frac{H_y{}''}{H_y} \right) = \left(\frac{Z' - Z}{Z' + Z} \right)^2 = \left[\frac{\sqrt{\epsilon/\mu} - \sqrt{\epsilon'/\mu'}}{\sqrt{\epsilon/\mu} + \sqrt{\epsilon'/\mu'}} \right]^2 \tag{29-22}$$

In many common situations, the two media are non-magnetic and $\mu = \mu' = \mu_0$. Then, by (25-5), $\kappa_m = \kappa_m{}' = 1$ and, by (28-22),

$$n = \sqrt{\kappa_e} \tag{29-23}$$

so that, with the use of (22-5), we can write (29-22) as

$$R = \left(\frac{n - n'}{n + n'} \right)^2 \tag{29-24}$$

We see at once that $R < 1$ and that not all the incident power is reflected.

We also see from our results that, if the wave had been incident in the other direction, n and n' would simply be interchanged, but R would have the same value.

Now let us calculate the ratio of the transmitted amplitudes. We find from (29-17), (29-19), and (29-15) that

$$\frac{E_x'}{E_x} = \frac{2Z'}{Z' + Z} \quad \text{and} \quad \frac{H_y'}{H_y} = \frac{2Z}{Z' + Z} \tag{29-25}$$

If we define a transmission coefficient for power, T, as the ratio of the transmitted power to the incident power, we obtain

$$T = \frac{E_x' H_y'}{E_x H_y} = \frac{4Z'Z}{(Z' + Z)^2} \tag{29-26}$$

We can easily show from (29-22) and (29-26) that

$$R + T = 1 \tag{29-27}$$

This equation says that the sum of the reflected and transmitted power is exactly equal to the incident power. Thus (29-27) is an expression of the fact that the energy is conserved.

Now let us return for another look at the reflected wave. For the common case (29-23), we find that (29-20) becomes

$$\frac{E_x''}{E_x} = \frac{n - n'}{n + n'} \tag{29-28}$$

Therefore, if $n > n'$, the ratio E_x''/E_x is positive, and, if $n < n'$, it is negative. The latter result simply means that, if a wave is normally incident upon a medium of higher index of refraction, the phase of the electric field is reversed; that is, the reflected electric field oscillates oppositely to the incident one. In other words, there is a phase difference of π between them. On the other hand, if the reflection is against a surface of lower index, the phase is not reversed and the phase difference is zero. This result is the basis for the reversal of phase which is introduced in elementary discussions of optical interference where this phase change is equivalent to an additional optical path difference of half a wavelength.

We also see from (29-28) that, if $n' = n$, then $E_x'' = 0$ and that there is no reflected wave. This is just what one should expect since then there is no real surface of discontinuity.

29-3 Fresnel's equations

When we come to consider incidence at an arbitrary value of θ, we see from Fig. 29-3 that we can divide the problem into two parts by resolving

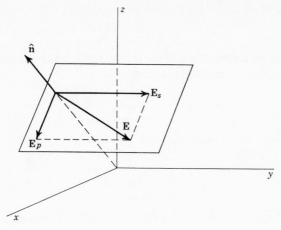

Fig. 29-3

$\mathbf{E}$ into two components. One component, $\mathbf{E}_s$, is perpendicular to the plane of incidence, while the other, $\mathbf{E}_p$, is parallel to the plane of incidence (xz plane). After we have found how each of these components is affected at the surface of separation, we can recombine them to find the behavior of $\mathbf{E}$ itself.

E *perpendicular to the plane of incidence*

The direction of $\mathbf{E}$ is therefore parallel to the y axis. This situation is illustrated in Fig. 29-4 where the y axis is directed into the paper; it will be convenient to choose our directions of $\mathbf{E}$ as indicated by "in" or "out." (If we have made a wrong guess about the positive sense of any electric field, our results will give us the correct sign.) The directions of $\mathbf{H}$ shown are then found from the condition that $\mathbf{E} \times \mathbf{H}$ be in the direction of propagation.

The electric field has only y components, which are tangential components and equal to the magnitudes. We must have $E_y + E_y'' = E_y'$, by (29-1), or

$$E - E'' = E' \tag{29-29}$$

The tangential components of the magnetic fields are

$$H_x = -H \cos \theta = -\frac{E}{Z} \cos \theta \tag{29-30}$$

$$H_x' = -\frac{E'}{Z'} \cos \theta', \quad H_x'' = -\frac{E''}{Z} \cos \theta \tag{29-31}$$

and, by (29-1), we must have

$$H_x + H_x'' = H_x'$$ (29-32)

If we substitute (29-30) and (29-31) into (29-32) and then eliminate E' between the result and (29-29), we find that

$$\frac{E''}{E} = \frac{Z \cos \theta' - Z' \cos \theta}{Z \cos \theta' + Z' \cos \theta}$$ (29-33)

This can be put into a more convenient form. Using (28-38), (28-20), and (29-13), we find that

$$\frac{Z}{Z'} = \frac{\mu \sin \theta}{\mu' \sin \theta'}$$ (29-34)

so that, upon substitution of (29-34) into it, (29-33) becomes

$$\frac{E''}{E} = \frac{\mu \tan \theta - \mu' \tan \theta'}{\mu \tan \theta + \mu' \tan \theta'}$$ (29-35)

When $\mu = \mu'$ (including non-magnetic media), (29-35) simplifies to

$$\frac{E''}{E} = \frac{\sin (\theta - \theta')}{\sin (\theta + \theta')}$$ (29-36)

This is our basic result for the case when **E** is perpendicular to the plane of incidence, and it is one of Fresnel's equations.

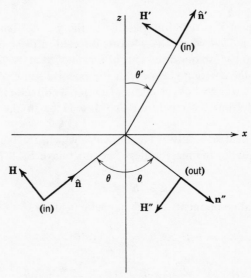

Fig. 29-4

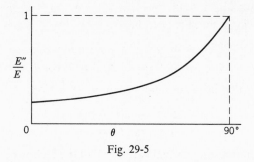

Fig. 29-5

We can now obtain our previous result for normal incidence as a special case of (29-36). As $\theta \to 0$, (29-14) becomes $n\theta = n'\theta'$ and $\theta' \to 0$ also. Then we obtain

$$\frac{E''}{E} \xrightarrow[\theta \to 0]{} \frac{\theta - \theta'}{\theta + \theta'} = \frac{n' - n}{n' + n} \qquad (29\text{-}37)$$

which we see is the same as (29-28) when we remember that the directions of the reflected electric field were oppositely chosen in the two cases.

At the other extreme of grazing incidence, $\theta = 90°$, and (29-36) becomes $E''/E = \cos \theta'/\cos \theta' = 1$. The general behavior of this ratio (29-36) is shown in Fig. 29-5 when $n' > n$. We shall come back to the case $n' < n$ later.

E *parallel to the plane of incidence*

This situation is illustrated in Fig. 29-6 where we are assuming **H** to be into the paper for all waves; again the directions of the electric fields are determined so that **E** × **H** is in the direction of propagation. This time, **H** has only y, or tangential, components given by

$$H_y = \frac{E}{Z}, \quad H_y' = \frac{E'}{Z'}, \quad H_y'' = \frac{E''}{Z} \qquad (29\text{-}38)$$

We must have, therefore,

$$H_y + H_y'' = H_y' \qquad (29\text{-}39)$$

The tangential components of **E** are seen to be

$$E_x = E \cos \theta, \quad E_x' = E' \cos \theta', \quad E_x'' = -E'' \cos \theta \qquad (29\text{-}40)$$

and we must have

$$E_x + E_x'' = E_x' \qquad (29\text{-}41)$$

Using (29-34) and (29-38) through (29-41), we find the ratio of the reflected to incident amplitude to be given by

$$\frac{E''}{E} = \frac{\mu \sin \theta \cos \theta - \mu' \sin \theta' \cos \theta'}{\mu \sin \theta \cos \theta + \mu' \sin \theta' \cos \theta'} \tag{29-42}$$

and, if $\mu = \mu'$, this becomes another Fresnel equation,

$$\frac{E''}{E} = \frac{\tan (\theta - \theta')}{\tan (\theta + \theta')} \tag{29-43}$$

There is an interesting special case of (29-43) which is not contained in the result (29-36) which was found for the electric field perpendicular to the plane of incidence. When $\theta + \theta' = 90°$, then $\tan (\theta + \theta')$ is infinite, $E'' = 0$ and there is no reflected wave. When θ has the correct value to make this so, it is called the *polarizing angle* θ_p. Suppose we have unpolarized radiation incident at the polarizing angle. By "unpolarized" we mean a combination of the two types we have just considered; that is, the electric fields have components both parallel and perpendicular to the plane of incidence. Then only the radiation with its electric field perpendicular to the plane is reflected. The reflected radiation then consists completely of waves with their electric fields all in the same direction; it is then said to be *polarized*. This is the way in which the polarization properties of light were discovered experimentally, and it provides additional evidence that light waves are electromagnetic waves. The law of refraction (29-14) now

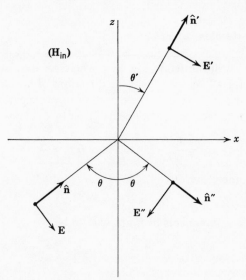

Fig. 29-6

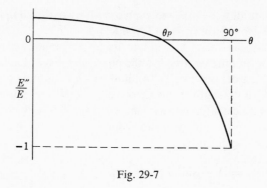

Fig. 29-7

takes an interesting form. When $\theta_p + \theta_p' = 90°$, $\sin \theta_p' = \cos \theta_p$ and (29-14) becomes

$$\tan \theta_p = \frac{n'}{n} = \frac{v}{v'} \qquad (29\text{-}44)$$

This result is known as *Brewster's law*.

When $\theta > \theta_p$, $\tan (\theta + \theta') < 0$; hence E''/E is negative. This means that the phase of the electric vector is suddenly reversed at the polarizing angle. In the limit of grazing incidence when $\theta = 90°$, (29-43) becomes $E''/E = -1$ so that the radiation is completely reflected. We have seen that this is also true when **E** is perpendicular to the plane of incidence. Therefore electromagnetic radiation is *always* completely reflected from the surface of a dielectric for grazing incidence. This fact can be easily demonstrated by looking at a light source by reflection from the surface of a *rough* sheet of paper as the angle of incidence is gradually increased to 90°. The behavior of the ratio E''/E as the function of θ given by (29-43) is shown in Fig. 29-7.

29-4 Total reflection

Let us go back to the case $n' < n$, so that our wave is incident upon a medium of lower index of refraction. From (29-14) we see that if θ has the value θ_c given by

$$\sin \theta_c = \frac{n'}{n} \qquad (29\text{-}45)$$

then $\theta' = 90°$. Now it is certainly possible to have $\theta > \theta_c$, but then (29-14) gives $\sin \theta' > 1$, indicating that θ' is imaginary. This is not really a difficulty, for if we look back at (29-4) we see that the actual reason for introducing θ' at all was simply to enable us to write the components of $\hat{n}'$ in the convenient form $\hat{n}' = n_x \hat{i} + n_y \hat{k} = \sin \theta' \hat{i} + \cos \theta' \hat{k}$, which it takes after (29-4) has been brought to its final simplified form with the help of (29-11). In other words, θ is the physically determinable angle and θ' is actually then defined by (29-14), and we can continue to use all our formulas. Let us, therefore, put these values into our equations to see what type of physical situation we shall have when $\theta > \theta_c$.

The value of $\sin \theta'$ can be found from (29-14). We also need $\cos \theta'$ which we find to be given by

$$\cos \theta' = (1 - \sin^2 \theta')^{\frac{1}{2}} = i\left[\left(\frac{n}{n'} \right)^2 \sin^2 \theta - 1 \right]^{\frac{1}{2}} = i\tau \quad (29\text{-}46)$$

when written completely in terms of θ.

According to (29-7), (29-10), and (29-11), the wave in the second medium has the form

$$\mathbf{E}' = \mathbf{E}_0' e^{i\omega[(x \sin \theta' + z \cos \theta')/v' - t]}$$

which, with the use of (29-46) and (29-13), becomes

$$\mathbf{E}' = \mathbf{E}_0' e^{-(\omega\tau/v')z} e^{i\omega[(x \sin \theta'/v') - t]} \quad (29\text{-}47)$$

This is a wave in the medium of lower index of refraction which is traveling in the positive x direction and therefore parallel to the surface separating the two media. The speed of this wave is $v'/\sin \theta'$, which is less than v', the normal speed in this medium, since $\sin \theta' > 1$. We also see that the amplitude decreases as z increases, that is, as one gets farther from the surface. This decrease of amplitude is so great for ordinary materials that the field has essentially vanished in a distance of only a few wavelengths from the surface. Therefore it is practically impossible to detect this field, although it has been observed by means of quite ingenious experimental arrangements.

By computing the Poynting vector, it can be shown that no net energy is carried into the second medium; hence the name *total reflection* correctly describes this case. The angle θ_c is called the *critical angle*; therefore, for angles of incidence which are greater than the critical angle, all the incident energy is reflected at the bounding surface.

It is interesting to see what Fresnel's equations tell us about the fields when we use these values of $\sin \theta'$ and $\cos \theta'$ given by (29-14) and (29-46). We consider first the case in which $\mathbf{E}$ is perpendicular to the plane, and we find that (29-36) becomes

$$\left(\frac{E''}{E} \right)_s = \frac{\sin \theta \cos \theta' - \cos \theta \sin \theta'}{\sin \theta \cos \theta' + \cos \theta \sin \theta'} = -\left[\frac{\cos \theta - i(n'\tau/n)}{\cos \theta + i(n'\tau/n)} \right] \quad (29\text{-}48)$$

When **E** is parallel to the plane, (29-43) becomes

$$\left(\frac{E''}{E}\right)_p = \frac{\cos\theta - i(n\tau/n')}{\cos\theta + i(n\tau/n')}$$ (29-49)

Both of these equations have the general form

$$\frac{E''}{E} = \mp\frac{a^*}{a} = \mp\frac{(\rho e^{-i\varphi})}{(\rho e^{i\varphi})} = \mp e^{-2i\varphi}$$ (29-50)

so that $|E''/E| = 1$. This means that the amplitude is not changed in magnitude and hence the total reflected energy equals the total incident energy, as we said above. However, (29-50) shows us that the *phase* of the reflected wave is changed. It turns out that the phase change is different for the fields perpendicular or parallel to the plane of incidence. The general consequence of this is that, if a linearly polarized wave is reflected from the boundary at an incident angle greater than the critical angle, the reflected wave will be elliptically polarized.

We can show in the following way that the last statement is correct. We assume that the incident wave is linearly polarized; by this we mean

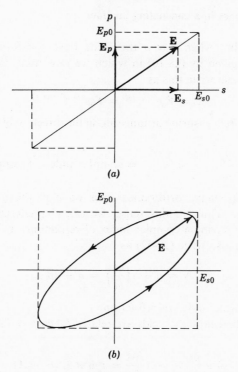

(a)

(b)

Fig. 29-8

the oscillating electric field always lies along the same direction as shown in Fig. 29-8a. If we write the fields in their real forms, the components of the linearly polarized field can be written

$$E_s = E_{s0} \cos \omega t, \quad E_p = E_{p0} \cos \omega t$$

After reflection, each of these components will have had its phase changed by different amounts; they can then be written

$$E_s'' = E_{s0} \cos (\omega t - \phi), \quad E_p'' = E_{p0} \cos (\omega t - \psi)$$

Now the components no longer vanish nor reach their maxima simultaneously, and, when we add them to find the resultant E, we obtain the curve shown in Fig. 29-8b in which the tip of E now traces out an ellipse and, therefore, is said to be elliptically polarized.

Next we consider reflection from the surfaces of absorbing media, particularly those which are good conductors. But, before we do this, we have to consider the general properties of plane waves in more detail than we did in Chapter 28.

29-5 Plane waves in a conducting medium

We found that when $\sigma \neq 0$ the fields have the form (28-8) where $\gamma = k + i\alpha$ is given by (28-10) in which we now need use only the plus sign. We can also write this as

$$E = E_0 e^{i(\gamma\zeta - \omega t)} = E_0 e^{i\omega[(N/c)\zeta - t]} \qquad (29\text{-}51)$$

where now we are measuring distance along the direction of propagation by ζ and where

$$N = \frac{c\gamma}{\omega} = \frac{c}{\omega}(k + i\alpha) = \text{complex index of refraction} \qquad (29\text{-}52)$$

since (29-51) formally corresponds to a wave in the ζ direction with "velocity" c/N. Thus, in this sense, we can characterize an absorbing medium as one having a complex index of refraction. Using (28-17) and (28-20), we can also write (29-52) as

$$N = n + i\left(\frac{c\alpha}{\omega}\right) = n + i\beta \qquad (29\text{-}53)$$

where n is the usual index of refraction.

In order to find how the fields are related when $\sigma \neq 0$, we use (29-51) and (28-27):

$$\hat{n} \times \frac{\partial E}{\partial \zeta} = -\mu \frac{\partial H}{\partial t} = i\gamma \hat{n} \times E = i\omega\mu H$$

Then

$$\mathbf{H} = \frac{(k + i\alpha)}{\omega\mu}(\hat{\mathbf{n}} \times \mathbf{E}) = \left[\frac{\epsilon}{\mu}\left(1 + \frac{i\sigma}{\epsilon\omega}\right)\right]^{\frac{1}{2}}(\hat{\mathbf{n}} \times \mathbf{E}) \qquad (29\text{-}54)$$

The average energy densities, (28-48) and (28-49), then become

$$\bar{u}_e = \tfrac{1}{4}\epsilon\,|\mathbf{E}_0|^2 e^{-2\alpha\zeta} \qquad (29\text{-}55)$$

$$\bar{u}_m = \tfrac{1}{4}\mu|\mathbf{H}_0|^2 e^{-2\alpha\zeta} = \tfrac{1}{4}\epsilon\left[1 + \left(\frac{\sigma}{\epsilon\omega}\right)^2\right]^{\frac{1}{2}}|\mathbf{E}_0|^2 e^{-2\alpha\zeta} \qquad (29\text{-}56)$$

if we use (29-54) and the form (29-51) for the fields. Therefore we see that

$$\bar{u}_m = \left[1 + \left(\frac{\sigma}{\epsilon\omega}\right)^2\right]^{\frac{1}{2}}\bar{u}_e \qquad (29\text{-}57)$$

and that the average magnetic and electric energy densities are different within a conducting medium, in contrast to the previous cases where they were equal, as found in (28-52). In fact, as $\sigma \to \infty$, $\bar{u}_e/\bar{u}_m \to 0$. This means that the electric energy density vanishes faster than the magnetic in the limit of a perfect conductor.

We now want to investigate these results more closely for a case of great practical importance, namely, when

$$\frac{\sigma}{\epsilon\omega} \gg 1 \qquad (29\text{-}58)$$

This relation is valid for practically all metallic conductors for frequencies less than optical frequencies, and, in particular, it is a very good approximation for microwave frequencies which correspond to wavelengths of centimeters to millimeters. Combining (29-58) and (28-10), we get as an approximation $\gamma \simeq \sqrt{i\sigma\mu\omega}$. We can write $i = e^{i\frac{1}{2}\pi}$, so that $\sqrt{i} = e^{i\frac{1}{4}\pi} = \cos(\pi/4) + i\sin(\pi/4) = (1 + i)/\sqrt{2}$, and therefore

$$\gamma = k + i\alpha \simeq \sqrt{\frac{\sigma\mu\omega}{2}}(1 + i) = \frac{(1 + i)}{\delta} \qquad (29\text{-}59)$$

Inserting (29-59) into (29-51), we find that the fields are now given by

$$\mathbf{E} = \mathbf{E}_0 e^{-(\zeta/\delta)} e^{i[(\zeta/\delta) - \omega t]}$$
$$\mathbf{H} = \mathbf{H}_0 e^{-(\zeta/\delta)} e^{i[(\zeta/\delta) - \omega t]} \qquad (29\text{-}60)$$

We see that both fields decrease exponentially with the distance traveled within the conducting material as we briefly noted after (28-54). The fields will have decreased to $1/e$ of their surface values after they have penetrated a distance $\delta = \sqrt{2/\mu\sigma\omega}$. This distance δ is called the *skin depth,* and it represents roughly the depth of penetration of a wave into a conductor. If σ is infinite, $\delta = 0$ and hence both **E** and **H** are zero inside a perfect conductor. (**E** must be zero inside, for otherwise there would be an infinite current density in the interior.)

Now let us consider the relative magnitudes of the fields in the conductor. When (29-58) is applicable, we can approximate (29-54) as

$$\mathbf{H} \simeq \sqrt{\frac{i\sigma}{\mu\omega}}\,(\hat{\mathbf{n}} \times \mathbf{E}) \tag{29-61}$$

Then the ratio of the magnitudes of the fields is approximately given by

$$\frac{|\mathbf{E}|}{|\mathbf{H}|} = \sqrt{\frac{\mu\omega}{\sigma}} \tag{29-62}$$

For large values of σ, this ratio is practically zero; hence in the interior of a good conductor the electric field can generally be neglected as compared to the magnetic field.

29-6   Reflection at the surface of an absorbing medium

We now want to consider effects like those we previously discussed by means of Fresnel's equations, except that now they involve conductivity and energy can be absorbed from the waves. These problems can be worked out by the same method of satisfying boundary conditions which we have used, but the general results are much too complicated for our purposes. Accordingly, we shall consider only a simplified situation which will, however, show us the essential features of these phenomena. We shall assume that a plane wave is traveling in a transparent (non-absorbing) medium and is incident upon an absorbing medium at normal incidence $(\theta = 0)$.

The result for normal incidence upon non-absorbing media is given by (29-28). The primed quantities will refer to the absorbing medium, and we saw in (29-53) that we can describe it by the complex index of refraction, $N' = n' + i\beta'$. *Nothing* in our derivation of (29-28) required that the indices of refraction be real; therefore we can say at once that the solution for the present situation is given by

$$\frac{E''}{E} = \frac{n - N'}{n + N'} = \frac{(n - n') - i\beta'}{(n + n') + i\beta'} \tag{29-63}$$

Then, since the magnetic fields are proportional to the electric fields, the reflection coefficient will be given by

$$R = \left|\frac{E''}{E}\right|^2 = \frac{(n - n')^2 + \beta'^2}{(n + n')^2 + \beta'^2} \tag{29-64}$$

First of all, we see from this equation that, the larger β' is, the more nearly is R equal to unity. In other words, waves which are most strongly absorbed are very strongly reflected. A good example is afforded by the optical properties of thin sheets of gold. They appear yellowish by reflection; this means that, in the originally white light transmitted through the sheets, the yellow is practically all absorbed. As a result, the transmitted light appears greenish or bluish.

We now want to obtain a good approximation to R which will hold for very good conductors, that is, when $(\sigma'/\epsilon\omega) \gg 1$. We saw before in (29-59) that this means that $k' \simeq \alpha' \simeq \sqrt{\sigma'\mu'\omega/2}$. Then, from (29-52) and (29-53), we find that

$$n' \simeq \beta' \simeq \sqrt{\frac{\sigma'}{2\omega\epsilon_0}} \gg 1 \qquad (29\text{-}65)$$

Since $n' \gg n$, we can approximate (29-64):

$$R \simeq \frac{(n - n')^2 + n'^2}{(n + n')^2 + n'^2} = \frac{1 + [1 - (n/n')]^2}{1 + [1 + (n/n')]^2}$$

$$\simeq \frac{1 + [1 - 2(n/n')]}{1 + [1 + 2(n/n')]} \simeq \left(1 - \frac{n}{n'}\right)\left(1 - \frac{n}{n'}\right) \simeq 1 - 2\frac{n}{n'}$$

and, upon using (29-65), we find that this becomes

$$R \simeq 1 - 2n\sqrt{\frac{2\omega\epsilon_0}{\sigma'}} \qquad (29\text{-}66)$$

which, because of (29-58), has the form $R = 1 -$ (a small quantity). We see from (29-66) that the reflection coefficient will be close to unity for large conductivity and low frequency and that essentially all the energy will be reflected as is commonly observed for metals. What little energy does flow into the conductor is rapidly dissipated by the heat loss associated with the induced currents; this is the physical basis for the damping of the fields described by (29-60).

Now we are in a position to take up our next topic.

29-7 Boundary conditions at the surface of a perfect conductor

The general boundary conditions at a surface of discontinuity in the electromagnetic properties are given by (20-4), (20-8), (20-13), and (20-16). We have just seen in the last section that all the fields vanish in a perfect conductor. Choosing medium 1 as the conductor, so that $\hat{n}$ is directed outward from the conducting surface, we can therefore set $\mathbf{E}_1$, $\mathbf{D}_1$, $\mathbf{B}_1$, and

H_1 equal to zero. Then we can drop the subscript 2 and our boundary conditions become

$$\hat{n} \cdot D = \sigma, \quad \hat{n} \times E = 0, \quad \hat{n} \cdot B = 0, \quad \hat{n} \times H = K \qquad (29\text{-}67)$$

Thus at the surface of a perfect conductor E is normal to the surface, and H is tangential to the surface. To put it another way, E has no tangential component, while H has no normal component. It is possible to have a finite surface current density K even though $E_{tang} = 0$ since the conductivity is infinite. In fact, it is precisely these induced surface currents that keep H_{tang} from being zero at the surface, even though it is zero inside.

These boundary conditions (29-67) will be of great help to us in the next chapter when we discuss electromagnetic fields in finite regions, as we shall be able to simplify the discussion considerably by assuming the regions to be bounded by perfectly conducting surfaces.

Exercises

29-1. Find the ratio of the transmitted to the incident electric field for E both perpendicular to and parallel to the plane of incidence.

29-2. A plane wave traveling in a medium of impedance Z_1 is normally incident at $z = 0$ upon a second medium of impedance Z_2. The second medium has a thickness L and behind it is another medium of impedance Z_3 which occupies the rest of space. Find the value of the reflected amplitude in the incident medium, taking into account that there are reflected and transmitted waves arising at each surface of discontinuity. Show that the reflected wave will be zero when L equals a quarter wavelength in medium 2 and $Z_2 = \sqrt{Z_1 Z_3}$.

29-3. What are the conditions which must be satisfied in order that one can obtain circularly polarized light by one total reflection?

29-4. The resistivity of silver is about 1.58×10^{-6} ohm-centimeter. Find the skin depth of silver for waves of wavelength 300 meters, 1 centimeter, and 5000 angstroms.

29-5. Find the reflection coefficient for silver for a wavelength of 10 microns. (One micron is a millionth of a meter.)

30 Normal modes of the electromagnetic field

In this chapter we want to consider time-dependent solutions of Maxwell's equations within bounded regions. It is evident that the solutions will not generally be plane waves, that is, have constant values over an infinite plane, because the fields must simultaneously satisfy Maxwell's equations and the boundary conditions at the limits of the region. For simplicity, we shall assume vacuum properties for our medium, and that all bounding surfaces are perfect conductors.

Under these conditions, we see by (28-7) that each component of **E** or **H** separately satisfies the three-dimensional wave equation

$$\nabla^2 U - \frac{1}{c^2} \frac{\partial^2 U}{\partial t^2} = 0 \tag{30-1}$$

where $c = 1/\sqrt{\mu_0 \epsilon_0}$ through (28-21). In addition, the fields must satisfy (29-67).

We already know that the time variation can be separated out as

$$U(x, y, z, t) = u(x, y, z)T(t) = u(x, y, z)e^{-i\omega t} \tag{30-2}$$

so that the equation satisfied by the spatial part of the component is

$$\nabla^2 u + k_0^2 u = 0 \tag{30-3}$$

where

$$k_0^2 = \left(\frac{\omega}{c}\right)^2 = \left(\frac{2\pi}{\lambda_0}\right)^2 \tag{30-4}$$

where λ_0 is the wavelength which a plane wave of circular frequency ω would have in free space, and hence λ_0 is called the free space wavelength. We have also seen, for instance in Sec. 21-4, that we can separate (30-3) in rectangular coordinates by writing

$$u(x, y, z) = X(x)Y(y)Z(z) \tag{30-5}$$

By substituting (30-5) into (30-3), we obtain separate equations satisfied by the functions X, Y, Z of the form

$$\frac{d^2 X}{dx^2} + k_1^2 X = 0, \quad \frac{d^2 Y}{dy^2} + k_2^2 Y = 0, \quad \frac{d^2 Z}{dz^2} + k_3^2 Z = 0 \tag{30-6}$$

where

$$k_1^2 + k_2^2 + k_3^2 = k_0^2 \tag{30-7}$$

These equations must be solved subject to the boundary conditions required of the field component represented by or related to the scalar u. Calling upon our past experience with similar situations, we can expect to find that the satisfaction of the boundary conditions will determine a set of allowed values of k_1, k_2, k_3 and thence, by (30-7) and (30-4), a set of allowed (or normal) frequencies. In other words, we can conclude that, in regions with perfect conductors as boundaries, we shall find characteristic modes of the electromagnetic field, similar in concept and origin to the normal modes of a vibrating string or membrane. An arbitrary field in general would then be some *superposition* of these electromagnetic normal modes, much as the general displacement of a string was written as a superposition of its normal modes. We shall now illustrate this procedure with a specific example.

30-1   Fields in a closed rectangular cavity

We consider a closed vacuum region with perfectly conducting rectangular walls of sides A, B, C as illustrated in Fig. 30-1. The equation $(d^2X/dx^2) + k_1^2 X = 0$ has the general solution $X(x) = a_1 \cos k_1 x + b_1 \sin k_1 x$, where a_1 and b_1 are constants, so that a solution of (30-1) of the form (30-5) for one of the components of $\mathbf{E}$ is

$$E_x = (a_1 \cos k_1 x + b_1 \sin k_1 x)(a_2 \cos k_2 y + b_2 \sin k_2 y)$$
$$\times (a_3 \cos k_3 z + b_3 \sin k_3 z)e^{-i\omega t} \quad (30\text{-}8)$$

Now E_x is a tangential component for the faces perpendicular to the y and z axes, and therefore $E_x = 0$ when $y = 0$, $y = B$, $z = 0$, and $z = C$. In order for (30-8) to vanish always when y and z equal zero, we see that we must have $a_2 = a_3 = 0$. So that (30-8) may vanish at the other two faces, we must have $\sin k_2 B = \sin k_3 C = 0$ or

$$k_2 = \frac{n\pi}{B}, \quad k_3 = \frac{p\pi}{C} \quad (30\text{-}9)$$

where n and p are positive integers. At this stage, therefore, we have

$$E_x = (a_1 \cos k_1 x + b_1 \sin k_1 x) \sin k_2 y \sin k_3 z \, e^{-i\omega t} \quad (30\text{-}10)$$

Similarly, we find that

$$E_y = \sin k_1 x (a_2 \cos k_2 y + b_2 \sin k_2 y) \sin k_3 z \, e^{-i\omega t} \quad (30\text{-}11)$$

$$E_z = \sin k_1 x \sin k_2 y (a_3 \cos k_3 z + b_3 \sin k_3 z) \, e^{-i\omega t} \quad (30\text{-}12)$$

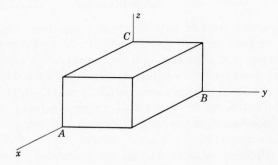

Fig. 30-1

where

$$k_1 = \frac{m\pi}{A} \qquad (30\text{-}13)$$

If we substitute (30-9) and (30-13) into (30-7) and (30-4), we find that the normal frequencies of oscillation are given by

$$\left(\frac{\omega}{c}\right)^2 = \pi^2\left[\left(\frac{m}{A}\right)^2 + \left(\frac{n}{B}\right)^2 + \left(\frac{p}{C}\right)^2\right] \qquad (30\text{-}14)$$

Although the field components (30-10), (30-11), and (30-12) satisfy the boundary conditions on $\mathbf{E}$ and are solutions of the wave equation (30-1), they are not yet necessarily a solution of Maxwell's equations. This is so because the wave equation is simply a consequence of Maxwell's equations and by itself does *not* imply Maxwell's equations. In particular, we must have div $\mathbf{E} = 0$; when the expressions given above for E_x, E_y, and E_z are substituted in this, we find that we obtain

$$-(k_1 a_1 + k_2 a_2 + k_3 a_3)\sin k_1 x \sin k_2 y \sin k_3 z$$
$$+[(k_1 b_1 \cos k_1 x \sin k_2 y \sin k_3 z)$$
$$+(k_2 b_2 \sin k_1 x \cos k_2 y \sin k_3 z)$$
$$+ (k_3 b_3 \sin k_1 x \sin k_2 y \cos k_3 z)] = 0 \qquad (30\text{-}15)$$

We now see that we cannot possibly hope to satisfy this equation for all values of x, y, z unless $b_1 = b_2 = b_3 = 0$. If we set $a_1 = E_1$, $a_2 = E_2$, $a_3 = E_3$, we find that (30-15) becomes

$$k_1 E_1 + k_2 E_2 + k_3 E_3 = 0 \qquad (30\text{-}16)$$

and (30-10), (30-11), and (30-12) become

$$E_x = E_1 \cos k_1 x \sin k_2 y \sin k_3 z \, e^{-i\omega t} \qquad (30\text{-}17a)$$

$$E_y = E_2 \sin k_1 x \cos k_2 y \sin k_3 z \, e^{-i\omega t} \qquad (30\text{-}17b)$$

$$E_z = E_3 \sin k_1 x \sin k_2 y \cos k_3 z \, e^{-i\omega t} \qquad (30\text{-}17c)$$

If we insert into these equations the possible values of the k_i given by (30-9) and (30-13), we get the electric field components for this mode which has the frequency given by (30-14).

The magnetic field of this mode can be obtained by inserting (30-17) into curl $\mathbf{E} = -\mu_0 \, \partial\mathbf{H}/\partial t = i\omega\mu_0\mathbf{H}$. We can easily show that the magnetic field obtained in this way automatically satisfies the boundary condition of having no normal component; we shall illustrate this for H_x. Using (30-17), we find that

$$i\omega\mu_0 H_x = \frac{\partial E_z}{\partial y} - \frac{\partial E_y}{\partial z}$$

$$= (k_2 E_3 - k_3 E_2) \sin k_1 x \cos k_2 y \cos k_3 z \, e^{-i\omega t} \quad (30\text{-}18)$$

and we see at once that $H_x = 0$ when $x = 0$ or A, as it should.

If we define a vector $\mathbf{k}$ with components k_1, k_2, k_3 and other vectors $\mathbf{E}_0$ and $\mathbf{H}_0$ with components E_1, E_2, E_3 and $k_2 E_3 - k_3 E_2, \ldots$, respectively, we see that (30-16) can be written

$$\mathbf{k} \cdot \mathbf{E}_0 = 0 \quad (30\text{-}19)$$

while

$$\mathbf{H}_0 = \mathbf{k} \times \mathbf{E}_0$$

so that in this situation we can introduce a set of mutually perpendicular vectors much as we did for the plane wave in free space, and the two vectors $\mathbf{E}_0$ and $\mathbf{H}_0$ can be regarded as the amplitudes of the electric and magnetic fields.

If the sides A, B, and C are all different, we see from (30-14) that the normal frequencies will generally be different, although there still may be degeneracy if A, B, C have simple integral relations of the type we discussed in connection with the vibrating membrane. A fundamental degeneracy still remains, however, because there are two independent, mutually perpendicular directions along which $\mathbf{E}_0$ can be chosen and still satisfy (30-19), that is, $\mathbf{E}_0$ being perpendicular to $\mathbf{k}$. Therefore, for each possible value of $\mathbf{k}$, there are two independent possible directions of the polarization of the amplitude $\mathbf{E}_0$ and of the corresponding $\mathbf{H}_0$. (This is similar to the problem of finding the directions of the principal axes of inertia of a rigid body which has an axis of symmetry.)

The problem of finding the normal modes of the fields within cavities of other shapes, such as cylinders and spheres, is approached in exactly the same manner. The results differ in detail, of course, from what we obtained above because we would use coordinate systems, such as cylindrical or spherical, which are more convenient for the purposes of separating the variables and of stating the boundary conditions in terms of appropriate components.

30-2 Fields in a wave guide

In this section, we consider possible transfer of electromagnetic energy along a wave guide, which is simply a long tube with open ends. We shall

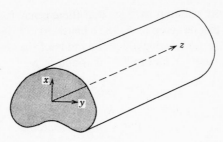

Fig. 30-2

consider a guide of arbitrary cross section in the xy plane which extends indefinitely along z, and whose walls are perfect conductors (Fig. 30-2). The field components must satisfy (30-1) within the guide and (29-67) at the walls.

We try to find a solution of (30-1) in the form of a wave traveling in the z direction and thus of the form

$$U(x, y, z, t) = u(x, y)e^{i(k_g z - \omega t)} \tag{30-20}$$

We note that this is not a plane wave because its amplitude varies over the cross section. The guide propagation constant k_g is related to the guide wavelength λ_g by

$$k_g = \frac{2\pi}{\lambda_g} \tag{30-21}$$

If we substitute (30-20) into (30-1), use (30-4), and cancel out the common exponent, we find the equation for $u(x, y)$ to be

$$\frac{\partial^2 u}{\partial x^2} + \frac{\partial^2 u}{\partial y^2} + k_c^2 u = 0 \tag{30-22}$$

where

$$k_c^2 = k_0^2 - k_g^2 \tag{30-23}$$

Equation (30-22) is now to be solved and the appropriate boundary conditions satisfied. We can expect that, when this is done, we shall find a set of possible values of k_c, and thence of λ_c defined by

$$k_c = \frac{2\pi}{\lambda_c} \tag{30-24}$$

Thus we can also write (30-23) as

$$\frac{1}{\lambda_c^2} = \frac{1}{\lambda_0^2} - \frac{1}{\lambda_g^2} \tag{30-25}$$

Before we go on, we want to show that there is a definite physical interpretation which can be given to k_c (and hence to λ_c). Suppose that k_c is fixed; then we are considering a definite mode of the guide. Since ω, and therefore k_0, is given, we find that k_g is found to be

$$k_g^2 = k_0^2 - k_c^2 \tag{30-26}$$

When $k_0 > k_c, k_g^2 > 0$; when $k_0 < k_c, k_g^2 < 0$, hence k_g is imaginary and can be written $k_g = i |k_g|$. In this second case, (30-20) becomes

$$U = ue^{-|k_g|z}e^{-i\omega t} \tag{30-27}$$

This is not a wave, but rather a harmonically oscillating disturbance whose amplitude is steadily attenuated as we go along the guide in the direction of increasing z. On the other hand, if $k_0 > k_c$ so that k_g is real, (30-20) does represent a wave propagating along z. Therefore we cannot propagate waves for which $k_0 < k_c$. To state this in terms of wavelength, we use (30-24) and (30-4), and we see that a wave whose frequency corresponds to a free space wavelength $\lambda_0 > \lambda_c$ will not be propagated along the guide but will be attenuated instead. For this reason, λ_c is called the *cutoff wavelength*; the corresponding frequency is called the *cutoff frequency*, and we have seen that a guide acts as a sort of high-pass filter in the sense that one can only propagate waves along it whose frequencies are greater than the cutoff frequency.

The fields **E** and **H** must satisfy Maxwell's equations as well as the wave equation. Since there are no charges or currents in the vacuum within the guide, the equations (28-1) through (28-4) become

$$\text{div } \mathbf{E} = 0 \qquad \text{div } \mathbf{H} = 0$$

$$\text{curl } \mathbf{E} = -\mu_0 \frac{\partial \mathbf{H}}{\partial t} \qquad \text{curl } \mathbf{H} = \epsilon_0 \frac{\partial \mathbf{E}}{\partial t} \tag{30-28}$$

Since each of the components has the form (30-20), we can write

$$\mathbf{E} = \mathscr{E}(x, y)e^{i(k_g z - \omega t)} \tag{30-29}$$

$$\mathbf{H} = \mathscr{H}(x, y)e^{i(k_g z - \omega t)} \tag{30-30}$$

If we substitute (30-29) and (30-30) into (30-28), we obtain the following eight equations involving the amplitudes $\mathscr{E}$ and $\mathscr{H}$:

$$\frac{\partial \mathscr{E}_x}{\partial x} + \frac{\partial \mathscr{E}_y}{\partial y} + ik_g\mathscr{E}_z = 0 \tag{30-31}$$

$$\frac{\partial \mathscr{H}_x}{\partial x} + \frac{\partial \mathscr{H}_y}{\partial y} + ik_g\mathscr{H}_z = 0 \tag{30-32}$$

$$\frac{\partial \mathscr{E}_y}{\partial x} - \frac{\partial \mathscr{E}_x}{\partial y} = i\omega\mu_0\mathscr{H}_z \qquad (30\text{-}33a)$$

$$\frac{\partial \mathscr{E}_z}{\partial y} = i\omega\mu_0\mathscr{H}_x + ik_g\mathscr{E}_y \qquad (30\text{-}33b)$$

$$-\frac{\partial \mathscr{E}_z}{\partial x} = i\omega\mu_0\mathscr{H}_y - ik_g\mathscr{E}_x \qquad (30\text{-}33c)$$

$$\frac{\partial \mathscr{H}_y}{\partial x} - \frac{\partial \mathscr{H}_x}{\partial y} = -i\omega\epsilon_0\mathscr{E}_z \qquad (30\text{-}34a)$$

$$\frac{\partial \mathscr{H}_z}{\partial y} = -i\omega\epsilon_0\mathscr{E}_x + ik_g\mathscr{H}_y \qquad (30\text{-}34b)$$

$$-\frac{\partial \mathscr{H}_z}{\partial x} = -i\omega\epsilon_0\mathscr{E}_y - ik_g\mathscr{H}_x \qquad (30\text{-}34c)$$

It turns out, as we shall see in detail as we go along, that it is possible to classify all the modes of the wave guides into two types:

(1) $\mathscr{E}_z = 0$. For this type, **E** is entirely in the xy plane and therefore perpendicular to the direction of propagation. This is called a *transverse electric* or *TE* mode.

(2) $\mathscr{H}_z = 0$. For this type, **H** is perpendicular to the direction of propagation. This is called a *transverse magnetic* or *TM* mode.

Let us consider the two types separately.

TE mode

Since $\mathscr{E}_z = 0$, some of the equations (30-31) through (30-34) simplify to become

$$\frac{\partial \mathscr{E}_x}{\partial x} + \frac{\partial \mathscr{E}_y}{\partial y} = 0 \qquad (30\text{-}31')$$

$$k_g\mathscr{E}_y = -\omega\mu_0\mathscr{H}_x \qquad (30\text{-}33b')$$

$$k_g\mathscr{E}_x = \omega\mu_0\mathscr{H}_y \qquad (30\text{-}33c')$$

$$\frac{\partial \mathscr{H}_y}{\partial x} - \frac{\partial \mathscr{H}_x}{\partial y} = 0 \qquad (30\text{-}34a')$$

and the other four are unchanged.

If we eliminate $\mathscr{E}_y$ from (30-34c) by using (30-33b'), we find that

$$\frac{\partial \mathscr{H}_z}{\partial x} = i\left(k_g - \frac{\omega^2\mu_0\epsilon_0}{k_g}\right)\mathscr{H}_x = \frac{i}{k_g}(k_g^2 - k_0^2)\mathscr{H}_x = -i\frac{k_c^2}{k_g}\mathscr{H}_x \qquad (30\text{-}35)$$

with the help of (28-21), (30-4), and (30-23). Similarly, from (30-34b) and (30-33c'), we find that

$$\frac{\partial \mathcal{H}_z}{\partial y} = -i\frac{k_c^{\,2}}{k_g}\,\mathcal{H}_y \tag{30-36}$$

Now if we let

$$\mathcal{H}_t = \mathcal{H}_x\hat{\mathbf{i}} + \mathcal{H}_y\hat{\mathbf{j}} = \text{transverse component of } \mathcal{H} \tag{30-37}$$

and remember that $\mathcal{H}_z$ depends only on x and y, we can combine (30-35) and (30-36) to obtain

$$\text{grad }\mathcal{H}_z = \frac{\partial \mathcal{H}_z}{\partial x}\hat{\mathbf{i}} + \frac{\partial \mathcal{H}_z}{\partial y}\hat{\mathbf{j}} = -i\frac{k_c^{\,2}}{k_g}\,\mathcal{H}_t \tag{30-38}$$

We also find from (30-33b'), (30-33c'), and (30-37) that

$$\mathcal{H}_t = \frac{k_g}{\omega\mu_0}(-\mathcal{E}_y\hat{\mathbf{i}} + \mathcal{E}_x\hat{\mathbf{j}}) = \frac{k_g}{\omega\mu_0}(\hat{\mathbf{k}} \times \mathcal{E}_t) \tag{30-39}$$

where

$$\mathcal{E}_t = \mathcal{E}_x\hat{\mathbf{i}} + \mathcal{E}_y\hat{\mathbf{j}} = \text{transverse component of } \mathcal{E} \tag{30-40}$$

(Actually, $\mathcal{E}_t$ is the only component of $\mathcal{E}$ in this TE case.) The coefficient in (30-39) can be rewritten

$$\frac{k_g}{\omega\mu_0} = \sqrt{\frac{\epsilon_0}{\mu_0}}\frac{k_g}{\omega\sqrt{\mu_0\epsilon_0}} = \frac{k_g}{Z_0}\frac{c}{\omega} = \frac{k_g}{Z_0 k_0} = \frac{\lambda_0}{Z_0\lambda_g}$$

where we have introduced the free space impedance from (28-39). Therefore, if we define a guide impedance Z_{ge} by

$$Z_{ge} = Z_0\left(\frac{k_0}{k_g}\right) = Z_0\left(\frac{\lambda_g}{\lambda_0}\right) \tag{30-41}$$

we can write (30-39) as

$$\mathcal{H}_t = \frac{\hat{\mathbf{k}} \times \mathcal{E}_t}{Z_{ge}} \tag{30-42}$$

which is reminiscent of (28-36) and (28-38) combined.

If we look back at what we have done, we see that, if we know $\mathcal{H}_z$, $\mathcal{H}_t$ can be found from (30-38), and then $\mathcal{E}_t$ can be found from (30-42). In other words, for the TE case, a knowledge of $\mathcal{H}_z$ is enough to determine the rest of the fields.

TM mode

Here $\mathscr{H}_z = 0$. We can proceed in exactly the same way as above and obtain the following results:

$$\text{grad } \mathscr{E}_z = -i\frac{k_c^2}{k_g}\mathscr{E}_t \tag{30-43}$$

$$\mathscr{H}_t = \frac{\hat{\mathbf{k}} \times \mathscr{E}_t}{Z_{gm}} \tag{30-44}$$

$$Z_{gm} = Z_0\left(\frac{k_g}{k_0}\right) = Z_0\left(\frac{\lambda_0}{\lambda_g}\right) \tag{30-45}$$

Therefore, in the TM case, a knowledge of $\mathscr{E}_z$ is sufficient to determine the rest of the fields. (We note again that, since both $\mathscr{E}_z$ and $\mathscr{H}_z$ are functions only of x and y, their gradients lie entirely in the xy plane, as they should by (30-38) and (30-43)).

The results (30-42) and (30-44) show that in both cases the transverse components $\mathscr{H}_t$ and $\mathscr{E}_t$ are mutually perpendicular in the xy plane, which in turn is perpendicular to z, the direction of propagation. This is illustrated for a TE mode in Fig. 30-3.

Now let us consider the boundary conditions in the two cases. At the surface of the guide, $\mathscr{E}_{\text{tang}} = 0$, i.e., $\mathscr{E}_z = 0$, and also $\mathscr{H}_{\text{norm}} = 0$, i.e. $(\mathscr{H}_t)_{\text{norm}} = 0$, or $(\text{grad } \mathscr{H}_z)_{\text{norm}} = 0$ if (30-38) is applicable. These conditions will ultimately determine the values of k_c.

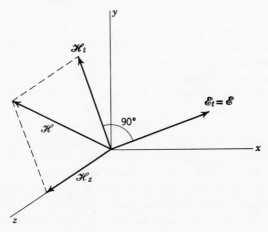

Fig. 30-3

If we keep all these facts in mind, we can now outline a systematic procedure for calculating all the fields for a given mode:

$$\textbf{TE } (\mathscr{E}_z = 0) \qquad\qquad\qquad \textbf{TM } (\mathscr{H}_z = 0)$$

Find a solution $u(x, y)$ of (30-22) for which

$$(\operatorname{grad} u)_{\text{norm}} = 0 \qquad \Big| \qquad u = 0$$

on the surface of the guide. Call this solution

$$\mathscr{H}_z \qquad\qquad \Big| \qquad\qquad \mathscr{E}_z$$

(In the TM case, since $u = 0$ everywhere on the wall, grad u will be normal to the wall.)

Then calculate

$$\mathscr{H}_t = \frac{ik_g}{k_c^{\,2}} \operatorname{grad} \mathscr{H}_z \qquad\qquad \Big| \qquad\qquad \mathscr{E}_t = \frac{ik_g}{k_c^{\,2}} \operatorname{grad} \mathscr{E}_z$$

(Thus we have made sure that $\mathscr{H}_t$ is parallel to the surface at the surface and that $\mathscr{E}_t$ is perpendicular to the surface at the surface.)

Then find

$$\mathscr{E}_t \ \text{ from } \ \mathbf{\hat{k}} \times \mathscr{E}_t = Z_{ge}\mathscr{H}_t \qquad \Big| \qquad \mathscr{H}_t = \frac{\mathbf{\hat{k}} \times \mathscr{E}_t}{Z_{gm}}$$

(Since $\mathscr{H}_t$ is parallel to the wall, we make sure that $\mathscr{E}_t$ is perpendicular to the wall at the wall so that its tangential component is zero; in the TM case, $\mathscr{H}_t$ will be automatically parallel to the surface at the surface and hence will have no normal component.)

Therefore, for every solution of the scalar equation (30-22) which vanishes on the boundary, we shall obtain a TM wave, and, for every solution whose normal derivative vanishes on the boundary, we shall get a TE wave. We should expect to find an infinite number of solutions of each type, each corresponding to a particular cutoff wavelength; we could then classify our solutions in some convenient manner in terms of the cutoff wavelengths, for instance in order of decreasing magnitude (or increasing frequency).

It can be shown quite generally that all transverse components can be expressed in terms of $\mathscr{E}_z$ and $\mathscr{H}_z$ which satisfy the same differential equation. Since the boundary conditions are different for these two components, the solutions will generally correspond to different frequencies, so that it is not possible to have $\mathscr{E}_z$ and $\mathscr{H}_z$ simultaneously different from zero. Thus all the modes are either TE or TM.

We can also see from our results as outlined above that we cannot have a mode which is simultaneously transverse for **E** and **H** in the hollow pipe we are considering. This would require $\mathscr{E}_z = \mathscr{H}_z = 0$, and we see from above that all the fields would be zero. Such a mode is called *transverse electromagnetic* (TEM) and it can exist under rather different circumstances from those we have here; we shall discuss it later in another way.

Next we want to illustrate these general procedures by a detailed calculation of the fields in an important practical type of wave guide.

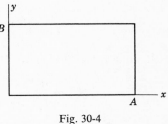

Fig. 30-4

30-3   Rectangular guide

This guide has a rectangular cross section in the xy plane with sides A and B as shown in Fig. 30-4. Now (30-22) is the two-dimensional form of (30-3) with k_c replacing k_0 because u is now to be independent of z. Therefore we can use the results (30-7) and (30-8) and immediately write the solution of (30-22) which we would get by separating variables:

$$u(x, y) = (a_1 \cos k_1 x + b_1 \sin k_1 x)(a_2 \cos k_2 y + b_2 \sin k_2 y) \quad (30\text{-}46)$$

where

$$k_1{}^2 + k_2{}^2 = k_c{}^2 \quad (30\text{-}47)$$

TE mode

We now let (30-46) be called $\mathscr{H}_z$. The component of grad $\mathscr{H}_z$ which will be the normal component at $x = 0$ and $x = A$ is

$$\frac{\partial \mathscr{H}_z}{\partial x} = k_1(-a_1 \sin k_1 x + b_1 \cos k_1 x)(a_2 \cos k_2 y + b_2 \sin k_2 y) \quad (30\text{-}48)$$

In order for this to vanish when $x = 0$ and $x = A$, we see that we must have $b_1 = 0$ and $k_1 A = m\pi$ or

$$k_1 = \frac{m\pi}{A} \quad (30\text{-}49)$$

where m is a positive integer. Similarly, by requiring that $\partial \mathscr{H}_z/\partial y$ be zero when $y = 0$ or B, we find that $b_2 = 0$ and

$$k_2 = \frac{n\pi}{B} \quad (30\text{-}50)$$

so that (30-46) now can be written

$$\mathscr{H}_z = H_0 \cos k_1 x \cos k_2 y \quad (30\text{-}51)$$

and the values of $k_c{}^2$ as given by (30-47) are

$$k_c{}^2 = \pi^2\left[\left(\frac{m}{A}\right)^2 + \left(\frac{n}{B}\right)^2\right]$$

(30-52)

and we can have an infinite set of TE waves. The guide propagation constant and guide wavelength are then obtained by putting (30-52) into (30-26) with the result that

$$k_g{}^2 = \left(\frac{\omega}{c}\right)^2 - \left(\frac{\pi m}{A}\right)^2 - \left(\frac{\pi n}{B}\right)^2 = \left(\frac{2\pi}{\lambda_g}\right)^2$$

(30-53)

If we now use (30-51) in (30-38), we find that

$$\mathcal{H}_x = \frac{ik_g}{k_c{}^2}\frac{\partial \mathcal{H}_z}{\partial x} = -H_0 \frac{ik_g k_1}{k_c{}^2}\sin k_1 x \cos k_2 y$$

(30-54)

$$\mathcal{H}_y = \frac{ik_g}{k_c{}^2}\frac{\partial \mathcal{H}_z}{\partial y} = -H_0 \frac{ik_g k_2}{k_c{}^2}\cos k_1 x \sin k_2 y$$

(30-55)

From (30-42) and (30-41), we can write

$$\hat{\mathbf{k}} \times \mathcal{E}_t = -\mathcal{E}_y\hat{\mathbf{i}} + \mathcal{E}_x\hat{\mathbf{j}} = Z_{ge}\mathcal{H}_t = Z_0 \frac{k_0}{k_g}(\mathcal{H}_x\hat{\mathbf{i}} + \mathcal{H}_y\hat{\mathbf{j}})$$

and therefore, with the use of (30-54) and (30-55), we find that

$$\mathcal{E}_x = Z_0\frac{k_0}{k_g}\mathcal{H}_y = -H_0 Z_0 \frac{ik_0 k_2}{k_c{}^2}\cos k_1 x \sin k_2 y$$

(30-56)

$$\mathcal{E}_y = -Z_0\frac{k_0}{k_g}\mathcal{H}_x = H_0 Z_0 \frac{ik_0 k_1}{k_c{}^2}\sin k_1 x \cos k_2 y$$

(30-57)

and, of course, $\mathcal{E}_z = 0$.

The actual fields are then obtained by multiplying each of these amplitudes by $e^{i(k_g z - \omega t)}$ according to (30-29) and (30-30). For example, if we do this, and also insert the explicit values of k_1 and k_2 given by (30-49) and (30-50) into (30-54), we obtain

$$H_x = -H_0\frac{ik_g}{k_c{}^2}\left(\frac{m\pi}{A}\right)\sin\left(\frac{m\pi x}{A}\right)\cos\left(\frac{n\pi y}{B}\right)e^{i(k_g z - \omega t)}$$

(30-58)

We still would have to take the real part of the complex solution (30-58) and insert the values given by (30-52) and (30-53) to get finally the explicit expression for the field H_x.

Example. Let us suppose that $A > B$ and look only at the mode with the smallest k_c (largest λ_c). From (30-52), we see that $m = n = 0$ would make $k_c = 0$; but then by (30-51) $\mathcal{H}_z = $ const. and all the other fields would be zero. In this case $k_g = \omega/c$ by (30-53), and we would apparently have a solution of the form $H_z = H_0 e^{i\omega[(z/c)-t]}$, that is, only a magnetic field propagating down the guide with speed c. However, we must still have div $\mathbf{H} = 0 = \partial H_z/\partial z = (i\omega/c)H_z$ so that $\omega = 0$ and $H_z = $ const. In other words, the complete electromagnetic field for $k_c = 0$ is merely a constant magnetic field in the guide; while this is certainly possible, it is of no interest to us here.

Therefore the smallest value of k_c which will give a wave for $A > B$ corresponds to $m = 1, n = 0$, so that $\lambda_c = 2A$ from (30-52) and (30-24). Then $k_1 = k_c = (\pi/A), k_2 = 0, k_g{}^2 = k_0{}^2 - (\pi/A)^2$, and (30-54) through (30-57) give us $\mathscr{E}_x = \mathscr{E}_z = \mathscr{H}_y = 0$ and the only remaining components are

$$E_y = H_0 Z_0 i \left(\frac{k_0 A}{\pi}\right) \sin\left(\frac{\pi x}{A}\right) e^{i(k_g z - \omega t)} \qquad (30\text{-}59)$$

$$H_x = -H_0 i \left(\frac{k_g A}{\pi}\right) \sin\left(\frac{\pi x}{A}\right) e^{i(k_g z - \omega t)} \qquad (30\text{-}60)$$

$$H_z = H_0 \cos\left(\frac{\pi x}{A}\right) e^{i(k_g z - \omega t)} \qquad (30\text{-}61)$$

To find the actual fields we must take the real parts of these equations. Let us assume, for simplicity, that H_0 is real; then we find that the only non-zero field components are

$$E_y = -H_0 Z_0 \left(\frac{k_0 A}{\pi}\right) \sin\left(\frac{\pi x}{A}\right) \sin(k_g z - \omega t) \qquad (30\text{-}62)$$

$$H_x = H_0 \left(\frac{k_g A}{\pi}\right) \sin\left(\frac{\pi x}{A}\right) \sin(k_g z - \omega t) \qquad (30\text{-}63)$$

$$H_z = H_0 \cos\left(\frac{\pi x}{A}\right) \cos(k_g z - \omega t) \qquad (30\text{-}64)$$

As an elementary check on our results, we see that they really do satisfy the boundary conditions at $x = 0, A$ and $y = 0, B$; that is, $\mathbf{E}_{\text{tang}} = 0$ and $\mathbf{H}_{\text{norm}} = 0$.

The values of E_y are independent of y; hence the electric field lines are straight with their maximum value in the center at $x = \frac{1}{2}A$. The lines of H_x are also straight lines in the xy plane with maximum value in the center. The values of H_z, on the other hand, are zero in the center and have opposite signs on the two sides of the center. These fields are shown, *at a given time*, in Fig. 30-5. In (a), the fields in the xy plane are shown, $\mathbf{E}$ being given by the solid lines and $\mathbf{H}$ dashed; the short arrows below indicate the variation in magnitude of H_x with position. When

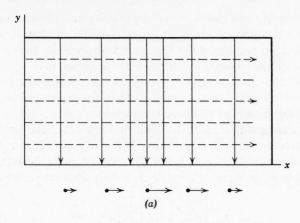

(a)

$H_z = 0$ $E_y = H_x = 0$ $H_z = 0$

$\frac{1}{2}\lambda_g$

(b)

Fig. 30-5

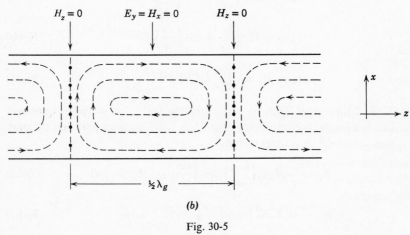

Fig. 30-6

the z dependence of the fields is considered at a given time, we see that E_y and H_x are both zero when $|H_z|$ is a maximum, and $|E_y|$ and $|H_x|$ have maximum values when H_z is zero; these results are illustrated in Fig. 30-5b.

Since our solutions represent waves, the picture of the behavior of the fields in time can be obtained by imagining these figures traveling steadily in the positive z direction with the guide velocity $v_g = \omega/k_g$.

As there are non-zero tangential components of **H**, (29-67) tells us that there are currents on the surface of the guide given by $\mathbf{K} = \hat{\mathbf{n}} \times \mathbf{H}$. They can be calculated from this formula and their directions are shown by the solid lines in Fig. 30-6.

TM mode

For this we need the solution of the general form (30-46) which vanishes at the walls. This clearly has the form

$$\mathscr{E}_z = E_0 \sin\left(\frac{m\pi x}{A}\right) \sin\left(\frac{n\pi y}{B}\right) \tag{30-65}$$

and the values of $k_c{}^2$ are again given by (30-52) so that the TE and TM modes of a rectangular guide have the same set of cutoff wavelengths. However, the case $m = 1, n = 0$, which we discussed above does *not* exist as a TM mode because we see from (30-65) that all the fields will vanish; hence this lowest mode exists only for a TE wave. If we wished, we could now go ahead from (30-65) and find all the rest of the field components for the TM modes of a rectangular guide.

There are other guides with different cross-sectional shapes which can be discussed in the same manner as we used above; we shall not discuss these, however, but another type of mode instead.

30-4 Principal modes

An interesting and practical situation would arise if we could somehow make k_c zero, for then we could use the guide to transmit energy of any frequency or wavelength. Such a mode is called a principal mode. We can use some of our previous results to show what sort of properties we could expect of a principal mode. As $k_c \to 0$, we see from (30-23) that k_g will become equal to k_0, the free space propagation constant. Therefore the wave in the principal mode is propagated with speed c. Now, if we look at our results for the TM case, for example, where $\mathscr{H}_z = 0$, we see from

(30-43) that grad $\mathscr{E}_z = 0$ when $k_c = 0$, so that $\mathscr{E}_z =$ const. over the cross section of the guide. But $\mathscr{E}_z$ is a tangential component and must vanish at the walls; therefore $\mathscr{E}_z = 0$ everywhere. In other words, the principal mode has no components in the direction of propagation, and hence **E** and **H** are simultaneously transverse and the principal mode is a TEM mode. The same conclusion follows from (30-38) for the TE case. Also, when $k_g = k_0$, (30-42) and (30-44) both become

$$\mathscr{H}_t = \frac{\hat{\mathbf{k}} \times \mathscr{E}_t}{Z_0} \tag{30-66}$$

where Z_0 is the free space impedance. Thus the principal mode possesses many of the characteristics of a plane wave in free space.

We can obtain the components of the TEM mode from a solution of the two-dimensional form of Laplace's equation. We can show this in the following way: If $\mathscr{H}_z = 0$ and $\mathscr{E}_z = 0$, then (30-31) and (30-33a) become

$$\frac{\partial \mathscr{E}_x}{\partial x} + \frac{\partial \mathscr{E}_y}{\partial y} = 0 \quad \text{and} \quad \frac{\partial \mathscr{E}_y}{\partial x} - \frac{\partial \mathscr{E}_x}{\partial y} = 0 \tag{30-67}$$

If we define $\phi(x, y)$ by the equations $\mathscr{E}_x = -\partial\phi/\partial x$ and $\mathscr{E}_y = -\partial\phi/\partial y$, that is,

$$\mathscr{E}_t = -\text{grad } \phi \tag{30-68}$$

then the second equation in (30-67) is satisfied, and the first becomes

$$\frac{\partial^2 \phi}{\partial x^2} + \frac{\partial^2 \phi}{\partial y^2} = 0 \tag{30-69}$$

Therefore, if we take *any* solution of the appropriate two-dimensional *electrostatic* potential problem, which gives an electric field which is normal to the perfectly conducting bounding surface, call this field $\mathscr{E}_t$, and then find $\mathscr{H}_t$ from (30-66), we get a TEM mode for the system. The two-dimensional field pattern obtained in this way will then be propagated down the guide with the free space speed c.

We saw previously that the hollow pipe wave guide cannot have a TEM mode. We shall show below that a principal mode can exist only if the wave guide consists of at least two separate conductors, such as two parallel wires. Actually, the reason for this can be seen quite easily if we look at the limiting case of very low frequency. A zero frequency current (direct current) can be transmitted along a line consisting of two or more conductors since they can be insulated from each other and thereby suited to carry the current. If there is only one conductor, as for a hollow pipe, then, if we were to connect the source of the direct current, we would obviously have a short circuit and any propagation would be impossible. Now let us also prove this analytically.

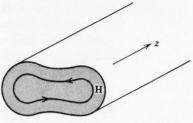

Fig. 30-7

We must still have

$$\text{div } \mathbf{H} = 0 \tag{30-70}$$

and

$$\text{curl } \mathbf{H} = \mathbf{J} + \epsilon_0 \frac{\partial \mathbf{E}}{\partial t} \tag{30-71}$$

for a TEM mode. If $\mathbf{H}$ is to lie only in the transverse xy plane, then (30-70) says that the lines of $\mathbf{H}$ must form closed loops in this plane as shown in Fig. 30-7. Evidently, if we calculate the line integral of $\mathbf{H}$ around one of these loops, we obtain

$$\oint_{\text{loop}} \mathbf{H} \cdot d\mathbf{s} \neq 0 \tag{30-72}$$

But we can also calculate this line integral with the help of (30-71) as

$$\oint \mathbf{H} \cdot d\mathbf{s} = \int \text{curl } \mathbf{H} \cdot d\mathbf{a} = \int J_z \, da + \epsilon_0 \frac{\partial}{\partial t} \int E_z \, da = \int J_z \, da = I \tag{30-73}$$

since $E_z = 0$ by hypothesis; I is the total current passing through the area enclosed by the loop.

Now, if there is not an inner conductor, $I = 0$ and the line integral is zero, from (30-73). But this contradicts the result (30-72) obtained from another of Maxwell's equations, and therefore a TEM wave is not possible if there is no inner conductor. On the other hand, if there is an inner conductor, $I \neq 0$ and (30-72) and (30-73) are compatible and a TEM mode is possible, as we stated above.

To illustrate these ideas in detail, we shall discuss the simplest possible principal mode of a very important type of guide.

Example.   Coaxial line. This consists of two concentric cylinders of different radii with a vacuum between them as illustrated in Fig. 30-8. We shall use polar coordinates r and φ in the plane of the cross section. Then, since ϕ is independent of z, we find from (18-21) that (30-69) becomes

$$\nabla^2 \phi = \frac{1}{r} \frac{\partial}{\partial r}\left(r \frac{\partial \phi}{\partial r} \right) + \frac{1}{r^2} \frac{\partial^2 \phi}{\partial \varphi^2} = 0 \tag{30-74}$$

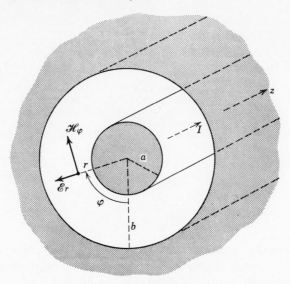

Fig. 30-8

Let us look for a solution of the form $\phi = \phi(r)$. Then (30-74) becomes

$$\frac{d}{dr}\left(r\frac{d\phi}{dr}\right) = 0$$

so that

$$\frac{d\phi}{dr} = \frac{A}{r}$$

and

$$\phi = (A \ln r) + B \qquad (30\text{-}75)$$

where A and B are constants. Therefore, from (30-75) and (30-68), we see that $\mathscr{E}_t$ has only a radial component given by

$$\mathscr{E}_r = -\frac{d\phi}{dr} = -\frac{A}{r} \qquad (30\text{-}76)$$

Then from (30-66) we see that $\mathscr{H}_t$ has only a φ component given by

$$\mathscr{H}_\varphi = \frac{\mathscr{E}_r}{Z_0} \qquad (30\text{-}77)$$

Inserting these results into (30-29) and (30-30), we find the fields to be given by

$$E_r = \mathscr{E}_r e^{i\omega[(z/c)-t]} \qquad (30\text{-}78)$$

$$H_\varphi = \mathscr{H}_\varphi e^{i\omega[(z/c)-t]} \qquad (30\text{-}79)$$

since $k_g = k_0 = \omega/c$. These expressions can now be rewritten in terms of some experimentally significant quantities.

When E_r has its maximum value $\mathcal{E}_r = -d\phi/dr$, the potential difference between the conductors is a maximum, ϕ_0, which is given by

$$\phi_0 = \int_a^b \mathcal{E}_r \, dr = \phi_a - \phi_b = -A \ln \frac{b}{a}$$

after we have used (30-75). Therefore $A = -\phi_0/\ln(b/a)$ and (30-78) becomes

$$E_r = \frac{\phi_0 e^{i\omega[(z/c)-t]}}{r \ln(b/a)} \tag{30-80}$$

When H_φ has its maximum value $\mathcal{H}_\varphi$, the current has its maximum value I_0 and (30-73) becomes

$$\oint \mathbf{H} \cdot d\mathbf{s} = I_0 = \mathcal{H}_\varphi \oint ds = \mathcal{H}_\varphi 2\pi r$$

so that $\mathcal{H}_\varphi = I_0/2\pi r$ and (30-79) can be written

$$H_\varphi = \frac{I_0 e^{i\omega[(z/c)-t]}}{2\pi r} \tag{30-81}$$

If we now combine (30-76) and (30-77) with the last results, we obtain

$$Z_0 = \frac{\mathcal{E}_r}{\mathcal{H}_\varphi} = \frac{2\pi\phi_0}{I_0 \ln(b/a)}$$

so that

$$\frac{\phi_0}{I_0} = \frac{Z_0}{2\pi} \ln \frac{b}{a} = Z_c \tag{30-82}$$

where Z_c is called the characteristic impedance of the coaxial line.

Exercises

30-1. Verify (30-43) through (30-45).

30-2. Calculate the time average Poynting vector for a general TE mode in a rectangular guide. By integrating over the cross section of the guide find the total power transmitted along the guide.

30-3. Find the general expressions for the fields in a TM mode of a rectangular guide. What is the smallest possible value of k_c?

30-4. What is the lowest normal frequency of a closed cavity when $A = B = C$? Find all components of the electric and magnetic fields for this case. Make a sketch of the directions of the fields in the cavity at a given time, and verify that they satisfy the appropriate boundary conditions.

31 Scalar and vector potentials

Up to this point, we have considered time-dependent electromagnetic fields (essentially only those which are waves) without being concerned about how we could produce them. Now we want to see how the fields can be related to their sources, that is, how we can find the fields from a knowledge of the time-dependent charge and current distributions. It is most convenient to treat this problem by means of the scalar and vector potentials.

31-1   Definition of the potentials

Maxwell's equations in general form are

$$\text{div } \mathbf{D} = \rho \tag{31-1}$$

$$\text{curl } \mathbf{E} = -\frac{\partial \mathbf{B}}{\partial t} \tag{31-2}$$

$$\text{div } \mathbf{B} = 0 \tag{31-3}$$

$$\text{curl } \mathbf{H} = \mathbf{J} + \frac{\partial \mathbf{D}}{\partial t} \tag{31-4}$$

We see again that curl $\mathbf{E}$ and curl $\mathbf{H}$ are generally different from zero; hence we cannot use the simple scalar potentials previously introduced. However, (31-3), which was the basis for introducing the vector potential, still holds and we can write

$$\mathbf{B} = \text{curl } \mathbf{A} \tag{31-5}$$

where now $\mathbf{A}$ must be assumed to be a function of t as well as of x, y, z. We still need to find how to satisfy the other three equations and obtain a method for calculating $\mathbf{A}$.

If we substitute (31-5) into (31-2), we obtain

$$\text{curl } \mathbf{E} = -\frac{\partial}{\partial t} \text{curl } \mathbf{A} = -\text{curl}\frac{\partial \mathbf{A}}{\partial t}$$

so that

$$\text{curl}\left(\mathbf{E} + \frac{\partial \mathbf{A}}{\partial t}\right) = 0 \tag{31-6}$$

Since the curl of the quantity in parentheses is zero, it can be written as the gradient of a scalar, i.e., $\mathbf{E} + (\partial \mathbf{A}/\partial t) = -\text{grad } \phi$, or

$$\mathbf{E} = -\text{grad } \phi - \frac{\partial \mathbf{A}}{\partial t} \tag{31-7}$$

Therefore we can satisfy (31-2) by introducing the scalar potential $\phi(x, y, z, t)$.

As we go on from here, we shall get reasonably simple results only if we assume that $\mathbf{D} = \epsilon \mathbf{E}$ and $\mathbf{B} = \mu \mathbf{H}$, where ϵ and μ are constants independent of position. It is also convenient to take account of the fact that the free current density $\mathbf{J}$ can result from external sources, as well as being produced by the field itself in a medium of conductivity σ. Therefore we write

$$\mathbf{J} = \mathbf{J}' + \sigma \mathbf{E} \tag{31-8}$$

where $\mathbf{J}'$ is the current produced by external sources.

Multiplying (31-4) through by μ, using (31-5), (31-7), and (31-8), we obtain

$$\text{curl } \mathbf{B} = \mu \mathbf{J}' + \mu \sigma \mathbf{E} + \mu \epsilon \frac{\partial \mathbf{E}}{\partial t}$$

$$= \text{curl curl } \mathbf{A} = \text{grad div } \mathbf{A} - \nabla^2 \mathbf{A}$$

$$= \mu \mathbf{J}' - \left(\mu \sigma + \mu \epsilon \frac{\partial}{\partial t} \right) \left(\text{grad } \phi + \frac{\partial \mathbf{A}}{\partial t} \right)$$

so that

$$\nabla^2 \mathbf{A} - \mu \epsilon \frac{\partial^2 \mathbf{A}}{\partial t^2} - \mu \sigma \frac{\partial \mathbf{A}}{\partial t} - \text{grad} \left(\text{div } \mathbf{A} + \mu \epsilon \frac{\partial \phi}{\partial t} + \mu \sigma \phi \right) = -\mu \mathbf{J}' \quad (31\text{-}9)$$

Similarly, from the remaining Maxwell equation, we get

$$\nabla^2 \phi - \mu \epsilon \frac{\partial^2 \phi}{\partial t^2} - \mu \sigma \frac{\partial \phi}{\partial t} + \frac{\partial}{\partial t} \left(\text{div } \mathbf{A} + \mu \epsilon \frac{\partial \phi}{\partial t} + \mu \sigma \phi \right) = -\frac{\rho}{\epsilon} \quad (31\text{-}10)$$

These are the equations from which we can calculate the potentials $\mathbf{A}$ and ϕ. If they are inserted into (31-5) and (31-7), the fields $\mathbf{E}$ and $\mathbf{B}$ will automatically satisfy (31-1) through (31-4).

These equations, (31-9) and (31-10), can be further simplified if we remember that the vector $\mathbf{A}$ has not yet been completely defined because we have only specified curl $\mathbf{A}$ everywhere by means of (31-5). Therefore we are free to choose div $\mathbf{A}$ in any convenient manner. A glance at (31-9) and (31-10) shows that a simple way of doing this is to choose

$$\text{div } \mathbf{A} + \mu \epsilon \frac{\partial \phi}{\partial t} + \mu \sigma \phi = 0 \tag{31-11}$$

for then (31-9) and (31-11) become

$$\nabla^2 \mathbf{A} - \mu\epsilon \frac{\partial^2 \mathbf{A}}{\partial t^2} - \mu\sigma \frac{\partial \mathbf{A}}{\partial t} = -\mu \mathbf{J}' \qquad (31\text{-}12)$$

$$\nabla^2 \phi - \mu\epsilon \frac{\partial^2 \phi}{\partial t^2} - \mu\sigma \frac{\partial \phi}{\partial t} = -\frac{\rho}{\epsilon} \qquad (31\text{-}13)$$

The requirement (31-11) is called the Lorentz condition. The advantages of this particular choice of div **A** are that it makes the equations for **A** and ϕ independent of each other and makes them have the same form, so we have only one general problem to solve.

The general procedure in solving an electromagnetic problem involving known sources would then be the following: We assume that we know the distribution of external charges and currents, that is, we are given the functions $\mathbf{J}'(x, y, z, t)$ and $\rho(x, y, z, t)$; then we solve (31-12) and (31-13), making sure that **A** and ϕ satisfy (31-11); we can then find **B** and **E** from (31-5) and (31-7). If we desire, we can find $\mathbf{H} = \mathbf{B}/\mu$ and $\mathbf{D} = \epsilon\mathbf{E}$; we can also calculate the polarization and magnetization by $\mathbf{P} = (\kappa_e - 1)\epsilon_0 \mathbf{E}$ and $\mathbf{M} = [(\kappa_m - 1)/\kappa_m \mu_0]\mathbf{B}$.

From now on, we shall consider only situations for which $\sigma = 0$ and $\mathbf{J} = \mathbf{J}'$. Then (31-11), (31-12), and (31-13) become

$$\nabla^2 \mathbf{A} - \frac{1}{v^2} \frac{\partial^2 \mathbf{A}}{\partial t^2} = -\mu \mathbf{J} \qquad (31\text{-}14)$$

$$\nabla^2 \phi - \frac{1}{v^2} \frac{\partial^2 \phi}{\partial t^2} = -\frac{\rho}{\epsilon} \qquad (31\text{-}15)$$

$$\text{div } \mathbf{A} + \frac{1}{v^2} \frac{\partial \phi}{\partial t} = 0 \qquad (31\text{-}16)$$

where $v^2 = c^2/n^2$ as in (28-20). These differential equations for **A** and ϕ are similar both to Poisson's equation and the wave equation. If we define the D'Alembertian operator by

$$\square^2 = \nabla^2 - \frac{1}{v^2} \frac{\partial^2}{\partial t^2} \qquad (31\text{-}17)$$

the equations for **A** and ϕ take on the compact form

$$\square^2 \mathbf{A} = -\mu \mathbf{J}, \quad \square^2 \phi = -\frac{\rho}{\epsilon} \qquad (31\text{-}18)$$

These equations possess an interesting property which we want to consider now; it is that the potentials calculated in this way are not unique, although the electromagnetic fields calculated from them are unique. To show this, let us define two new quantities $\mathbf{A}'$ and ϕ' by

$$\mathbf{A}' = \mathbf{A} - \text{grad } \psi, \quad \phi' = \phi + \frac{\partial \psi}{\partial t} \tag{31-19}$$

where $\psi = \psi(x, y, z, t)$. From (31-5) we see that

$$\mathbf{B} = \text{curl } \mathbf{A} = \text{curl } (\mathbf{A}' + \text{grad } \psi) = \text{curl } \mathbf{A}' \tag{31-20}$$

since curl grad $\psi = 0$. From (31-7), we find that

$$\mathbf{E} = -\text{grad } \phi - \frac{\partial \mathbf{A}}{\partial t} = -\text{grad } \phi' - \frac{\partial \mathbf{A}'}{\partial t} \tag{31-21}$$

Therefore we get the same fields whether we use the set $(\mathbf{A}, \phi)$ or $(\mathbf{A}', \phi')$. The kind of transformation defined by (31-19) is called a *gauge transformation*; thus (31-20) and (31-21) show that Maxwell's equations are invariant with respect to a gauge transformation, or to a change of gauge. There are certain restrictions on ψ, however, as we want both sets of potentials to satisfy the Lorentz condition (31-16). If we substitute (31-19) into (31-16), we find that

$$\text{div } \mathbf{A}' + \frac{1}{v^2} \frac{\partial \phi'}{\partial t} + \nabla^2 \psi - \frac{1}{v^2} \frac{\partial^2 \psi}{\partial t^2} = 0$$

so that $\mathbf{A}'$ and ϕ' will also satisfy (31-16) provided that

$$\nabla^2 \psi - \frac{1}{v^2} \frac{\partial^2 \psi}{\partial t^2} = 0 \tag{31-22}$$

In other words, ψ can be any solution of the homogeneous wave equation.

Equations (31-18) can be solved in general by a method similar to that we used to solve Poisson's equation in Secs. 21-2 and 21-3. The derivations of these solutions, as well as the results themselves, are quite complicated, and since we shall not have use for them in what follows we shall not discuss them in any detail. The potentials obtained this way are called retarded potentials; the expressions for them are much like those given in (21-9) and (25-18), except that the integrands have to be evaluated at a time earlier than that at which it is desired to evaluate the fields, in order to take account of the finite speed of propagation of electromagnetic effects given by $v = c/n$.

31-2 Hertz vector in free space

Hertz was able to show that in regions where there are no charges and currents the electromagnetic field can be described in terms of only *one* vector. We designate it $\mathbf{\Pi}$; it is called the *Hertz vector* or *polarization potential*. We shall discuss it only for the simpler case of free space where $\mu = \mu_0$, $\epsilon = \epsilon_0$, and $v = c$; we also require $\mathbf{J}$ and ρ to be zero. Then (31-14), (31-15), and (31-16) become

$$\nabla^2 \mathbf{A} - \frac{1}{c^2} \frac{\partial^2 \mathbf{A}}{\partial t^2} = 0 \qquad (31\text{-}14')$$

$$\nabla^2 \phi - \frac{1}{c^2} \frac{\partial^2 \phi}{\partial t^2} = 0 \qquad (31\text{-}15')$$

$$\text{div } \mathbf{A} + \frac{1}{c^2} \frac{\partial \phi}{\partial t} = 0 \qquad (31\text{-}16')$$

We define the Hertz vector $\mathbf{\Pi}$ by

$$\mathbf{A} = \frac{1}{c^2} \frac{\partial \mathbf{\Pi}}{\partial t} \qquad (31\text{-}23)$$

$$\phi = -\text{div } \mathbf{\Pi} \qquad (31\text{-}24)$$

Substitution of (31-23) and (31-24) into (31-16') shows that the Lorentz condition is satisfied by these definitions. If we also substitute (31-23) and (31-24) into (31-14') and (31-15'), we easily find that these last two equations are also satisfied provided that

$$\nabla^2 \mathbf{\Pi} - \frac{1}{c^2} \frac{\partial^2 \mathbf{\Pi}}{\partial t^2} = 0 \qquad (31\text{-}25)$$

Therefore we see that any solution of the vector wave equation (31-25) defines a possible electromagnetic field by means of the equations given above, except in source regions where $\mathbf{J} \neq 0$ and $\rho \neq 0$, for then the equations in (31-18), rather than (31-14') and (31-15'), apply.

It is convenient to express the fields directly in terms of $\mathbf{\Pi}$. From (31-5) and (31-23), we obtain

$$\mathbf{H} = \frac{1}{\mu_0} \text{curl } \mathbf{A} = \frac{1}{\mu_0 c^2} \text{curl} \left(\frac{\partial \mathbf{\Pi}}{\partial t} \right) = \epsilon_0 \frac{\partial}{\partial t} \text{curl } \mathbf{\Pi} \qquad (31\text{-}26)$$

while we find from (31-7), (31-23), (31-24), and (31-25) that

$$\mathbf{E} = \text{grad div } \mathbf{\Pi} - \frac{1}{c^2} \frac{\partial^2 \mathbf{\Pi}}{\partial t^2} = \text{curl curl } \mathbf{\Pi} \qquad (31\text{-}27)$$

These can be written even more compactly by defining $\mathbf{C} = \text{curl } \mathbf{\Pi}$ for they then become just $\mathbf{H} = \epsilon_0(\partial \mathbf{C}/\partial t)$ and $\mathbf{E} = \text{curl } \mathbf{C}$.

32 *Electric dipole radiation*

We look for the simplest possible solution of (31-25) in spherical coordinates in order to get a Hertz vector $\mathbf{\Pi}$ which may correspond to a source at the origin. Therefore we try to find a $\mathbf{\Pi}$ which depends only on r and t, i.e., $\mathbf{\Pi}(r, t)$. Then, with the use of (18-22), we find that (31-25) becomes

$$\frac{\partial^2 \mathbf{\Pi}}{\partial r^2} + \frac{2}{r} \frac{\partial \mathbf{\Pi}}{\partial r} - \frac{1}{c^2} \frac{\partial^2 \mathbf{\Pi}}{\partial t^2} = 0 \tag{32-1}$$

If we separate variables by writing

$$\mathbf{\Pi}(r, t) = \mathbf{F}(r)e^{-i\omega t} \tag{32-2}$$

and substituting this into (32-1), we find the equation for $\mathbf{F}$ to be

$$\frac{d^2 \mathbf{F}}{dr^2} + \frac{2}{r} \frac{d\mathbf{F}}{dr} + k^2 \mathbf{F} = 0 \tag{32-3}$$

where

$$k = \frac{\omega}{c} = \frac{2\pi}{\lambda} \tag{32-4}$$

We can also write (32-3) as

$$\frac{d^2}{dr^2}(r\mathbf{F}) + k^2(r\mathbf{F}) = 0$$

which has a solution $r\mathbf{F} = \textbf{const.}e^{ikr}$. If we write the **const.** as $\mathbf{p}_0/4\pi\epsilon_0$, where $\mathbf{p}_0$ is a constant vector, we can substitute this value for $\mathbf{F}$ into (32-2) and get

$$\mathbf{\Pi} = \frac{\mathbf{p}_0 e^{i(kr - \omega t)}}{4\pi\epsilon_0 r} \tag{32-5}$$

This corresponds to a wave traveling outward from the origin and with a speed c in the r direction. The amplitude decreases inversely with the distance r from the origin. We also see that (32-5) has a singularity at the origin where this solution no longer satisfies the wave equation (31-25). After we have obtained the fields corresponding to this $\mathbf{\Pi}$, we shall be able to interpret this singularity as a particular type of source for these fields.

According to (31-26), we now need to find curl $\mathbf{\Pi}$. Using (32-5), (25-24), and the fact that

$$\text{grad } f(r) = \frac{df}{dr} \hat{\mathbf{r}} = \frac{df}{dr}\left(\frac{\mathbf{r}}{r}\right) \tag{32-6}$$

we find that

$$\text{curl } \mathbf{\Pi} = \frac{1}{4\pi\epsilon_0} \text{ curl}\left[\left(\frac{e^{ikr}}{r}\right)(\mathbf{p}_0 e^{-i\omega t})\right]$$

$$= \frac{1}{4\pi\epsilon_0}\left[\text{grad}\left(\frac{e^{ikr}}{r}\right) \times (\mathbf{p}_0 e^{-i\omega t})\right]$$

$$= \frac{1}{4\pi\epsilon_0}\left[\frac{d}{dr}\left(\frac{e^{ikr}}{r}\right)\right](\hat{\mathbf{r}} \times \mathbf{p}_0 e^{-i\omega t}) \tag{32-7}$$

If we now substitute (32-7) into (31-26) and use

$$\frac{\partial \mathbf{\Pi}}{\partial t} = -i\omega \mathbf{\Pi} \tag{32-8}$$

$$\frac{d}{dr}\left(\frac{e^{ikr}}{r}\right) = k^2\left[\frac{i}{kr} - \frac{1}{(kr)^2}\right]e^{ikr} \tag{32-9}$$

we find that

$$\mathbf{H} = -\frac{i\omega k^2}{4\pi}\left[\frac{i}{kr} - \frac{1}{(kr)^2}\right](\hat{\mathbf{r}} \times \mathbf{p}_0)e^{i(kr-\omega t)} \tag{32-10}$$

Before we discuss this result, let us first calculate **E** from the first form given in (31-27).

Using (32-4) and (32-8), we obtain

$$-\frac{1}{c^2}\frac{\partial^2 \mathbf{\Pi}}{\partial t^2} = \frac{k^3}{4\pi\epsilon_0}\left[\frac{\mathbf{p}_0 e^{i(kr-\omega t)}}{kr}\right] \tag{32-11}$$

Substituting (32-5) into the vector identity following (23-6), we find

$$\text{div } \mathbf{\Pi} = \frac{1}{4\pi\epsilon_0} \text{ div}\left[\left(\frac{e^{ikr}}{r}\right)(\mathbf{p}_0 e^{-i\omega t})\right]$$

$$= \frac{1}{4\pi\epsilon_0} \text{ grad}\left(\frac{e^{ikr}}{r}\right) \cdot (\mathbf{p}_0 e^{-i\omega t})$$

$$= \frac{1}{4\pi\epsilon_0}\left[\frac{1}{r}\frac{d}{dr}\left(\frac{e^{ikr}}{r}\right)\right](\mathbf{r} \cdot \mathbf{p}_0 e^{-i\omega t}) \tag{32-12}$$

with the help of (32-6).

Now if we use

$$\text{grad }(uv) = v \text{ grad } u + u \text{ grad } v$$

$$\text{grad }(\mathbf{r} \cdot \mathbf{p}_0) = \text{grad }(xp_{0x} + yp_{0y} + zp_{0z})$$

$$= p_{0x}\hat{\mathbf{i}} + p_{0y}\hat{\mathbf{j}} + p_{0z}\hat{\mathbf{k}} = \mathbf{p}_0$$

we find from (32-12) and (32-6) that

$$\text{grad div } \mathbf{\Pi} = \frac{1}{4\pi\epsilon_0}\left\{\hat{\mathbf{r}}(\hat{\mathbf{r}}\cdot\mathbf{p}_0)\left[\frac{d^2}{dr^2}\left(\frac{e^{ikr}}{r}\right) - \frac{1}{r}\frac{d}{dr}\left(\frac{e^{ikr}}{r}\right)\right]\right.$$

$$\left. + \mathbf{p}_0\left[\frac{1}{r}\frac{d}{dr}\left(\frac{e^{ikr}}{r}\right)\right]\right\}e^{-i\omega t} \quad (32\text{-}13)$$

From (32-9), we also find that

$$\frac{1}{r}\frac{d}{dr}\left(\frac{e^{ikr}}{r}\right) = k^3\left[\frac{i}{(kr)^2} - \frac{1}{(kr)^3}\right]e^{ikr} \quad (32\text{-}14)$$

$$\frac{d^2}{dr^2}\left(\frac{e^{ikr}}{r}\right) = k^3\left[-\frac{1}{kr} - \frac{2i}{(kr)^2} + \frac{2}{(kr)^3}\right]e^{ikr} \quad (32\text{-}15)$$

If we now substitute (32-14) and (32-15) into (32-13), and then substitute the resulting expression plus (32-11) into (31-27), we find that

$$\mathbf{E} = \frac{k^3}{4\pi\epsilon_0}\left\{\hat{\mathbf{r}}(\hat{\mathbf{r}}\cdot\mathbf{p}_0)\left[-\frac{1}{kr} - \frac{3i}{(kr)^2} + \frac{3}{(kr)^3}\right]\right.$$

$$\left. + \mathbf{p}_0\left[\frac{1}{kr} + \frac{i}{(kr)^2} - \frac{1}{(kr)^3}\right]\right\}e^{i(kr-\omega t)} \quad (32\text{-}16)$$

As we see, the expressions for the fields given in (32-10) and (32-16) consist of several parts which depend on r in different ways. Both fields are waves traveling outward from the origin but with amplitudes which depend on distance and angles in a complicated manner. The easiest way to understand the significance of our results is to consider what they become in two standard limiting cases.

Near zone

Here $kr \ll 1$, i.e., $r \ll \lambda$; hence we are close to the origin on a wavelength scale of distance. We can therefore use the approximation

$$e^{ikr} \simeq 1 \quad (32\text{-}17)$$

We see that the predominant term in (32-10) will be that which goes as $(kr)^{-2}$; then we get as a good approximation

$$\mathbf{H}_N \simeq \frac{i\omega}{4\pi r^2}(\hat{\mathbf{r}}\times\mathbf{p}_0)e^{-i\omega t} = \frac{1}{4\pi r^2}\left[\frac{d}{dt}(\mathbf{p}_0 e^{-i\omega t})\right]\times\hat{\mathbf{r}} \quad (32\text{-}18)$$

In (32-16), the predominant terms are those which involve $(kr)^3$ in the denominator. We see that these did not come from (32–11), and now from (31-27) we can write

$$\mathbf{E}_N \simeq \operatorname{grad}\,(\operatorname{div}\,\mathbf{\Pi})_N = -\operatorname{grad}\,\phi_N \qquad (32\text{-}19)$$

where ϕ_N is obtained from (32-12) and (32-17) and is

$$\phi_N = -(\operatorname{div}\,\mathbf{\Pi})_N = \frac{(\mathbf{p}_0 e^{-i\omega t}) \cdot \hat{\mathbf{r}}}{4\pi\epsilon_0 r^2} \qquad (32\text{-}20)$$

These results enable us to interpret the constant of integration, $\mathbf{p}_0$. If we compare (32-20) and (19-26), we see that the electric field in the near zone is exactly that derived from the potential of an *electric dipole* located at the origin, whose dipole moment is $\mathbf{p}_0 e^{-i\omega t}$.

This interpretation is also consistent with the result (32-18) for $\mathbf{H}_N$. If we compare (32-18) and (19-31), we see that $\mathbf{H}_N$ is exactly the magnetic field due to a current element $i\,d\mathbf{s}$ given by

$$i\,d\mathbf{s} = \frac{d}{dt}\,(\mathbf{p}_0 e^{-i\omega t}) = \frac{d\mathbf{p}}{dt} \qquad (32\text{-}21)$$

But this is the current element which would arise from an electric dipole whose charge varied periodically, for, if the dipole moment is $\mathbf{p} = q\,d\mathbf{s}$,

$$\frac{d\mathbf{p}}{dt} = \frac{dq}{dt}\,d\mathbf{s} = i\,d\mathbf{s} \qquad (32\text{-}22)$$

since dq/dt is the current which flows as the charges on the dipole are changing. We see that (32-22) is the same as (32-21).

Therefore we are justified in concluding that the fields (32-10) and (32-16) are the result of an oscillating electric dipole located at the origin.

Radiation zone

Here $kr \gg 1$; hence $r \gg \lambda$. The predominant terms in (32-10) and (32-16) are now those with kr in the denominator; we can no longer use (32-17). Therefore we get

$$\mathbf{E}_R \simeq \frac{k^2}{4\pi\epsilon_0 r}\,[\mathbf{p}_0 - \hat{\mathbf{r}}(\hat{\mathbf{r}} \cdot \mathbf{p}_0)]e^{i(kr-\omega t)}$$

$$= \frac{k^2}{4\pi\epsilon_0 r}\,[\hat{\mathbf{r}} \times (\mathbf{p}_0 \times \hat{\mathbf{r}})]e^{i(kr-\omega t)} \qquad (32\text{-}23)$$

$$\mathbf{H}_R \simeq \frac{\omega k}{4\pi r}\,(\hat{\mathbf{r}} \times \mathbf{p}_0)e^{i(kr-\omega t)}$$

$$= -\frac{1}{4\pi cr}\left\{\hat{\mathbf{r}} \times \frac{d^2}{dt^2}\,[\mathbf{p}_0 e^{i(kr-\omega t)}]\right\} \qquad (32\text{-}24)$$

with the help of (1-21) and (32-4).

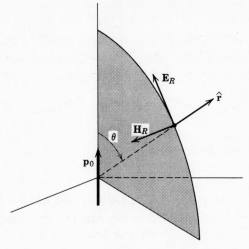

Fig. 32-1

We see that the fields in the radiation zone have amplitudes which now vary only as $1/r$, and they are proportional to the second time derivative of the dipole moment or to the rate of change of current in the oscillator.

We can easily find the relation between the fields from (32-23) and (32-24); it is

$$\mathbf{H}_R = \frac{\omega \epsilon_0}{k} (\hat{\mathbf{r}} \times \mathbf{E}_R) = c\epsilon_0(\hat{\mathbf{r}} \times \mathbf{E}_R) = \sqrt{\frac{\epsilon_0}{\mu_0}} (\hat{\mathbf{r}} \times \mathbf{E}_R) \qquad (32\text{-}25)$$

There are several comments to be made about these results:

(1) Since $\hat{\mathbf{r}}$ is in the direction of propagation, (32-23) and (32-24) show that both $\mathbf{E}_R$ and $\mathbf{H}_R$ are perpendicular to the direction of propagation. In other words, at large distances, the fields become *transverse waves*.

(2) From (32-25), we see that $\mathbf{E}_R$ and $\mathbf{H}_R$ are mutually perpendicular. We also see from (32-24) that $\mathbf{H}_R$ is perpendicular to the plane containing $\hat{\mathbf{r}}$ and $\mathbf{p}_0$. The mutual directions among these vectors are illustrated in Fig. 32-1, which shows the fields at a given time.

(3) The ratio of the magnitudes is found from (32-25) to be $E_R/H_R = \sqrt{\mu_0/\epsilon_0} = Z_0$. Therefore these fields in the radiation zone have the characteristics of a plane wave in free space.

(4) Since $|\hat{\mathbf{r}} \times \mathbf{p}_0| \to 0$ as $\theta \to 0$, both $\mathbf{E}_R$ and $\mathbf{H}_R$ become zero for a direction of propagation along the axis of the dipole. In other words, the electric dipole emits no radiation in the direction of its axis. Similarly, the fields have maximum amplitude in a direction perpendicular to the dipole axis.

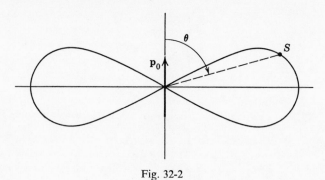

Fig. 32-2

The direction of the Poynting vector $\mathbf{S}$ is seen to be radially outward from Fig. 32-1. We can calculate the time average value $\bar{\mathbf{S}}$ by putting (32-23) and (32-24) into (28-47) and using $|\hat{\mathbf{r}} \times \mathbf{p}_0| = |\hat{\mathbf{r}} \times (\mathbf{p}_0 \times \hat{\mathbf{r}})| = |\mathbf{p}_0| \sin \theta$. The result is

$$\bar{\mathbf{S}} = \frac{\omega k^3 |p_0|^2 \sin^2 \theta}{32\pi^2 \epsilon_0 r^2} \, \hat{\mathbf{r}} = S\hat{\mathbf{r}} \tag{32-26}$$

and, since this is positive, there is a net outward flow of energy from the dipole. The magnitude S in (32-26) can be rewritten with the use of (32-4) and (28-21) as

$$S = \frac{\mu_0 \omega^4 |p_0|^2}{32\pi^2 c r^2} \sin^2 \theta \tag{32-27}$$

Thus the energy flux (intensity) is seen to vary as $1/r^2$, which is the familiar inverse square law for radiation intensity. The intensity varies with angle as $\sin^2 \theta$; this is illustrated in Fig. 32-2, where S is plotted as a function of θ.

By integrating (32-27) over the surface of a sphere of radius r, we can find the total energy radiated per second by the dipole. This is

$$-\frac{dU}{dt} = \int \bar{\mathbf{S}} \cdot d\mathbf{a} = \int S \, da = \int_0^{2\pi} \int_0^{\pi} S r^2 \sin \theta \, d\theta \, d\varphi = \frac{\mu_0 \omega^4 |p_0|^2}{12\pi c} \tag{32-28}$$

and is proportional to the fourth power of the frequency and to the square of the dipole moment.

Electric dipole radiation is the most common type observed in the light emitted by excited atoms. At the other extreme, a radio antenna can often be approximated as an electric dipole radiator, and (32-28) can be used to calculate its total radiation rate.

Exercises

32-1. Find the amplitudes of the electric and magnetic fields in the radiation from a 100-watt lamp at a distance of 3 meters, if it is assumed that all energy supplied to the lamp is radiated.

32-2. If there is an alternating current of maximum value i_0 in a vertical antenna of length l, and assuming that it can be treated as a dipole, find the total rate of radiation. Show that this power loss is the same as that which would be dissipated in the "radiation resistance" R given by $R = (2\pi/3) Z_0(l/\lambda)^2$.

32-3. Show that an accelerated charge q can be formally treated as a dipole of moment $q\mathbf{a}/\omega^2$, where $\mathbf{a}$ is the acceleration, and therefore the instantaneous rate of radiation from the charge would be $q^2a^2/6\pi\epsilon_0c^3$.

Part Three

Interactions of

Electromagnetic Fields and Matter

33 Electron theory of matter and scattering

In our discussion of plane waves, we found that Maxwell's equations provide a connection between the propagation properties of the waves and the electromagnetic constants of the medium. For example, we found in (28-22) that the index of refraction is given by $n = \sqrt{\kappa_e \kappa_m}$. We have also pointed out that the Maxwell theory does not tell us the values of these quantities, so they must be determined from experiment or from some microscopic theory of matter. In other words, all our experience with Maxwell's equations has made us so confident of their basic correctness that we determine the quantities ϵ, μ, σ by comparing experimental results with the predictions of the theory. Then, of course, we would like to be able to account for their numerical values and other properties by theoretical calculations based on some model of the properties of matter.

When we consider all that we know about individual atoms and molecules, as well as their various states of aggregation, we suspect that the fulfillment of this aim will be very complicated to carry out exactly. This turns out to be true, and, as a matter of fact, it is still being vigorously worked on, even though very much has been accomplished in the past. Nevertheless, a simple, yet surprisingly satisfactory, theory of this general subject can be developed by using the concepts of the *electron theory of matter*. What one attempts to do in this theory is to calculate the electromagnetic properties of matter by considering the *mechanical* behavior of a collection of charged mass points under the influence of applied fields. Although the theory we shall develop is admittedly only a first approximation, the ideas introduced thereby are basically still the same as those used in more sophisticated discussions, and these ideas and the results to which they lead give us an adequate understanding of what is going on.

33-1 Basic ideas of the electron theory

We assume that each molecule contains charged particles which can be acted on by electric and magnetic fields, that these charges have mass, and that they act as if they were held to equilibrium positions by forces proportional to the displacement, that is, by restoring forces of harmonic-oscillator type. (We recall from our results in mechanics that this holds for any law of force if the displacements from equilibrium are sufficiently small.) In addition, it is desirable to assume that these charged particles are also subject to a frictional damping force of some sort, which, as usual, is assumed to be proportional to the velocity. (We shall not need to inquire into the precise nature or origin of this damping force; it can be shown, however, that, for a harmonically oscillating charge, the radiated energy leads to an effect equivalent to a damping force proportional to the velocity.)

Therefore, for each charge, we can write an equation of motion of the form $m\ddot{\mathbf{r}} = \mathbf{F} - m\gamma\dot{\mathbf{r}} - m\omega_0^2\mathbf{r}$, where $\mathbf{r}$ is the displacement. If we also use (19-34), we can write this as

$$m\ddot{\mathbf{r}} + m\gamma\dot{\mathbf{r}} + m\omega_0^2\mathbf{r} = \mathbf{F} = e(\mathbf{E} + \dot{\mathbf{r}} \times \mathbf{B}) \tag{33-1}$$

where e is the charge which we shall always take to be the electronic charge -1.60×10^{-19} coulomb.

For simplicity, we shall always be considering the interaction between the medium and a plane wave. Then we see from (28-38) and (33-1) that we can estimate the ratio of the magnetic force to the electric force as

$$\frac{F_m}{F_e} \approx \frac{e\dot{r}B}{eE} = \frac{\dot{r}}{v} \simeq \frac{\dot{r}}{c} \tag{33-2}$$

where v is the speed of the wave in the medium, which we can take as not too much different from c, as we shall consider only cases in which n is of the order of magnitude of unity. We can reasonably expect the velocity of the charges to be small enough that $\dot{r} \ll c$; then we see from (33-2) that $F_m \ll F_e$. Therefore we can simplify (33-1) by neglecting the term $e\dot{\mathbf{r}} \times \mathbf{B}$. Justification for this simplification is provided by some famous experiments by Wiener on interference phenomena involving standing light waves. These experiments showed, at least for photographic plates, that optical effects are produced by $\mathbf{E}$ and not by $\mathbf{B}$.

With only $\mathbf{E}$ appearing in (33-1), the displacement $\mathbf{r}$ will be parallel to $\mathbf{E}$. Then the problem reduces to a one-dimensional one, and we can adopt the scalar equation of motion

$$m\ddot{x} + m\gamma\dot{x} + m\omega_0^2x = eE \tag{33-3}$$

as the basic equation of our theory.

33-2 Scattering

If we assume that the wavelength of our incident plane wave is large compared to the size of the molecule, the electric field will be approximately constant over the space occupied by the molecule; thus we can assume the same value for E at a given time for all the molecular charges.

Therefore only the time variation of the electric field of the plane wave remains, and (33-3) becomes

$$m\ddot{x} + m\gamma\dot{x} + m\omega_0^2 x = eE_0 e^{-i\omega t} \tag{33-4}$$

where E_0 is the amplitude. As in Chapter 5, we find that the steady state displacement as obtained from (33-4) is

$$x = \frac{(e/m)E_0 e^{-i\omega t}}{\omega_0^2 - \omega^2 - i\gamma\omega} = x_0 e^{-i\omega t} \tag{33-5}$$

Because of the much greater mass of the positively charged nucleus, we can assume it to be at rest at the equilibrium position. Hence the oscillatory motion of the electron is equivalent to an *induced* electric dipole whose moment is

$$p = ex = p_0 e^{-i\omega t} \tag{33-6}$$

where

$$p_0 = \frac{(e^2/m)E_0}{\omega_0^2 - \omega^2 - i\gamma\omega} \tag{33-7}$$

and therefore

$$|p_0|^2 = \frac{(e^2/m)^2 |E_0|^2}{(\omega_0^2 - \omega^2)^2 + (\gamma\omega)^2} \tag{33-8}$$

As a result of its forced oscillation, this induced dipole will radiate energy in all directions as described by (32-27). This energy, which is absorbed from the incident wave and then re-radiated, is called the scattered energy. The total rate is obtained by substituting (33-8) into (32-28); it is

$$-\frac{dU}{dt} = \frac{\mu_0(e^2/m)^2\omega^4 |E_0|^2}{12\pi c[(\omega_0^2 - \omega^2)^2 + (\gamma\omega)^2]} \tag{33-9}$$

For many purposes, particularly in comparing the scattering properties of different atoms and molecules, it is desirable to eliminate the arbitrary incident field term $|E_0|^2$ appearing in (33-9). This can be done by introducing the incident intensity I_0, that is, the energy flow per unit area of the incident plane wave; this is equal to the time average Poynting vector given by (28-51) as

$$I_0 = \bar{S} = \frac{1}{2}\sqrt{\frac{\epsilon_0}{\mu_0}} |E_0|^2 \tag{33-10}$$

A convenient quantity for our purposes is the *scattering cross section* σ_s, which is defined as the ratio of the total scattered energy rate to the total incident intensity. Therefore, using (33-9), (33-10), and (28-21), we find that

$$\sigma_s = \frac{1}{I_0}\left(-\frac{dU}{dt}\right) = \frac{8\pi r_0^2}{3} \cdot \frac{\omega^4}{[(\omega_0^2 - \omega^2)^2 + (\gamma\omega)^2]} \qquad (33\text{-}11)$$

where

$$r_0 = \frac{e^2}{4\pi\epsilon_0 mc^2} \qquad (33\text{-}12)$$

r_0 is called the classical radius of the electron. We see that σ_s has the dimensions of an area; it can be regarded as sort of an effective area of the charge for scattering since, if we write (33-11) as $(-dU/dt) = \sigma_s I_0$, we see that the total scattered energy is exactly equal to that passing through, and thereby intercepted by, the area σ_s.

Thomson scattering

Let us assume that $\omega \gg \omega_0$. This is almost the same as assuming $\omega_0 \simeq 0$ and $\gamma \simeq 0$; that is, the electron is essentially *free*. This turns out to be a good approximation for the frequencies of X-rays. Then (33-11) becomes

$$\sigma_s \simeq \frac{8\pi r_0^2}{3} \qquad (33\text{-}13)$$

so that for very high frequency the scattering cross section is independent of frequency. This formula was first derived for a completely free electron by Thomson and agrees well with experiment.

Rayleigh scattering

We now assume that $\omega \ll \omega_0$. This is the condition found for many materials when ω corresponds to the frequency of visible light and ω_0 corresponds to the ultraviolet. Then (33-11) becomes

$$\sigma_s \simeq \frac{8\pi r_0^2}{3}\left(\frac{\omega}{\omega_0}\right)^4 \sim \frac{1}{\lambda^4} \qquad (33\text{-}14)$$

where λ is the incident wavelength. Therefore, the shorter the wavelength, the more strongly is the incident light scattered. This is the result that is used to account for the blue color of the sky; the light entering the eye has been strongly scattered away from its direct path from the sun by the air molecules and, since the shortest visible wavelength corresponds to blue light, this is what one mainly sees. Similarly, the red color of a sunset arises because the light coming to the eye through a thick layer of air has had virtually all the blue light scattered out of this almost direct path, leaving only the long wavelength (red) component of the light left to be seen.

Resonance scattering

The maximum value of σ_s occurs when $\omega \simeq \omega_0$, and then (31-11) becomes

$$\sigma_s \simeq \frac{8\pi r_0^2}{3}\left(\frac{\omega_0}{\gamma}\right)^2 \tag{33-15}$$

which is generally very large compared to the free electron cross section given by (33-13). One example of resonance scattering occurs when sodium vapor is illuminated with the characteristic yellow sodium radiation. The whole volume of the vapor then becomes luminous because it is strongly scattering radiation of its natural frequency.

Polarization properties

The induced molecular dipoles have their axes parallel to the incident electric field, according to (33-3). Therefore, from (32-27), we see that there will also be no radiation scattered in this direction. If we now look in Fig. 33-1a at the scattered radiation in the direction OA, which is perpendicular both to the direction of the dipole axis and the direction of propagation of the incident wave, we see that not only is the radiation a maximum in this direction (or in any direction in this same plane) but

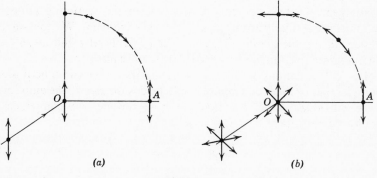

(a)   *(b)*

Fig. 33-1

also that it is polarized in the sense that the scattered electric field is parallel to the incident electric field. The arrows on the dashed line indicate the dependence of the intensity of the scattered radiation upon the angle from *OA*.

Now let us consider Fig. 33-1*b*, which shows what occurs when the incident radiation is unpolarized; that is, the incident electric fields have all possible directions. Then we see that the molecular dipoles will have all possible directions of oscillation as well, but they will all lie in the plane transverse to the incident direction, and the scattered radiation will *still* be polarized with the electric field in the plane perpendicular to the direction of incidence.

The fact that scattered light is polarized can be verified by observing the light scattered from the sky, and one finds that it has an appreciable degree of polarization. It was first shown by means of scattering experiments that X-rays can be polarized, and those results provided some of the early evidence that X-rays are also electromagnetic waves.

33-3   Coherence and incoherence

In the preceding sections we calculated the scattering from a single electron when a plane wave acts on it. When we discussed the results, we implicitly assumed that what is characteristic of a single induced dipole is characteristic of a collection of them. That is, if there are N scatterers, we have assumed that

Total scattered intensity $= N$

$\times$ (scattered intensity from a single dipole)   (33-16)

In practice, it is found that (33-16) holds very well for a *gas* but is not always generally true, as, for example, when the scattering atoms or molecules are regularly arranged, as in a crystalline solid. We now want to consider this whole question in more detail and thereby find under what conditions our assumption stated in (33-16) can be justified.

Maxwell's equations are linear; therefore they obey the superposition principle, that is, the total amplitude of a field is the *sum* of the amplitudes of the individual waves. For example, if we consider any component of the electric field, then

$$E_{\text{total}} = E = \sum_j E_j \qquad (33\text{-}17)$$

where E_j is the amplitude produced by the *j*th scatterer. Then, from

(28-51), the total scattered intensity will be proportional to the time average of the square of (33-17); that is,

$$I \sim \overline{E^2} = \overline{\left(\sum_j E_j\right)^2} \neq \sum_j \overline{E_j^2} \qquad (33\text{-}18)$$

will be generally true. Since the intensity I_j produced by the jth scatterer will be proportional to $\overline{E_j^2}$, we see that (33-18) says that

$$I \neq \sum_j I_j \qquad (33\text{-}19)$$

will ordinarily obtain. In other words, we must expect that the total scattered intensity is not necessarily equal to the sum of the individual intensities; on the other hand, (33-16) says that the total intensity *is* equal to the sum of the individual intensities, and this is often found to be true in practice.

The key to this apparent contradiction is to be found in the relations among the phases of the waves involved in the superposition (33-17). If the phases have fixed relations with respect to each other, they are said to be *coherent*; if the phases have random relations with respect to each other, they are said to be *incoherent*. We shall find below that, when we have coherence, we must always be sure to add the amplitudes; if we have incoherence, we can safely add intensities as in (33-16).

Since the waves are all proportional to $e^{i(\mathbf{k} \cdot \mathbf{r} - \omega t)}$, we see that the field at a given point due to a given source can be written

$$E_j = E_{0j} e^{-i(\omega t - \alpha_j)} \qquad (33\text{-}20)$$

where the phase α_j will depend on the distance from the scatterer, the distance from the primary source of the incident radiation, the initial conditions, etc. Assuming E_{0j} to be real, and taking the real part of (33-20), we find that we can write

$$E_j = E_{0j} \cos(\omega t - \alpha_j) \qquad (33\text{-}21)$$

and that, when we insert (33-21) into (33-17) to find the resultant amplitude, we obtain

$$E = \left(\sum_j E_{0j} \cos \alpha_j\right) \cos \omega t + \left(\sum_j E_{0j} \sin \alpha_j\right) \sin \omega t \qquad (33\text{-}22)$$

Using the relations immediately following (28-45), we find the time average of the square of (33-22) to be

$$\overline{E^2} = \frac{1}{2}\left[\left(\sum_j E_{0j} \cos \alpha_j\right)^2 + \left(\sum_j E_{0j} \sin \alpha_j\right)^2\right] \qquad (33\text{-}23)$$

Let us consider one of these terms in (33-23). It can be written

$$\left(\sum_j E_{0j} \cos \alpha_j\right)^2 = (E_{01} \cos \alpha_1 + E_{02} \cos \alpha_2 + \cdots)^2$$

$$= \sum_j E_{0j}{}^2 \cos^2 \alpha_j + \sum_j \sum_{\substack{k \\ k \neq j}} E_{0j} E_{0k} \cos \alpha_j \cos \alpha_k \quad (33\text{-}24)$$

Now let us assume that we are dealing with identical scatterers; let us also assume that the phases are incoherent and therefore completely independent. The cosines are just as likely to be positive as they are to be negative, and for a large number of scatterers the last sum in (33-24) will be zero as a result of mutual cancellation of terms, and we shall be left with only the first term on the right. We shall obtain a similar result for the summation involving $\sin \alpha_j$; hence, for incoherent phases, (33-23) becomes simply

$$\overline{E^2} = \tfrac{1}{2} \sum_j E_{0j}{}^2 (\cos^2 \alpha_j + \sin^2 \alpha_j) = \sum_j \tfrac{1}{2} E_{0j}{}^2 = \sum_j \overline{E_j{}^2} \quad (33\text{-}25)$$

because of (33-21). Therefore (33-25) represents a situation in which intensities add; if the scatterers are identical, $E_{0j} = E_0$ and $\overline{E^2} = N(\tfrac{1}{2}E_0{}^2)$, which is equivalent to (33-16).

If the phases are coherent, with fixed relations among them, we cannot say that the last sum in (33-24) will be zero; hence we shall generally have a situation in which (33-19) applies, although the exact value of I cannot be found until the precise relationships among the phases are known. As an extreme illustration, let us consider the situation in which all phases are equal, and, for simplicity, let us set $\alpha_j = 0$. Then (33-23) becomes $\overline{E^2} = \tfrac{1}{2}(\sum_j E_{0j})^2$. If, in addition, all the amplitudes are equal so that $E_{0j} = E_0$, then, by (33-22), $E = NE_0 \cos \omega t$ and $\overline{E^2} = N^2(\tfrac{1}{2}E_0{}^2)$, giving for this case the result

Total intensity $= N^2$

$\times$ (scattered intensity from a single dipole)   (32-26)

which is considerably different from (33-16).

The situations involving coherent phases in which the resultant amplitude can range from zero to the sum of the magnitudes of the individual amplitudes, depending on the precise relations among the phases, are exactly the phenomena called *interference and diffraction* in optics. We shall consider some of these phenomena in detail in later chapters.

Now let us apply these ideas of coherence to the problem of scattering by gas molecules. The phase of the scattered wave at the point P shown in Fig. 33-2a, arising from a molecule located at 1, will depend on the distance the wave has traveled from the source to 1, and from 1 to P. Since the molecules of a gas have no permanent locations with respect to each other,

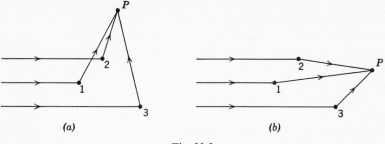

Fig. 33-2

their path lengths will be randomly related, their phases will be incoherent, and we shall be justified in adding intensities, as stated in (33-16) and observed experimentally. This procedure would not be permissible, for example, in discussing the scattering of X-rays in crystals, where the various atoms have fixed positions in the lattice, so that one observes interference instead.

The use of (33-16) would also not be very valid if we were looking at the radiation which is scattered from a gas and is observed in a direction close to the incident direction as is illustrated in Fig. 33-2b. If we are far enough in front, the path lengths are all about the same, the phases are approximately equal, and we get interference rather than incoherent scattering. In fact, this is the origin of the phenomenon of refraction, and we could show rigorously that it is the interference between the forward scattered waves and the original incident wave that produces a resultant wave traveling with the velocity given by (28-20), so that the medium can be described by the index of refraction, n. However, we shall not calculate n in this way; instead, in the next chapter, we shall use a simpler method which is based on (33-4) and gives basically the same results. We should not be too surprised, therefore, to find that the formulas we shall obtain bear a marked resemblance to those we have used in this chapter to describe scattering.

34 Dispersion

When we studied the propagation of plane waves in a conducting medium, we found that the medium could be described by a complex index of refraction which is given by (29-52), (29-53), and (28-10) as $N = n + i\beta = \{\kappa_e \kappa_m [1 + (i\sigma/\kappa_e \epsilon_0 \omega)]\}^{1/2}$, where n is the ordinary index of refraction. The existence of a complex index of refraction implied the absorption of energy from the wave. We have already pointed out that the quantities involved in the expression above are not constants because they are found to vary with frequency. This frequency dependence is called *dispersion* and is what we now want to calculate by means of the electron theory.

We consider first the case in which the medium is non-conducting; that is, $\sigma = 0$. If we also assume the very common situation in which the material is non-magnetic, $\kappa_m = 1$, and the complex index of refraction is given by the easily remembered formula

$$n + i\beta = \sqrt{\kappa_e} \qquad (34\text{-}1)$$

One might wonder why we are still including the imaginary part β in (34-1) since we have assumed zero conductivity. Our equation of motion for the electron (33-3) includes a damping term, and, as we found in Chapter 5, this will also lead to energy absorption. Hence we can expect, in advance, that there should be some absorption in a non-conducting medium, an effect which we have not previously included.

It is now very easy to outline the procedure by which we shall calculate the index of refraction by means of (34-1). Starting from our equation of motion, we find the displacement of the electron under the influence of the field. Then we can find P, the average electric dipole moment per unit volume as defined in (19-16). Finally, we get $\kappa_e = 1 + \chi_e = 1 + (P/\epsilon_0 E)$ as given by (22-2) and (22-4), and then substitute the resulting expression into (34-1). We shall illustrate this procedure by beginning with the simplest example.

34-1 Gases

The molecules in a gas can be assumed to be so far apart on the average that the interactions among the molecules can be neglected. Therefore we can safely assume that the field acting on the charges is that of the incident wave. The steady state displacement is then given again by (33-5) and the induced dipole moment by (33-6). Therefore, by (19-16), the polarization is

$$P = \frac{N(e^2/m)E}{\omega_0^2 - \omega^2 - i\gamma\omega} \qquad (34\text{-}2)$$

where N is the number of charges per unit volume.

So far we have assumed that there is only one type of charge which is characterized by the constants ω_0^2 and γ. It is quite reasonable to expect that the electrons are not all in identical situations within the molecules, and that there should be different pairs of characteristic frequencies ω_j^2 and associated damping factors γ_j, each pair reflecting the particular environment in which the given type of electron is found. Therefore, if we define N_j = number of electrons per unit volume characterized by the constants ω_j^2 and γ_j, we can easily generalize (34-2) so that the total polarization of the material is now given by

$$P = E \sum_j \frac{N_j(e^2/m)}{\omega_j^2 - \omega^2 - i\gamma_j\omega} \qquad (34\text{-}3)$$

and, if we use (22-2) and (22-4), we obtain

$$\kappa_e = 1 + \sum_j \frac{N_j(e^2/m\epsilon_0)}{\omega_j^2 - \omega^2 - i\gamma_j\omega} \qquad (34\text{-}4)$$

If $\omega = 0$, this becomes

$$\kappa_e = 1 + \frac{e^2}{m\epsilon_0} \sum_j \left(\frac{N_j}{\omega_j^2}\right) \qquad (34\text{-}5)$$

and shows how the static value of the dielectric constant can be related to the natural frequencies of the electrons.

For gases, it turns out that the summation in (34-4) is very small compared to unity, so that, when we insert (34-4) into (34-1), we can use the approximation $\sqrt{1 + x} \simeq 1 + \frac{1}{2}x$ and get

$$n + i\beta = 1 + \frac{1}{2} \sum_j \frac{N_j(e^2/m\epsilon_0)}{\omega_j^2 - \omega^2 - i\gamma_j\omega} \qquad (34\text{-}6)$$

We can find n and β separately by multiplying the numerator and denominator of the summation by $(\omega_j^2 - \omega^2 + i\gamma_j\omega)$ and equating real and imaginary parts of both sides; the results are

$$n = 1 + \frac{1}{2} \sum_j \frac{(N_j e^2/m\epsilon_0)(\omega_j^2 - \omega^2)}{(\omega_j^2 - \omega^2)^2 + (\gamma_j\omega)^2} \qquad (34\text{-}7)$$

$$\beta = \frac{1}{2} \sum_j \frac{(N_j e^2/m\epsilon_0)\gamma_j\omega}{(\omega_j^2 - \omega^2)^2 + (\gamma_j\omega)^2} \qquad (34\text{-}8)$$

As a qualitative check on the reasonableness of our results, we note first of all that, if $\gamma_j = 0$, $\beta = 0$. Thus, as we expected, it is the damping terms in the equations of motion which lead to the absorption of energy from the wave. Also, $\beta = 0$ if $\omega = 0$; hence there is no energy absorbed from a static field.

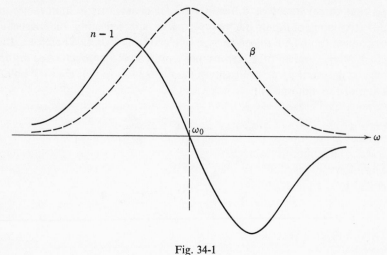

Fig. 34-1

In order to see the general nature of the variation with frequency predicted by these equations, let us assume only one set of constants, ω_0^2 and γ. Then (34-7) and (34-8) become

$$n - 1 = \frac{1}{2} \frac{(Ne^2/m\epsilon_0)(\omega_0^2 - \omega^2)}{[(\omega_0^2 - \omega^2)^2 + (\gamma\omega)^2]} \qquad (34\text{-}7')$$

$$\beta = \frac{1}{2} \frac{(Ne^2/m\epsilon_0)\gamma\omega}{[(\omega_0^2 - \omega^2)^2 + (\gamma\omega)^2]} \qquad (34\text{-}8')$$

These are plotted as functions of ω in Fig. 34-1. The frequency region near ω_0 in which both the index of refraction and the absorption factor are changing rapidly is called the region of anomalous dispersion. In the general case, (34-7) and (34-8), the dispersion curve will consist of a superposition of curves like those of Fig. 34-1, with an anomalous dispersion region around each of the ω_j. This is actually the type of dispersion curve that is observed in gaseous media; by fitting a curve like this to that observed, one can evaluate the parameters ω_j, γ_j, and N_j.

34-2   Liquids and solids

In these materials, the molecules are sufficiently close to each other that the effect of interactions among the molecules can be neglected no longer. Since the material is polarized, we expect that the actual electric field on a given charge will have a contribution from the polarization and hence it will be different from the applied field. The usual way of approximating this is to imagine a small sphere centered at the position of the electron in question to be cut out of the material as shown in Fig. 34-2a. The sphere is to be large enough that the material outside of it can be described in terms of the continuous polarization P. Then, because of the discontinuity in P, there are bound surface charges on the sphere which contribute to the local field E'. Using (22-11) and Fig. 34-2b, we see that this surface charge density is $\sigma_P = P_n = P \cos \theta$, and therefore the magnitude of the field produced by the charge on the area da is $dE' = \sigma_P \, da/4\pi\epsilon_0 r^2$, according to (19-6). The components normal to the direction of P will clearly cancel; hence, upon integrating over all the surface, we find the local field E' to be parallel to P and equal to

$$E' = \int dE' \cos \theta = \frac{P}{4\pi\epsilon_0} \int_0^{2\pi} \int_0^{\pi} \frac{\cos^2 \theta \cdot r^2 \sin \theta \, d\theta \, d\varphi}{r^2} = \frac{P}{3\epsilon_0} \quad (34\text{-}9)$$

This result is the contribution to the local field from all the material outside the sphere. We still have to calculate the contribution due to the molecules within the small sphere. It can be shown that this contribution averages to zero in an isotropic material such as a liquid, or when the molecules are arranged on a cubic lattice.

Therefore, if E is still the applied electric field, the total electric field acting on the charge is

$$E_t = E + E' = E + \frac{P}{3\epsilon_0} \quad (34\text{-}10)$$

There are two ways in which we can use (34-10). The final results will contain the same information, of course, but they will be stated in somewhat different terms.

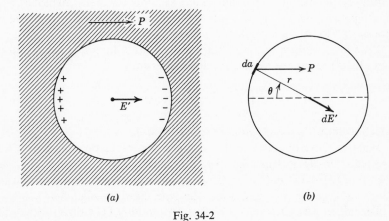

(a)   (b)

Fig. 34-2

The first method is to replace E by E_t in the *results* of our calculations for gases. Thus, for example, (34-3) becomes

$$P = \left(E + \frac{P}{3\epsilon_0}\right) \sum_j \frac{N_j(e^2/m)}{\omega_j{}^2 - \omega^2 - i\gamma_j\omega} \tag{34-11}$$

Now, using $P = (\kappa_e - 1)\epsilon_0 E$, we can easily show that

$$\frac{P}{E + (P/3\epsilon_0)} = 3\epsilon_0\left(\frac{\kappa_e - 1}{\kappa_e + 2}\right) \tag{34-12}$$

When we substitute (34-12) into (34-11) and use (34-1), we obtain

$$\frac{\kappa_e - 1}{\kappa_e + 2} = \frac{(n + i\beta)^2 - 1}{(n + i\beta)^2 + 2} = \frac{1}{3}\sum_j \frac{(N_je^2/m\epsilon_0)}{\omega_j{}^2 - \omega^2 - i\gamma_j\omega} \tag{34-13}$$

If we now let $f_j = N_j/N =$ fraction of the total number of charges per unit volume which are of type j, (34-13) can be written

$$\frac{(n + i\beta)^2 - 1}{(n + i\beta)^2 + 2} \cdot \frac{1}{N} = \frac{1}{3}\sum_j \frac{(f_je^2/m\epsilon_0)}{\omega_j{}^2 - \omega^2 - i\gamma_j\omega} \tag{34-14}$$

Since the right side is a function of ω, it will be constant for a given frequency.

As a special case, let us consider a transparent material for which $\beta = 0$. Then, for a fixed frequency, (34-14) gives

$$\left(\frac{n^2 - 1}{n^2 + 2}\right) \cdot \frac{1}{d} = \text{const.} \tag{34-15}$$

where d is the density, which is proportional to N. This relation is called the *Lorenz-Lorentz law*; it tells how the index of refraction depends on the density of the medium. It is amazingly accurate for many materials, even to the point of being approximately correct for the case in which a liquid transforms to the vapor phase.

If we let $\omega \to 0$, so that we obtain the condition for static fields, (34-13) and (34-14) together give the limiting expression

$$\left(\frac{\kappa_e - 1}{\kappa_e + 2}\right) \cdot \frac{1}{d} = \text{const.} \tag{34-16}$$

which is known as the *Clausius-Mossotti relation*.

What we have obtained in this manner, therefore, are equations which predict anomalous dispersion for the quantity $(n^2 - 1)/(n^2 + 2)$ rather than simply for n as in (34-7); the anomalous dispersion regions occur for the fixed frequencies ω_j and are of the type shown in Fig. 34-1.

The other way of using (34-10) is to put this field directly into the equation of motion (33-3). We shall not get simple results except by assuming that there is only one type of electron; in this case, (33-3) becomes

$$m\ddot{x} + m\gamma\dot{x} + m\omega_0^2 x = e[E + (P/3\epsilon_0)] \tag{34-17}$$

If we now substitute $P = Nex$, we find that (34-17) can be written

$$m\ddot{x} + m\gamma\dot{x} + m\omega_0'^2 x = eE \tag{34-18}$$

where

$$\omega_0'^2 = \omega_0^2 - (Ne^2/3m\epsilon_0) \tag{34-19}$$

This will lead at once to (34-6), except that now ω_0^2 will be replaced by $\omega_0'^2$. This will give us the same type of dispersion formula for the same quantities as those we found for gases, but now the natural frequencies ω_0' will be functions of the density since N is proportional to the density.

34-3 Metals

The simplest picture of conduction in metals which one can adopt is that some of the electrons are no longer bound to equilibrium positions but are *free* to travel through the metal and thereby carry the current. Therefore we can set $\omega_0^2 = 0$, and (33-3) becomes

$$m\ddot{x} + m\gamma\dot{x} = eE = eE_0 e^{-i\omega t} \tag{34-20}$$

If we assume a solution of the form

$$\dot{x} = \dot{x}_0 e^{-i\omega t} \tag{34-21}$$

and substitute this into (34-20), we find that

$$\dot{x} = \frac{eE}{m\gamma - im\omega} \tag{34-22}$$

Now the current density is

$$J = \rho v = Ne\dot{x} = \sigma E \tag{34-23}$$

from (19-1) and (24-7). If we substitute (34-22) into (34-23), we find that the conductivity is given by

$$\sigma = \frac{\sigma_0}{1 - i(\omega/\gamma)} \tag{34-24}$$

where

$$\sigma_0 = \frac{Ne^2}{m\gamma} \tag{34-25}$$

Therefore the conductivity shows dispersion in that it is a function of frequency. The constant σ_0 is the conductivity at zero frequency, as we see by putting $\omega = 0$ into (34-24). The result (34-25) also shows, as we would expect, that the damping term in the equation of motion leads to resistance; the smaller the value of γ is, the less is the resistance to the electron motion, and the greater the conductivity.

Now, if we look back at (28-10), we see that when $\kappa_m \simeq 1$, we have

$$n + i\beta = \left(\kappa_e + \frac{i\sigma}{\epsilon_0\omega}\right)^{\!\frac{1}{2}} \tag{34-26}$$

Hence the effect of conductivity, as far as wave propagation is concerned, is to make the dielectric constant complex and merely requires that we replace κ_e by $\kappa_e + (i\sigma/\epsilon_0\omega)$. Therefore, if we combine (34-26) and (34-4) and use (34-24), we get

$$(n + i\beta)^2 = \kappa_e + \left(\frac{i\sigma}{\epsilon_0\omega}\right) = 1 + \frac{(Ne^2/m\epsilon_0)}{-\omega^2 - i\gamma\omega} + \sum_j \frac{(N_je^2/m\epsilon_0)}{\omega_j{}^2 - \omega^2 - i\gamma_j\omega} \tag{34-27}$$

where N is now the number of free electrons per unit volume in the material. We see at once that the second term in (34-27), which is the contribution of the free electrons, is exactly of the form of the terms involved in the summation, except that $\omega_0{}^2$ is absent, since there are no restoring forces on these electrons. Therefore (34-27) tells us in general that the resultant absorption term β and the index of refraction n involve contributions from both the free and the bound electrons in the material. However, they do not contribute equally, and their relative importance in determining n and β also depends on the frequency region under consideration. This is most easily seen by beginning to find n and β separately.

If we write $(n + i\beta)^2 = (n^2 - \beta^2) + i2n\beta$ and then equate the real and imaginary parts on both sides of (34-27), we find

$$n^2 - \beta^2 = 1 - \frac{(\sigma_0/\gamma\epsilon_0)}{1 + (\omega/\gamma)^2} + \sum_j \frac{(N_je^2/m\epsilon_0)(\omega_j{}^2 - \omega^2)}{(\omega_j{}^2 - \omega^2)^2 + (\gamma_j\omega)^2} \tag{34-28}$$

$$2n\beta = \frac{(\sigma_0/\omega\epsilon_0)}{1 + (\omega/\gamma)^2} + \sum_j \frac{(N_je^2/m\epsilon_0)\gamma_j\omega}{(\omega_j{}^2 - \omega^2)^2 + (\gamma_j\omega)^2} \tag{34-29}$$

We could go on and solve these for n and β if we desired, but this is not necessary for our purposes.

We see that these formulas are quite complicated, but a few general things can be said about them. Let us begin by considering the low-frequency case; by this we mean $\omega \ll \sigma_0/\epsilon_0$ or $\sigma_0/\omega\epsilon_0 \gg 1$. We previously discussed exactly this situation in Sec. 29-5 in connection with the skin effect. As $\omega \to 0$, we see that (34-28) and (34-29) become

$$n^2 - \beta^2 \to 1 + \Delta \quad \text{and} \quad 2n\beta \to (\sigma_0/\omega\epsilon_0) \gg 1 \tag{34-30}$$

where Δ is a small quantity which never becomes very large because for $\omega \simeq 0$ there are no terms which can give resonance. Since the product $n\beta$ is very large, while the difference $n^2 - \beta^2$ remains practically constant and in fact, negligible compared to either n or β, (34-30) simply means that in this limiting case of low frequency

$$n \simeq \beta \simeq \left(\frac{\sigma_0}{2\omega\epsilon_0}\right)^{1/2}$$

These values are exactly those given in (29-65) and found by another method. Therefore, at low enough frequencies, all the propagation properties are completely determined by the conductivity and the effects of the bound electrons are masked by those of the free electrons.

For other frequency ranges, we shall have to content ourselves with qualitative remarks about the relative contributions of the electrons. At intermediate frequencies, by which we mean infrared or visible, the free and bound electrons are both important and the behavior of n and β can be quite complicated. As we get into high frequencies (ultraviolet and beyond), the effects of the bound electrons become dominant because of their many resonant frequencies in this region; in other words, the free electrons may as well not be there as far as the optical properties are concerned, and a metal acts like an insulator. In the extreme high-frequency case, in which $\omega \gg$ (any possible natural frequency), (34-28) and (34-29) become $n^2 - \beta^2 \rightarrow 1$ and $2n\beta \rightarrow 0$, so that $\beta \rightarrow 0$ and $n \rightarrow 1$. Hence the medium should be completely transparent according to this model. This is not what is observed, however, because effects of quantum theory become very important at extremely high frequencies, and these effects, of course, are not included in our simple classical electron theory of matter.

Exercises

34-1. Assuming that $\gamma_j \ll \omega_j$, show that for gases the maximum and minimum values of n in an anomalous region occur at frequencies where the value of β is half its maximum.

34-2. The quantity

$$\frac{n^2 - 1}{n^2 + 2} \frac{M}{d}$$

is called the molecular refractivity of a compound of molecular weight M. Neglecting damping terms, show that the molecular refractivity equals the sum of the atomic refractivities of the atoms forming the compound. What sort of experiments could you do to check this result? What possible applications can you make of this result?

35 Huygens' principle

Most of our discussion of electromagnetic waves so far has been limited to waves of infinite extent. The effect of boundaries on the region containing electromagnetic energy is of great importance because the situations most commonly encountered involve bounding surfaces of one sort or another. We considered one aspect of this problem in Chapter 30 when we discussed the normal modes of the field in regions with perfectly conducting bounding surfaces. Another aspect of the effect of boundaries arises when we consider what will happen when a plane wave of unlimited extent is incident upon a perfectly absorbing boundary, or screen, containing openings of assorted sizes and shapes. It is evident that some of the incident energy will be transmitted through the openings, but we should like to know how much of it will be transmitted, and how it will be distributed throughout the region on the other side of the screen. As we shall see, phenomena of this type involve the superposition of waves with coherent phases.

The simplest answer to the problem posed above is that given by geometrical optics. In this description, there is a discontinuity in the radiation: the fields have their normal values in the geometrically defined region into which the radiation could go if it traveled in straight lines; outside this region, i.e., in the *shadow*, the fields and their associated energy densities are zero.

It is a matter of common observation that this is approximately correct, since people, posts, buildings etc., all cast sharp shadows. However, if we investigate more closely we find that there is some radiation which does go into the geometric shadow region, so that the transition in energy density is not abrupt, but instead the intensity varies more or less rapidly as one penetrates into the shadow. It is also found that the intensity does not decrease smoothly to zero, but instead there are maxima and minima in the intensity variation. This behavior, which is characteristic of *all* types of waves, is known as *diffraction* and is what we now want to consider.

In order to solve this problem exactly, we should have to find solutions of the wave equation for **E** and **H** which satisfy Maxwell's equations in the absorbing screen as well as in all the rest of space. In addition, these fields would have to satisfy all the appropriate boundary conditions, taking into account the fact that the electromagnetic properties of these different regions (μ, ϵ, σ) are probably all different. If we could do all of this, we could expect that the solutions found in this way would answer all the

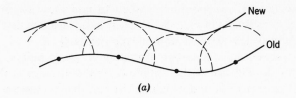

(a)

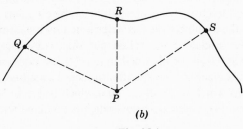

(b)

Fig. 35-1

possible questions we could ask about intensity, polarization, and directions of propagation of the waves. This overall problem is so difficult that it has not been solved in general, although it has been worked through for a few special cases. Diffraction of electromagnetic waves is a research field to which a considerable amount of work is being devoted at present, and more elaborate and successful methods of treating it have been devised than we are able to consider. We shall not attempt to treat this problem in general, but instead we shall discuss an approximate treatment which turns out to be surprisingly accurate for a large fraction of the possible cases and gives a basic idea of the physical situation which results in diffraction.

The concept, which is the basis of our considerations, is known as *Huygens' principle*. In its most elementary form it says that each point on a wave front can be regarded as a source of a new spherical wave which has a radius $v \, \Delta t$ after a time Δt. The new wave front is then considered to be the envelope of all these spherical "wavelets." Thus, as shown in Fig. 35-1a, Huygens' principle describes the progress of the wave front in this way. This construction is often used in elementary textbooks to derive the straight line propagation of light waves, as well as the laws of reflection and refraction. One of the difficulties of this elementary formulation is that it looks as if there should be a wave front going backward as well as forward, and this is definitely not observed. We shall come back to this point later on.

Fresnel and Young generalized and improved these ideas somewhat in the following way. Suppose one wished to find the wave amplitude at some point P as shown in Fig. 35-1b. Their basic idea was that one should add all the wavelets arriving from all the points $Q, R, S, \ldots$, assuming that the wavelets have a certain amplitude at these points, taking into account the dependence of the amplitude on the distance of the point on the wave front from P, and including the fact that all these wavelets will have different phase factors e^{ikr}. Actually, the surface $Q, R, S, \ldots$ need not be a wave front at all; it could be any closed surface for which the correct amplitude and phase could be assigned to each wavelet.

In general terms, therefore, what we shall mean by Huygens' principle is the statement that the amplitude at P is determined by the amplitude at all points on a surface enclosing P. When put this way, this principle is reminiscent of the solution we obtained in (21-32) for Poisson's equation by our use of Green's theorem. As a matter of fact, the method of attacking diffraction problems which we shall use, and which is due to Kirchhoff, is based on a solution of the wave equation which is obtained with the use of Green's theorem.

35-1   Kirchhoff's formulation of Huygens' principle

We found in (28-5) and (28-6) that **E** and **H** satisfy the equations

$$\nabla^2 \begin{bmatrix} \mathbf{E} \\ \mathbf{H} \end{bmatrix} = \frac{1}{v^2} \frac{\partial^2}{\partial t^2} \begin{bmatrix} \mathbf{E} \\ \mathbf{H} \end{bmatrix} \tag{35-1}$$

and the average intensity for these transverse waves is given in (28-50) as

$$\bar{\mathbf{S}} = \frac{1}{2} \sqrt{\frac{\epsilon}{\mu}} |\mathbf{E}|^2 \, \hat{\mathbf{n}} \sim |E|^2 \tag{35-2}$$

where E is the magnitude of the electric field.

This suggests the idea of representing the radiation by the single *scalar U*, which can be the magnitude of the electric field because the magnitude would be the only component in a properly chosen coordinate system. Then we would have

$$\nabla^2 U = \frac{1}{v^2} \frac{\partial^2 U}{\partial t^2} \tag{35-3}$$

$$\text{Intensity} = I \sim |U|^2 = UU^* \tag{35-4}$$

These two equations contain the basic assumption of our discussion of diffraction, namely, that the wave can be represented by a scalar quantity such that the intensity (energy flow) is proportional to the absolute square of this scalar.

If we discuss radiation of a single frequency (monochromatic), we can set

$$U = u(x, y, z)e^{-i\omega t} \tag{35-5}$$

Substituting (35-5) into (35-3), we obtain

$$\nabla^2 u + k^2 u = 0 \tag{35-6}$$

where, as usual,

$$k = \frac{\omega}{v} = \frac{2\pi}{\lambda} \tag{35-7}$$

We also find that (35-4) becomes

$$I \sim |u|^2 = uu^* \tag{35-8}$$

In Green's theorem (21-21), let us replace ϕ by u and ψ by v, where both u and v satisfy (35-6). Then

$$u \nabla^2 v - v \nabla^2 u = -k^2 uv + k^2 uv = 0$$

so that (21-21) becomes

$$\int_S (u \operatorname{grad} v - v \operatorname{grad} u) \cdot d\mathbf{a} = 0 \tag{35-9}$$

where S is some arbitrary closed surface.

Let us *choose* v to be the simplest solution of (35-6), that is, $v = v(r)$. We previously found that this is given in its dependence on r by (32-5) as

$$v = \frac{e^{ikr}}{r} \tag{35-10}$$

Since v becomes infinite at $r = 0$, that is, at the point P where we wish to find u, we must exclude a region about P from our volume of integration. We again do this by constructing a small sphere of radius R whose center is at P as shown in Fig. 35-2. Then the total surface of integration in (35-9) includes the surface of the sphere, Σ. The outer normal to Σ is directed toward P as shown. Then (35-9) and (35-10) combined become

$$\int_\Sigma \left[u \operatorname{grad} \left(\frac{e^{ikr}}{r} \right) - \left(\frac{e^{ikr}}{r} \right) \operatorname{grad} u \right] \cdot d\mathbf{a}$$

$$+ \int_S \left[u \operatorname{grad} \left(\frac{e^{ikr}}{r} \right) - \left(\frac{e^{ikr}}{r} \right) \operatorname{grad} u \right] \cdot d\mathbf{a} = 0 \tag{35-11}$$

As before, we are interested in the limiting value of the integral over Σ as the sphere is shrunk down to zero radius. We assume that u and grad u

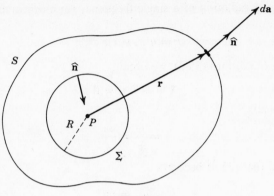

Fig. 35-2

are continuous and bounded everywhere. Proceeding exactly as in Sec. 21-3, we find that

$$\lim_{R \to 0} \int_\Sigma \left(\frac{e^{ikr}}{r}\right) \text{grad } u \cdot d\mathbf{a}$$

$$= \lim_{R \to 0} \left(\frac{e^{ikR}}{R}\right) |\text{grad } u|_P \, 4\pi R^2$$

$$= \lim_{R \to 0} \text{const. } R = 0 \tag{35-12}$$

To do the other integral over Σ, we use (32-6), (32-9), the fact that $\hat{\mathbf{r}} = -\hat{\mathbf{n}}$, and $d\mathbf{a} = \hat{\mathbf{n}} \, da$, and we find

$$\lim_{R \to 0} \int_\Sigma u \text{ grad}\left(\frac{e^{ikr}}{r}\right) \cdot d\mathbf{a}$$

$$= \lim_{R \to 0} u_P e^{ikR}\left(-\frac{ik}{R} + \frac{1}{R^2}\right)4\pi R^2 = 4\pi u_P \tag{35-13}$$

where u_P is the value of u at P. Combining (35-11), (35-12), and (35-13), we find that u_P is given by

$$u_P = \frac{1}{4\pi} \int_S \left[\left(\frac{e^{ikr}}{r}\right) \text{grad } u - u \text{ grad}\left(\frac{e^{ikr}}{r}\right)\right] \cdot d\mathbf{a} \tag{35-14}$$

which is our desired result and expresses the value of the solution of (35-6) at P in terms of its values and that of its gradient on the closed surface S surrounding P.

The question then naturally arises: What values would we adopt for u on the surface if, for example, the surface should consist of an absorbing screen with holes cut in it? The natural assumption to make is the one we shall adopt: We assume that the value of u is the same as it would be if the screen were not there. This obviously cannot be exactly correct, but it will work out sufficiently well for our purposes; actually, there is no reasonable alternative assumption which we can make since we are not able to solve the exact problem anyhow to find the true values of u on S.

Since we are going to apply (35-14) only to problems involving openings in perfectly absorbing screens, the only part of the surface integration which will contribute, i.e., where $u \neq 0$, is that from the integration over the openings, or over the *aperture* as it is called, and which we shall symbolize by $\mathscr{A}$. Thus we can now write (35-14) as

$$u_P = \frac{1}{4\pi} \int_{\mathscr{A}} \left[\left(\frac{e^{ikr}}{r} \right) \text{grad } u - u \text{ grad} \left(\frac{e^{ikr}}{r} \right) \right] \cdot d\mathbf{a} \qquad (35\text{-}15)$$

In order to obtain a definite expression for u, we shall specialize even further to a case in which the original source is a point source Q as shown in Fig. 35-3. Since the wave from Q is a spherical one whose amplitude depends only on r_1, the value of u must have the general form of (35-10), so that the value of u *at the aperture* due to Q is

$$u_{\mathscr{A}} = \frac{Ae^{ikr_1}}{r_1} \qquad (35\text{-}16)$$

where A is some amplitude. We can use (32-6) and (32-9) to evaluate grad u at $\mathscr{A}$; the result is

$$(\text{grad } u)_{\mathscr{A}} = \frac{A}{r_1} \left(ik - \frac{1}{r_1} \right) e^{ikr_1} \hat{\mathbf{r}}_1 \qquad (35\text{-}17)$$

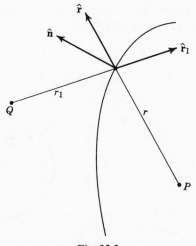

Fig. 35-3

If we put (35-16) and (35-17) into (35-15) and use (32-9), (1-7), and $d\mathbf{a} = \hat{\mathbf{n}}\, da$, we obtain

$$u_P = -\frac{A}{4\pi} \int_{\mathscr{A}} \frac{e^{ik(r+r_1)}}{rr_1} \left[\left(ik - \frac{1}{r}\right) \cos(\hat{\mathbf{r}}, \hat{\mathbf{n}}) - \left(ik - \frac{1}{r_1}\right) \cos(\hat{\mathbf{r}}_1, \hat{\mathbf{n}}) \right] da$$

(35-18)

where $(\hat{\mathbf{r}}, \hat{\mathbf{n}})$ is the angle between $\hat{\mathbf{r}}$ and $\hat{\mathbf{n}}$, etc.

We now further assume that $r \gg \lambda$ and $r_1 \gg \lambda$, so that, according to (35-7),

$$k \gg \frac{1}{r} \quad \text{and} \quad k \gg \frac{1}{r_1} \tag{35-19}$$

This assumption is true in virtually all practical cases at optical frequencies; it will not necessarily be correct at longer wavelengths, such as in the microwave region, unless you get very far from the source and aperture. Then we can simplify (35-18) even more to get

$$u_P = -\frac{ikA}{4\pi} \int_{\mathscr{A}} \frac{e^{ik(r+r_1)}}{rr_1} \left[\cos(\hat{\mathbf{r}}, \hat{\mathbf{n}}) - \cos(\hat{\mathbf{r}}_1, \hat{\mathbf{n}})\right] da \tag{35-20}$$

which expresses the value of u at P as a superposition of wavelets whose amplitudes have a complicated dependence on distance and direction.

The term in brackets in (35-20) is known as the obliquity factor, and it tells how the wavelet amplitude depends on angle. In order to illustrate its effect, let us consider the simple aperture shown in Fig. 35-4a. Since $\cos(\hat{\mathbf{r}}, \hat{\mathbf{n}}) = \cos \theta$, and $\cos(\hat{\mathbf{r}}_1, \hat{\mathbf{n}}) = \cos \pi = -1$, the obliquity factor is $1 + \cos \theta$. This is plotted in Fig. 35-4b, where we see that in the backward direction $(\theta = \pi)$ the wavelet amplitude is zero, showing that the wavelets do not travel backwards, thus removing the previous objection to our qualitative statement of Huygens' principle.

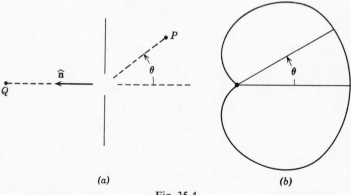

(a)   (b)

Fig. 35-4

We can still simplify (35-20) even more by assuming a situation which is almost always true in practice, namely, that r and r_1 are both very large as compared to the dimensions of the aperture. Then, as we integrate over the aperture, neither the obliquity factor nor the term rr_1 in the denominator will differ much from some appropriate average values. Therefore we can replace them by their average values and take them out from under the integral without introducing any appreciable error. We cannot make this simplification in the exponential term in (35-20), however, because both r and r_1 are multiplied by the large factor $k = 2\pi/\lambda$, and even small changes in r and r_1 can make a large change in the value of the exponential. If we do this, (35-20) becomes

$$u_P = u_0'' \int_{\mathscr{A}} e^{ik(r+r_1)} \, da \qquad (35\text{-}21)$$

where

$$u_0'' = - \frac{ikA}{4\pi \bar{r}\bar{r}_1} \, [\overline{\cos(\hat{\mathbf{r}}, \hat{\mathbf{n}})} - \overline{\cos(\hat{\mathbf{r}}_1, \hat{\mathbf{n}})}] \qquad (35\text{-}22)$$

We can make one more simplification of (35-21) in a way which corresponds to the most common experimental arrangements used to study diffraction, and which will not make us lose any of the essential features of diffraction phenomena. We shall assume that the source is so far away that the wave incident upon the aperture is a plane wave and is incident normally upon the aperture (or equivalently, that the wave has been made plane by some suitable lens system). Then the distance r_1 will be the same for each point of the aperture so that e^{ikr_1} will be a constant and can be taken out from under the integral in (35-21). Therefore, if we set

$$u_0' = u_0'' e^{ikr_1} \qquad (35\text{-}23)$$

we can write

$$u_P = u_0' \int_{\mathscr{A}} e^{ikr} \, da \qquad (35\text{-}24)$$

as our final formulation of Huygens' principle which we use together with (35-8). Actually, since we shall only be *comparing* intensities in what we shall do later, the constant of proportionality in (35-8) will always cancel out of every ratio we form; therefore we may as well set it equal to unity and write (35-8) simply as

$$I_P = |u_P|^2 \qquad (35\text{-}25)$$

35-2 Classification of diffraction phenomena

It turns out that essentially two types of diffraction are found: the pattern is observed at distances from the aperture which are comparable to

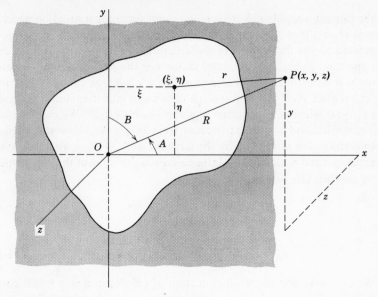

Fig. 35-5

the dimensions of the aperture, or at distances which are large compared to the dimensions of the aperture. In the first type, which is known as *Fresnel diffraction*, the illuminated part of the pattern has a size and shape comparable to that of the aperture; in the second type, which is known as *Fraunhofer diffraction*, the pattern has no resemblance to the aperture. We now want to find a mathematical criterion for distinguishing between these two.

Let us place the origin at a convenient point in the plane of the aperture, which we take as the xy plane so that z is normal to the plane (Fig. 35-5). The coordinates of P are x, y, z, and those of a point in the aperture ξ, η. Then we see that

$$r = [(x - \xi)^2 + (y - \eta)^2 + z^2]^{1/2} \qquad (35\text{-}26)$$

If we let

$$R = (x^2 + y^2 + z^2)^{1/2} \qquad (35\text{-}27)$$

be the distance of P from the origin, (35-26) can be written

$$r = [R^2 - 2(x\xi + y\eta) + \xi^2 + \eta^2]^{1/2} \qquad (35\text{-}28)$$

We also let α and β be the direction cosines of the line OP, so that

$$\alpha = \cos A = \frac{x}{R}, \quad \beta = \cos B = \frac{y}{R} \qquad (35\text{-}29)$$

and (35-28) can be written

$$r = R\left[1 - \frac{2(\alpha\xi + \beta\eta)}{R} + \left(\frac{\xi}{R}\right)^2 + \left(\frac{\eta}{R}\right)^2\right]^{\frac{1}{2}} \tag{35-30}$$

If we expand (35-30) in powers of ξ and η, using $(1 + x)^{\frac{1}{2}} = 1 + \frac{1}{2}x - \frac{1}{8}x^2 + \cdots$, and keeping only quadratic powers of ξ and η, we find that (35-30) becomes

$$r = R - (\alpha\xi + \beta\eta) + \frac{1}{2R}\left[\xi^2 + \eta^2 - (\alpha\xi + \beta\eta)^2\right] \tag{35-31}$$

If we now write (35-31) as

$$r = R + \phi(\xi, \eta) \tag{35-32}$$

and set

$$u_0 = u_0' e^{ikR} \tag{35-33}$$

then (35-24) becomes

$$u_P = u_0 \int_{\mathscr{A}} e^{ik\phi(\xi,\eta)}\, d\xi\, d\eta \tag{35-34}$$

where $\phi(\xi, \eta)$ is a power series in the coordinates (ξ, η) of the aperture and involves the constant value of R as well.

We can now classify the two types of diffraction in terms of ϕ.

Fresnel diffraction

The pattern is studied so close to the aperture that (ξ/R) and (η/R) are large enough that the quadratic terms cannot be neglected. Therefore, from (35-31) and (35-32),

$$\phi \text{ (Fresnel)} = -(\alpha\xi + \beta\eta) + \frac{1}{2R}\left[\xi^2 + \eta^2 - (\alpha\xi + \beta\eta)^2\right] \tag{35-35}$$

Fraunhofer diffraction

The pattern is studied so far from the aperture that (ξ/R) and (η/R) are small enough that we can neglect quadratic terms. Therefore

$$\phi \text{ (Fraunhofer)} = -(\alpha\xi + \beta\eta) \tag{35-36}$$

Exercise

35-1. Two apertures are said to be complementary if the openings in one are the same as the opaque portions of the other; that is, if the two apertures are superimposed, they form a completely opaque screen. Babinet's theorem says that the diffraction patterns produced by complementary screens are identical, except in the direction of the incident beam. Use (35-24) and (35-25) to prove this theorem.

36 Fraunhofer diffraction

Since Fraunhofer diffraction is the simpler type to study, both theoretically and experimentally, we shall begin with it.

36-1   Infinite slit

We let the aperture consist of a slit which is infinitely long in the y direction and has a width a, as shown in Fig. 36-1. We choose our origin at the center of the slit. Because of the infinite length of the slit, the intensity distribution as a function of angle will be the same in any plane parallel to the xz plane; hence we need only solve the two-dimensional problem in the xz plane. If we let θ be the angle between OP and the normal Oz, we see that $\alpha = \sin \theta$, $\beta = 0$, and (35-36) becomes

$$\phi = -\xi \sin \theta \qquad (36\text{-}1)$$

Then, if we substitute (36-1) into (35-34) and include the constant contribution from the integral over η in u_0, we obtain

$$u_P = u_0 \int_{-\frac{1}{2}a}^{\frac{1}{2}a} e^{-ik\xi \sin \theta}\, d\xi = u_0 a \left(\frac{e^{i\gamma} - e^{-i\gamma}}{2i\gamma} \right) = u_0 a \left(\frac{\sin \gamma}{\gamma} \right) \qquad (36\text{-}2)$$

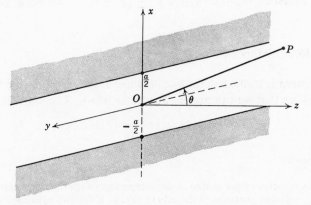

Fig. 36-1

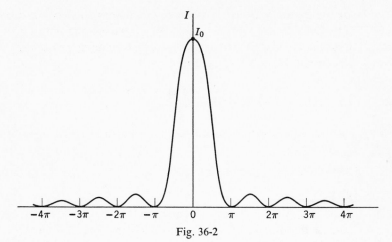

Fig. 36-2

where

$$\gamma = \frac{ka \sin \theta}{2} = \frac{\pi a \sin \theta}{\lambda} \tag{36-3}$$

Therefore (35-25) gives the intensity in the direction OP as

$$I = a^2 |u_0|^2 \left(\frac{\sin \gamma}{\gamma}\right)^2 = I_0 \left(\frac{\sin \gamma}{\gamma}\right)^2 \tag{36-4}$$

where I_0 is the maximum intensity.

We see that the intensity is a maximum in the direction corresponding to $\gamma = 0$, i.e., $\theta = 0$. The intensity is zero in directions corresponding to $\gamma = n\pi$ or, from (36-3), for angles given by the relation

$$a \sin \theta = n\lambda \tag{36-5}$$

where $n = \pm 1, \pm 2, \pm 3, \ldots$. The result (36-5) is the well-known condition for the minima in the diffraction pattern from a single slit.

A plot of the intensity as a function of γ, and thereby of θ by means of (36-3), is shown in Fig. 36-2. We see that there are alternately directions of minimum and maximum intensity. The positions of the maxima are *approximately* halfway between the minima, that is, when $\sin \gamma = 1$, or $\gamma = \pm \frac{3}{2}\pi, \pm \frac{5}{2}\pi, \ldots$. The relative values of the intensity at the maxima are then obtained by inserting these values of γ into (36-4); they are, approximately,

$$\frac{I}{I_0} = 1, \quad \left(\frac{2}{3\pi}\right)^2, \quad \left(\frac{2}{5\pi}\right)^2, \quad \ldots = 1, \quad 0.045, \quad 0.016, \quad \ldots \tag{36-6}$$

We see that the intensities of the maxima decrease very rapidly.

Most of the intensity of the diffracted radiation is therefore concentrated within the central maximum; in other words, most of the energy is contained in the angular spread between the first minima. This angular spread can be found from (36-5) and is

$$\Delta\theta = 2 \arcsin \left(\frac{\lambda}{a}\right) \simeq \frac{2\lambda}{a} \qquad (36\text{-}7)$$

We see that the pattern will be more spread out for the larger wavelengths or smaller slit widths.

36-2 Rectangular slit

Now suppose that the slit has a finite width b in the y direction as shown in Fig. 36-3. Then, if α and β are the direction cosines of OP, (35-34) and (35-36) become

$$u_P = u_0 \int_{-\frac{1}{2}a}^{\frac{1}{2}a} e^{-ik\alpha\xi}\, d\xi \int_{-\frac{1}{2}b}^{\frac{1}{2}b} e^{-ik\beta\eta}\, d\eta = u_0 ab \left(\frac{\sin\gamma}{\gamma}\right)\left(\frac{\sin\delta}{\delta}\right) \qquad (36\text{-}8)$$

where

$$\gamma = \frac{\pi a\alpha}{\lambda} \quad \text{and} \quad \delta = \frac{\pi b\beta}{\lambda} \qquad (36\text{-}9)$$

Therefore (35-25) becomes

$$I = I_0 \left(\frac{\sin\gamma}{\gamma}\right)^2 \left(\frac{\sin\delta}{\delta}\right)^2 \qquad (36\text{-}10)$$

Thus the pattern for this slit is a superposition of patterns, each of which is similar to that obtained from an infinite slit.

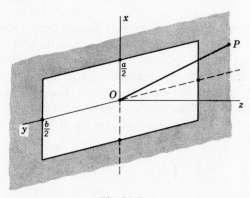

Fig. 36-3

36-3 Circular aperture

We let the radius of the circle be a and choose the origin at the center as shown in Fig. 36-4. The pattern will clearly be symmetric about the z axis; therefore we can pick P to be in the xz plane so that

$$\alpha = \sin \theta, \quad \beta = 0 \tag{36-11}$$

and $\phi = -\alpha\xi$. We introduce polar coordinates ρ and φ in the plane of the aperture so that $\xi = \rho \cos \varphi$, $\eta = \rho \sin \varphi$; then (35-34) becomes

$$u_P = u_0 \int_0^{2\pi} \int_0^a e^{-ik\alpha\rho \sin\varphi} \rho \, d\rho \, d\varphi \tag{36-12}$$

We can evaluate the double integral by expanding the exponential in a power series and integrating term by term; however, we still have to be able to recognize the series that is obtained, so we shall simply proceed directly by using the integral definition of J_0 and the relation between J_0 and J_1 $[xJ_0 = d(xJ_1)/dx]$, where J_0 and J_1 are Bessel functions:

$$\int_0^{2\pi} \int_0^a e^{-ik\alpha\rho \sin\varphi} \rho \, d\rho \, d\varphi = \int_0^a \rho \, d\rho \int_0^{2\pi} e^{-i(k\alpha\rho) \sin\varphi} \, d\varphi$$

$$= \int_0^a \rho \, d\rho \cdot 2\pi J_0(k\alpha\rho) = \frac{2\pi}{k^2\alpha^2} \int_0^{k\alpha a} x J_0(x) \, dx$$

$$= \frac{2\pi}{k^2\alpha^2} \Big[x J_1(x) \Big]_0^{k\alpha a} = 2\pi a^2 \frac{J_1(k\alpha a)}{k\alpha a} \tag{36-13}$$

Therefore (35-25) becomes

$$I = (2\pi a^2)^2 |u_0|^2 \left[\frac{J_1(k\alpha a)}{k\alpha a} \right]^2 \tag{36-14}$$

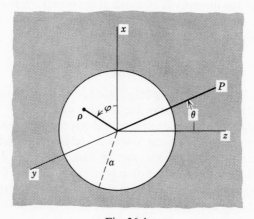

Fig. 36-4

If we use the power series expansion for $J_1(x)$, we find that

$$\frac{J_1(x)}{x} = \frac{1}{2} - \frac{x^2}{2!\,2^3} + \frac{x^4}{2!\,3!\,2^5} - \cdots \tag{36-15}$$

From the form of this series, we can see that the maximum intensity occurs when $x = k\alpha a = 0$, that is, $\alpha = \sin\theta = 0$ or $\theta = 0$; thus the maximum intensity is in the forward direction in the center of the pattern.

As θ increases from 0 to $\frac{1}{2}\pi$, J_1^2 goes through a series of zeroes, with maxima between, since $J_1(x)$ is an oscillating function of x. Therefore the pattern consists of a series of concentric bright circular fringes with dark circular fringes between. The intensities of successive maxima decrease as θ increases; the variation of intensity with angle is qualitatively similar to that shown in Fig. 36-2.

If we let x_n be the nth zero of J_1, i.e., $J_1(x_n) = 0$, the locations of the intensity minima can be found from (36-14) to be given by $k\alpha_n a = x_n = 2\pi a \sin\theta_n/\lambda$ with the use of (36-11). Here θ_n is the direction of the nth dark fringe and is therefore determined by

$$a \sin\theta_n = \left(\frac{x_n}{2\pi}\right)\lambda \tag{36-16}$$

which is a formula similar to (36-5) for a single slit. The values of x_n can be found in tables of the properties of Bessel functions. For example, $x_1 = 1.2197\pi$, and from (36-16), we obtain

$$a \sin\theta_1 = 0.61\lambda \tag{36-17}$$

and $a \sin\theta_2 = 1.16\lambda$, etc. Thus we see that, except for somewhat different numerical factors, the pattern from a circular aperture is about the same size as the pattern from a rectangular slit of comparable dimensions. As before, most of the intensity is included in the central ring, and we can say that the diffracted energy is approximately concentrated in a total angular spread given by

$$\Delta\theta = 2 \text{ arc sin}\left(\frac{0.61\lambda}{a}\right) \simeq 1.22\left(\frac{\lambda}{a}\right) \tag{36-18}$$

if we use (36-17); by comparing (36-7) and (36-18), we see that the angular spread is approximately the same for the two apertures.

The circular aperture is of great practical importance, as a large number of optical instruments such as cameras, telescopes, and microscopes involve circular apertures in one way or another. Thus the light which passes through the instrument is not only refracted to form the image but is diffracted by the aperture as well, and this can affect the properties of the instrument. As an example, we shall briefly consider one aspect of this problem.

Resolving power

Let us consider a telescope as an example, and let us suppose that the source is a distant star so that it will be like a point source. After passing through the telescope and being focused, the radiation from the star will not form a point image, but instead the image will consist of a bright central spot with a series of bright rings about it. If there is another point source, such as another distant star, which has only a small angular separation from the first, the two diffraction patterns will overlap; this is illustrated schematically in Fig. 36-5*a*. It is clear that if the angular separation is too small the two patterns will overlap so much that it will not be possible to interpret the resultant pattern as the result of two sources rather than one. On the other hand, if the angular separation of the sources is very large, the patterns will be well separated and the fact that there are two sources will be quite evident. Clearly, there must be some minimum value of the angular separation for which the patterns are just

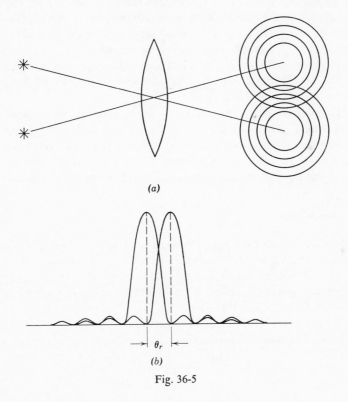

(a)

(b)

Fig. 36-5

recognizable as being due to two sources; they are then said to be *resolved*.

It is clear that an actual criterion which would enable us to state this ability of the instrument to distinguish between two sources, that is, its *resolving power*, would necessarily involve subjective factors which depend on who is actually looking through the telescope. Consequently, in order to obtain a quantitative measure of resolving power, we shall have to make some arbitrary, but reasonable, choice for our criterion. The one most frequently used, because of its simplicity, is due to Rayleigh. It is illustrated in Fig. 36-5*b*, and it states that, when the maximum of one central image falls exactly at the angular position of the first minimum of the other pattern, the sources are resolved. The corresponding angular separation between the sources, or the *minimum angle of resolution* θ_r, is therefore equal to the angular radius of the central bright image and, from (36-17), is given by

$$\theta_r = \theta_1 \simeq \frac{0.61\lambda}{a} \tag{36-19}$$

Thus we see that the larger the telescope radius or the smaller the wavelength observed, the better will be the resolving power. This is one of the reasons for the desirability of building large telescopes. It is also one of the reasons why modern radio telescopes are so large; since radio-frequency wavelengths are so very much longer than optical wavelengths, we see from (36-19) that a must be made correspondingly larger in order to obtain a tolerable resolving power.

Considerations like these can also be applied to microscopes with similar results. The resolving power of a microscope is widely used in the beginning development of quantum mechanics where it enables one to get a quantitative statement of the uncertainty principle, which itself is related to the diffraction phenomena characteristic of waves of all kinds.

36-4   Double slit

Before we consider the problem of an arbitrary number of slits, as in a diffraction grating, it will be useful to consider only two slits. We assume again that the slits are infinitely long in the y direction. The width is a, and the distance between centers is d; we choose the origin midway between the slits as illustrated in Fig. 36-6.

As in (36-2), we can include the constant contribution from the integral over η in u_0, so that (35-34) becomes

$$\frac{u_P}{u_0} = \int_{-d/2-a/2}^{-d/2+a/2} e^{-ik\alpha\xi}\,d\xi + \int_{d/2-a/2}^{d/2+a/2} e^{-ik\alpha\xi}\,d\xi \tag{36-20}$$

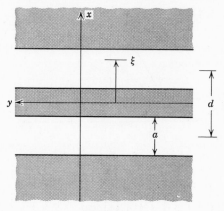

Fig. 36-6

If we change variables of integration by letting $\xi = -\frac{1}{2}d + \mu$ in the first integral and $\xi = \frac{1}{2}d + \nu$ in the second, (36-20) becomes

$$\frac{u_P}{u_0} = e^{\frac{1}{2}ik\alpha d} \int_{-a/2}^{a/2} e^{-ik\alpha\mu}\,d\mu + e^{-\frac{1}{2}ik\alpha d} \int_{-a/2}^{a/2} e^{-ik\alpha\nu}\,d\nu = 2a\left(\frac{\sin\gamma}{\gamma}\right)\cos\epsilon$$

$$(36\text{-}21)$$

since both integrals are the same as that over the single slit evaluated in (36-2); γ is again given by (36-3) and we have set

$$\epsilon = \frac{1}{2}k\alpha d = \frac{\pi d\sin\theta}{\lambda} \qquad (36\text{-}22)$$

If we insert (36-21) into (35-25), we obtain

$$I = (2a)^2\,|u_0|^2\left(\frac{\sin\gamma}{\gamma}\right)^2\cos^2\epsilon = I_0\left(\frac{\sin\gamma}{\gamma}\right)^2\cos^2\epsilon \qquad (36\text{-}23)$$

The condition that we actually have two slits is $\frac{1}{2}a < \frac{1}{2}d$, or $a < d$, and therefore, by (36-3) and (36-22), it is that $\gamma < \epsilon$. Very often, the slits are made very narrow compared to the separation between them, so that $a \ll d$ and therefore $\gamma \ll \epsilon$. Thus, as θ is increased, γ is a more slowly varying function of θ than is ϵ; that is, for a given change in θ, ϵ changes by much more than does γ. Then the oscillations in $\cos^2\epsilon$ are much more rapid than are those in $(\sin\gamma/\gamma)^2$, as illustrated in Fig. 36-7a. Since the intensity (36-23) is the product of these two curves, we see that we can speak of the resultant pattern as being produced by the modulation of the rapid oscillations of $\cos^2\epsilon$ by the more slowly varying single slit function $(\sin\gamma/\gamma)^2$; the resultant pattern constructed in this way is shown in Fig. 36-7b.

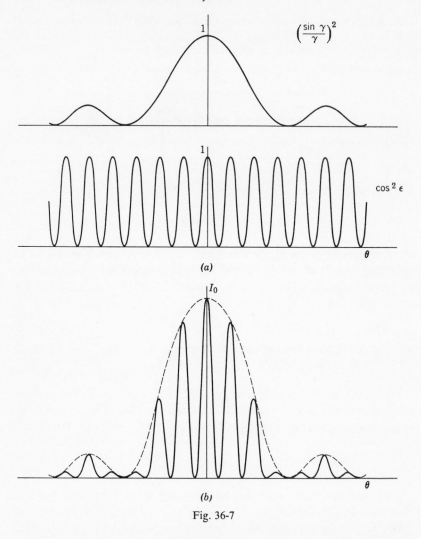

Fig. 36-7

If a is extremely small, the single slit function $(\sin \gamma/\gamma)^2$ will be essentially constant over a very large range of θ, and the resultant pattern of Fig. 36-7b will consist of a series of equally spaced, equally bright fringes; this is the characteristic pattern first found by Young for the double slit system. These maxima occur when $\cos^2 \epsilon = 1$ or $\epsilon = n\pi$, where $n = 0$, $\pm 1, \pm 2, \ldots$. Substituting this into (36-22), we obtain

$$d \sin \theta = n\lambda \qquad (36\text{-}24)$$

as the condition for maximum intensity for a double slit.

As a check on our results, we can consider what we have when $a = d$; that is, we have actually only a single slit of width $2a$. In this case, $\epsilon = \gamma$ and (36-23) becomes

$$I = I_0 \left(\frac{\sin \gamma \cos \gamma}{\gamma}\right)^2 = (2a)^2 |u_0|^2 \left(\frac{\sin 2\gamma}{2\gamma}\right)^2 \tag{36-25}$$

If we compare this with (36-3) and (36-4), we see that (36-25) is exactly the single slit result for a slit of width $2a$, as it should be.

36-5   N slits; the diffraction grating

We now calculate the diffraction pattern for an aperture consisting of N parallel slits, each of width a and with an equal distance d between centers of adjacent slits as shown in Fig. 36-8. We again assume the slits to be very long in the y direction; hence we need not consider the dependence on the η integral; then $\alpha = \sin \theta$, $\beta = 0$. We choose the origin at the center of the first slit and (35-34) becomes

$$\frac{u_P}{u_0} = \int_{-a/2}^{a/2} e^{-ik\alpha\xi} \, d\xi + \int_{d-a/2}^{d+a/2} [\quad] + \int_{2d-a/2}^{2d+a/2} [\quad] + \cdots + \int_{(N-1)d-a/2}^{(N-1)d+a/2} e^{-ik\alpha\xi} \, d\xi \tag{36-26}$$

We can proceed as in the last section by changing variables of integration: in the second integral let $\xi = d + \mu$; in the third let $\xi = 2d + \nu$, etc. Then, if we use (36-2) and (36-3), we find that each term in (36-26)

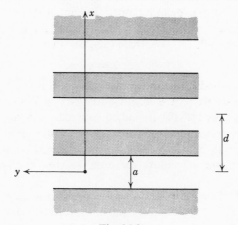

Fig. 36-8

has the single slit integral (36-2) as a common factor; thus

$$\frac{u_P}{u_0} = a \frac{\sin \gamma}{\gamma} [1 + e^{-ik\alpha d} + e^{-2ik\alpha d} + \cdots + e^{-i(N-1)k\alpha d}]$$

$$= a \frac{\sin \gamma}{\gamma} \frac{1 - e^{-iNk\alpha d}}{1 - e^{-ik\alpha d}} \tag{36-27}$$

since the term in brackets is a geometric series of N terms with the common ratio $e^{-ik\alpha d}$. When we insert (36-27) into (35-25) we obtain

$$I = I_s \frac{1 - \cos (Nk\alpha d)}{1 - \cos (k\alpha d)} = I_s \left(\frac{\sin N\epsilon}{\sin \epsilon}\right)^2 \tag{36-28}$$

where ϵ is again given by (36-22) and I_s is the characteristic single slit function (36-4). Thus we have gotten a result similar to that for the double slit in the sense that we can regard (36-28) as the interference pattern arising from the N slits, $(\sin N\epsilon/\sin \epsilon)^2$, modulated by the single slit diffraction pattern I_s. The properties of the last factor in (36-28) are what give the grating of N slits its interesting and important features.

First of all, the numerator of $(\sin N\epsilon/\sin \epsilon)^2$ has a relative maximum whenever $N\epsilon = (m + \frac{1}{2})\pi$, where $m = 0, \pm 1, \pm 2, \ldots$; when this is combined with (36-22), we obtain

$$Nd \sin \theta = (m + \frac{1}{2})\lambda \tag{36-29}$$

Thus these maxima are characteristic of the total distance Nd occupied by all the slits. If N is large, the values of θ do not change by very much between successive maxima, i.e., for a change in m of unity, so that the characteristic pattern of this function is one of closely spaced maxima.

However, these maxima do not all have the same value because of the factor $\sin^2 \epsilon$ in the denominator. In fact, the maximum value of $(\sin N\epsilon/\sin \epsilon)^2$ results when the denominator is zero, i.e., when $\epsilon = n\pi$, where $n = 0, \pm 1, \pm 2, \ldots$, or, from (36-22), when

$$d \sin \theta = n\lambda \tag{36-30}$$

These maxima are called *principal maxima*, and (36-30) shows that their direction depends only on the distance between adjacent slits. The other maxima described by (36-29) are called secondary maxima. It should be noted that the principal maxima do not occur at an angle where we would ordinarily expect to find a secondary maximum, but rather where we would expect a *zero* of sin $N\epsilon$, because, whenever sin $\epsilon = 0$, so does sin $N\epsilon$.

The result (36-30) is the equation most commonly used to describe the diffraction grating since the principal maxima are usually the ones of greatest interest; we now want to consider the reasons for this. Let us first calculate the intensity of a principal maximum. This is most simply done for the case $n = 0$, for then we find that, as $\epsilon \to 0$,

$$\left(\frac{\sin N\epsilon}{\sin \epsilon}\right)^2 \to \left(\frac{N\epsilon}{\epsilon}\right)^2 = N^2$$

so that

$$I \text{(prin. max.)} = N^2 I_s \tag{36-31}$$

The factor N^2 in (36-31) shows the effect of coherence among the N slits acting as radiation sources; we have seen N^2 appear once before in a situation involving coherence in the result (33-26) which we found in a somewhat different context.

Now let us find how rapidly the intensities of the secondary maxima decrease in relation to the principal maximum. Suppose that $N\epsilon = \frac{3}{2}\pi$, which gives the location of the first secondary maximum; then

$$\left(\frac{\sin N\epsilon}{\sin \epsilon}\right)^2 = \left(\sin \frac{3\pi}{2N}\right)^{-2} \simeq \left(\frac{3\pi}{2N}\right)^{-2} \simeq 0.045 N^2$$

If we combine this with (36-28) and (36-31), we find that

$$\frac{I \text{ (1st sec. max.)}}{I \text{ (prin. max.)}} \simeq 0.045 \tag{36-32}$$

The other secondary maxima are even smaller because the $\sin^2 \epsilon$ in the denominator is increasing.

The principal maxima are therefore really much more intense than are any of the others when N is large; therefore the appearance of the pattern is almost one in which only the bright fringes of the principal maxima are seen, with darkness between them. In spite of the fact that the intensity of

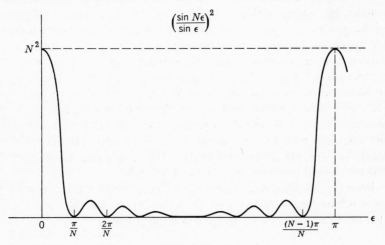

Fig. 36-9

the first secondary maximum is only about 4% of the principal maximum, it cannot be neglected completely, as we shall see shortly.

The general behavior of the term depending on the slit separation is shown in Fig. 36-9. Of course, we must remember that the actual intensity (36-28) is the product of this factor and the term describing the diffraction due to the finite width of the individual slit, i.e., the I_s given by (36-4); this would give us a final curve much like that for the double slit in Fig. 36-7b. However, it is common practice to rule gratings so that the slit width is very small compared to the slit separation. The result of this is to make γ a slowly changing function of θ as compared to ϵ, so that the factor I_s is almost constant and drops off very little for increasing values of θ. Thus we get the usual situation in which the principal maxima all appear to be of practically the same intensity.

Resolving power of a grating

We used the term "resolving power" first in connection with diffraction by a circular aperture for which we used it to express the ability of an optical system to distinguish between two point sources. This term is also used to describe a characteristic of the pattern produced by a diffraction grating. Since gratings are used so extensively to measure wavelengths very accurately, it is important to know the smallest wavelength difference which can be distinguished in order to make a proper assessment of the errors involved in wavelength determinations.

If a grating is illuminated with radiation consisting of several wavelengths, the resultant diffraction pattern will be a superposition of patterns of the type we have just considered, with one pattern arising from each of the wavelengths present. If the wavelengths are very nearly the same, the various principal maxima will almost coincide. Suppose $\Delta\lambda$ is the smallest wavelength difference which can be just distinguished, or resolved. In order to determine $\Delta\lambda$, we use an arbitrary criterion similar to that we used above for the circular aperture, and we say that two wavelengths, whose difference is $\Delta\lambda$, can be just distinguished when the principal maximum of one coincides with the first minimum from the corresponding principal maximum for the other wavelength. Hence a figure illustrating this criterion would be almost exactly like Fig. 36-5b.

If we use (36-30) and say that the principal maximum for λ occurs when $\alpha d = n\lambda$, or $N\alpha d = Nn\lambda$, we see from (36-28), or Fig. 36-9 and (36-22), that the first adjacent dark fringe will occur when

$$N\alpha d = (Nn + 1)\lambda = Nn(\lambda + \Delta\lambda) \qquad (36\text{-}33)$$

since this direction α is also to be the direction of the principal maximum for the wavelength $\lambda + \Delta\lambda$ according to our criterion. We find at once from (36-33) that

$$\text{Resolving power} = \frac{\lambda}{\Delta\lambda} = Nn \qquad (36\text{-}34)$$

We see, first of all, that the resolving power increases with the *order* of the principal maximum being observed; that is, it increases as n increases. In other words, as one goes out to larger angles from the normal to the grating surface, the pattern spreads apart and the various principal maxima have greater angular separation. Because the resolving power also increases as N increases, it is advantageous to use gratings with as large a number of illuminated slits as is feasible.

Exercises

36-1. What changes will result in our calculations of amplitude and intensity for the single slit if we choose the origin at an edge rather than in the center?

36-2. Show that the maxima of the single slit pattern are determined by the equation $\gamma = \tan\gamma$. Find the first three solutions of this equation and compare with the approximate solutions $\frac{3}{2}\pi$, $\frac{5}{2}\pi$, and $\frac{7}{2}\pi$.

36-3. Find the conditions for minimum intensity in the pattern from a rectangular slit whose length is twice its width.

36-4. Plot the intensity distribution for a grating of five equally spaced slits when $d = 3a$. What would be found in general if $d = 2a$ and there are an arbitrary number of slits?

36-5. A grating is formed from $2N$ narrow parallel slits, divided into two equal sets. Within each set, the infinitely long slits are equally spaced a distance d apart. However, the two sets are displaced from one another, so that each slit of the second set is at the distance $\frac{1}{3}d$ from its nearest neighbor of the first set. The net result is that the spacing between slits is $\frac{1}{3}d$, $\frac{2}{3}d$, $\frac{1}{3}d$, etc. Calculate the Fraunhofer diffraction pattern of this grating, and plot the resulting intensity distribution.

37 Fresnel diffraction

We recall that in this kind of diffraction observations are made close enough to the aperture that second order terms are important and ϕ is given by (35-35).

It will be possible to simplify our calculations considerably by restricting the type of problem to be considered. We shall calculate the intensity at points P on a screen which is parallel to the screen containing the openings

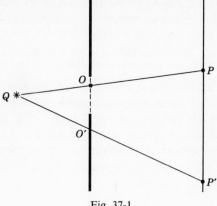

Fig. 37-1

of the aperture, as shown in Fig. 37-1. It will not be necessary to go over a very large range of coordinates of P in order to include all the regions in which the intensity has any appreciable variation and hence the values of α, β, and R will remain almost constant. We shall consider only arrangements in which the line connecting Q and P is almost always practically normal to the plane of the aperture. Hence we shall introduce very little error into our results if we simply set $\alpha = \beta = 0$; then (35-35) becomes

$$\phi = \frac{\xi^2 + \eta^2}{2R} \tag{37-1}$$

We also see from Fig. 37-1 that the coordinates of P will be almost the same as those of the corresponding point of the aperture. This figure also illustrates the particular way in which we shall find it convenient to choose the origin of coordinates for points *in the aperture*, that is, those points over which we perform the integration in (35-34). Even though Q is very far away from the screen in reality, the figure shows that the origin is chosen at the point where the line connecting Q and P intersects the plane of the screen containing the aperture, whether the line intersects an opening of the aperture or not. Thus, each time we choose a new point, such as P', at which to calculate the intensity, we shall automatically be choosing a new origin for the aperture coordinates, which would be O' for P'.

In addition, we shall consider only problems in which we can neglect the y dependence of the pattern, as for infinite slits; if we give a new meaning to u_0, as we did in the last chapter, then, when we insert (37-1) into (35-34), we obtain

$$u_P = u_0 \int_{\mathscr{A}} e^{ik\xi^2/2R} \, d\xi \tag{37-2}$$

If we confine ourselves to a discussion of a single slit, (37-2) becomes

$$u_P = u_0 \int_{\xi_1}^{\xi_2} e^{ik\xi^2/2R} \, d\xi \tag{37-3}$$

where ξ_1 and ξ_2 are the coordinates of the edges of the slit.

It is customary to change to dimensionless variables in (37-3). Let

$$\frac{k\xi^2}{2R} = \frac{\pi\xi^2}{R\lambda} = \frac{\pi s^2}{2} \tag{37-4}$$

Then

$$\xi = \sqrt{\frac{R\lambda}{2}} \, s \tag{37-5}$$

When (37-4) and (37-5) are substituted into (37-3), it becomes

$$u_P = \sqrt{\frac{R\lambda}{2}} \, u_0 \int_{s_1}^{s_2} e^{i\frac{1}{2}\pi s^2} \, ds \tag{37-6}$$

where

$$s_2 = \sqrt{\frac{2}{R\lambda}} \, \xi_2 \quad \text{and} \quad s_1 = \sqrt{\frac{2}{R\lambda}} \, \xi_1 \tag{37-7}$$

Let the x coordinate of P with respect to some conveniently chosen xyz coordinate system be x_P, and let the positions of the edges of the slit with respect to this system be a for the lower edge and b for the upper edge as shown in Fig. 37-2. Since we are using the assumption that $\alpha = 0$, the coordinate of the aperture origin O which is appropriate to P is the same as that of P, i.e., x_P. From the figure, we see that

$$\xi_2 = b - x_P, \quad \xi_1 = a - x_P \tag{37-8}$$

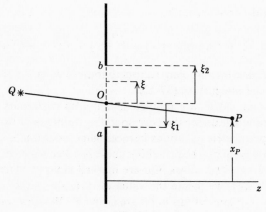

Fig. 37-2

so that from (37-7)

$$s_2 = \sqrt{\frac{2}{R\lambda}}\,(b - x_P), \quad s_1 = \sqrt{\frac{2}{R\lambda}}\,(a - x_P) \qquad (37\text{-}9)$$

If we write (37-6) as

$$u_P = \sqrt{\frac{R\lambda}{2}}\, u_0 \left[\int_{s_1}^{s_2} \cos\left(\frac{\pi s^2}{2}\right) ds + i \int_{s_1}^{s_2} \sin\left(\frac{\pi s^2}{2}\right) ds\right] \quad (37\text{-}10)$$

and substitute into (35-25), we obtain

$$I_P = \frac{I_0}{2} \left\{\left[\int_{s_1}^{s_2} \cos\left(\frac{\pi s^2}{2}\right) ds\right]^2 + \left[\int_{s_1}^{s_2} \sin\left(\frac{\pi s^2}{2}\right) ds\right]^2\right\} \quad (37\text{-}11)$$

The task of computing the intensity is now reduced to one of evaluating the integrals; we shall see the significance of $I_0 = \frac{1}{2} R\lambda\, |u_0|^2$ shortly. There are tables of these integrals available and (37-11) can be computed in this way. The expression (37-11) can also be put into a geometric form which is extremely helpful to the understanding of the basic features of Fresnel diffraction, and it can also be used for numerical computations; this is the procedure that we shall discuss next.

37-1   The Fresnel integrals and the Cornu spiral

The Fresnel integrals $C(\sigma)$ and $S(\sigma)$ are defined as

$$C(\sigma) = \int_0^\sigma \cos\left(\frac{\pi s^2}{2}\right) ds \quad \text{and} \quad S(\sigma) = \int_0^\sigma \sin\left(\frac{\pi s^2}{2}\right) ds \quad (37\text{-}12)$$

The integrals involved in (37-11) can be easily expressed in terms of the Fresnel integrals. For example,

$$\int_{s_1}^{s_2} \cos\left(\frac{\pi s^2}{2}\right) ds = \int_0^{s_2} [\quad] - \int_0^{s_1} [\quad] = C(s_2) - C(s_1) \quad (37\text{-}13)$$

Thus, for the present, we can restrict ourselves to a discussion of the properties of the integrals in (37-12).

Although their values are tabulated, it is also customary to give the values of these integrals for the corresponding values of σ by plotting the curve whose parametric equations in rectangular coordinates are given by $x = C(\sigma)$ and $y = S(\sigma)$. The resulting curve is called a *Cornu spiral* and is given in Fig. 37-3. The values of σ are marked along the curve; thus, to find $C(\sigma)$ and $S(\sigma)$, we locate the value of σ on the curve, and then the rectangular coordinates of this point are C and S. We now want to discuss some of the properties of this spiral.

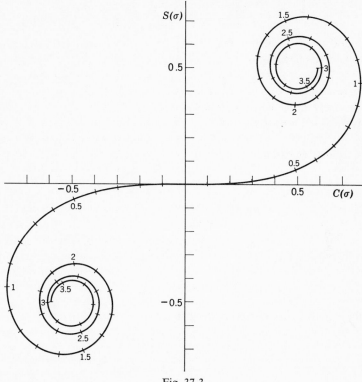

Fig. 37-3

It turns out that

$$C(\pm\infty) = S(\pm\infty) = \pm\tfrac{1}{2} \qquad (37\text{-}14)$$

Thus the limiting values as the spiral winds up tightly in each arm correspond to $\sigma = \pm\infty$. From (37-12), we find that the coordinate differentials are

$$dC = \cos\left(\frac{\pi\sigma^2}{2}\right) d\sigma \quad \text{and} \quad dS = \sin\left(\frac{\pi\sigma^2}{2}\right) d\sigma \qquad (37\text{-}15)$$

so that the slope of the curve is

$$\frac{dS}{dC} = \tan\left(\frac{\pi\sigma^2}{2}\right) \qquad (37\text{-}16)$$

Thus, when $\sigma = 0$, the slope is zero. As σ increases, the slope increases until $\sigma^2 = 1$, when the slope $= \tan(\tfrac{1}{2}\pi) = +\infty$; as σ increases further, the slope quickly becomes very large and negative. The slope decreases in magnitude with further increase in σ until $\sigma^2 = 2$, when the slope is again zero. Thus the point at the top of the curve corresponds to $\sigma = \sqrt{2}$. The slope then becomes positive, is infinite again when $\sigma^2 = 3$ or $\sigma = \pm\sqrt{3}$, and finally, when $\sigma^2 = 4$ or $\sigma = \pm 2$, the argument of the tangent has gone through a full range of 2π; then we are back at zero slope, and the whole cycle begins again. In other words, whenever σ^2 increases by 4, the curve swings around another loop; however, we still have not shown that the curve must actually have the spiral form shown.

From (37-15), we see that $(dC)^2 + (dS)^2 = (d\sigma)^2$; hence $d\sigma =$ length of arc of the curve between the two points corresponding to this difference in σ. Therefore we can say

$$\sigma_2 - \sigma_1 = \int_{\sigma_1}^{\sigma_2} d\sigma = \text{length of arc between the points}$$
$$\text{on the curve corresponding to } \sigma_1$$
$$\text{and } \sigma_2 \qquad (37\text{-}17)$$

Now we can show that the curve is a spiral. We saw above that one turn corresponds to $\Delta(\sigma^2) = 4$, or

$$\sigma_2{}^2 - \sigma_1{}^2 = 4 = (\sigma_2 - \sigma_1)(\sigma_2 + \sigma_1)$$

and the length of arc corresponding to one turn is

$$\sigma_2 - \sigma_1 = \frac{4}{\sigma_2 + \sigma_1} \qquad (37\text{-}18)$$

Therefore, as σ_1 and σ_2 increase, the denominator of (37-18) increases and the length of arc corresponding to one turn decreases; thus the turns become smaller and smaller, eventually winding up on themselves as shown in Fig. 37-3.

Use of the spiral

If we refer to Fig. 37-4, we can see how to use the Cornu spiral to evaluate (37-11). After s_2 and s_1 have been calculated from (37-9), we locate them on the spiral and draw a straight line connecting these two points. We see from the figure that the horizontal component of this line is $C(s_2) - C(s_1)$; the vertical component of this line is $S(s_2) - S(s_1)$. Therefore we have

$$L^2 = \text{square of the length of the line connecting}$$
$$\text{the points } s_2 \text{ and } s_1 \text{ on the spiral}$$
$$= [C(s_2) - C(s_1)]^2 + [S(s_2) - S(s_1)]^2 \qquad (37\text{-}19)$$

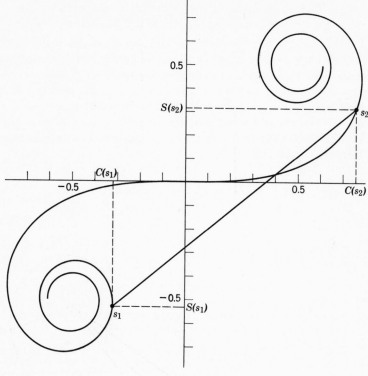

Fig. 37-4

Then (37-11) and (37-13) combined yield

$$I = \tfrac{1}{2}I_0L^2 \tag{37-20}$$

Thus the problem has been reduced to measuring distances on the spiral of Fig. 37-3.

Example. No Slit at All. Here $a = b = 0$, so that $s_1 = s_2$ from (37-9). Then $L = 0$ so that $I_P = 0$, as it should for a solid screen.

Example. No Screen at All. For *any* point P, $b = \infty$ and $a = -\infty$, so that $s_2 = \infty$ and $s_1 = -\infty$ from (37-9). Therefore, from (37-14) and (37-19), we see that the length of the line connecting the two wound-up points of the spiral is $\sqrt{2}$, so that $L^2 = 2$ and $I = I_0$ from (37-20). Thus I_0 has the significance of being the intensity in the fully illuminated region.

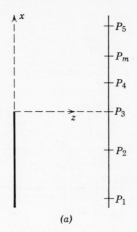

(a)

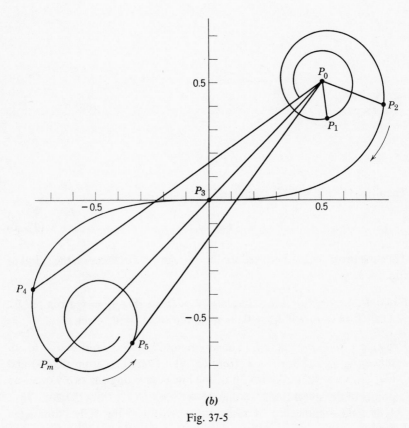

(b)

Fig. 37-5

37-2 Straight edge

Let the edge of a semi-infinite absorbing screen coincide with the y axis as shown in Fig. 37-5a. Hence $a = 0$ and $b = \infty$, and (37-9) gives

$$s_2 = \infty, \quad s_1 = -\sqrt{\frac{2}{R\lambda}}\, x_P \tag{37-21}$$

and the upper end of our line will always be at the upper limiting point $(\frac{1}{2}, \frac{1}{2})$, which we shall call P_0.

In Fig. 37-5b, we illustrate how the diffraction pattern of the straight edge is determined with the aid of the spiral. At a point P_1, well into the geometric shadow, x_P is large and negative and therefore s_1 is large and positive; the line connecting P_0 and P_1 is short, and the intensity is small. As we move along the screen up toward the lighted region, s_1 decreases and the line $P_0 P_i$ gradually unwinds along the upper end of the spiral; thus the length L is increasing, and the intensity is constantly increasing. At the point P_3, the edge of the geometric shadow, the line $P_0 P_3$ is of length $\frac{1}{2}\sqrt{2}$, the amplitude is half that in the fully illuminated region, and the intensity is $\frac{1}{4}I_0$ by (37-20).

As we pass P_3, s_1 becomes negative and increases in magnitude so that the lower end of the line starts to trace out the lower arm of the spiral. We

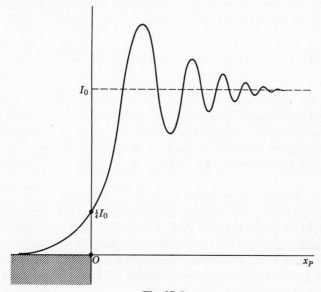

Fig. 37-6

see that the intensity still continues to increase since the length of the line is still increasing, until, at some point P_m, the line has maximum length and the intensity is a maximum. After P_m, the line gets shorter and the intensity decreases, until the length reaches a relative minimum and then begins to increase again. Therefore, as we continue moving up the screen, the lower end of the line winds around the lower end of the spiral with corresponding fluctuations in intensity; however, these fluctuations continually decrease in magnitude as the spiral becomes more tightly wound. Finally, we get way out in the illuminated region, the lower end of the curve is effectively always at the lower limit point $(-\frac{1}{2}, -\frac{1}{2})$, and the intensity is constant and equal to I_0. The resultant intensity variation with position along the screen which is obtained in this way is shown in Fig. 37-6.

37-3   Single slit

We choose the origin of the xyz axes at the center of the slit of width A so that $a = -\frac{1}{2}A$ and $b = \frac{1}{2}A$. Then (37-9) becomes

$$s_2 = \sqrt{\frac{2}{R\lambda}}(\tfrac{1}{2}A - x_P), \quad s_1 = \sqrt{\frac{2}{R\lambda}}(-\tfrac{1}{2}A - x_P) \qquad (37\text{-}22)$$

and we find from (37-17) that

$$\text{arc length} = s = s_2 - s_1 = \sqrt{\frac{2}{R\lambda}}\, A = \text{const.} \qquad (37\text{-}23)$$

Thus we can find the intensity distribution by imagining that we have a flexible tube of constant length s sliding along the spiral as shown in Fig. 37-7. The intensity is obtained by finding the square of the length of the line connecting the two ends of the tube as we slide it along the spiral to the positions corresponding to the locations of the various points on the screen.

When x_P is large and negative, we see from (37-22) that the tube is all wound up on itself at the upper end of the spiral and the intensity is zero, as it should be in the extreme shadow region. As x_P approaches $-\frac{1}{2}A$, s_1 approaches zero and one end of the tube reaches the origin. At this stage, we cannot say more about the qualitative behavior of the pattern unless we know something about the length of the arc; there are two extreme cases which can be easily discussed.

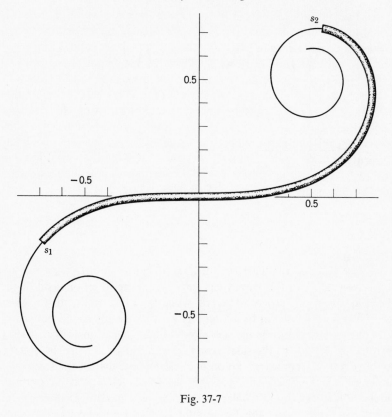

Fig. 37-7

Large s

We see from (37-23) that a large s will generally correspond to a wide slit, observation close to the slit, and short wavelength. In this case, when s_1 reaches the origin, s_2 will not have unwound much from the upper end, and the intensity will have uniformly increased in coming out of the shadow. As x_P increases, the tube will begin to wind up on the lower end of the spiral with resulting alternations in intensity like those from a straight edge. Then, for a while, s_2 will be at the upper end of the spiral, s_1 will be at the lower, and the intensity will be constant and equal to I_0. Finally, as x_P increases still more, the other end s_2 starts to unwind and we go through the stages outlined above, but in reverse order. In this extreme case, the resultant pattern is much like that obtained by the superposition of patterns from two straight edges, and, in effect, this is the way the pattern is formed. The intensity distribution for large s is shown in Fig. 37-8.

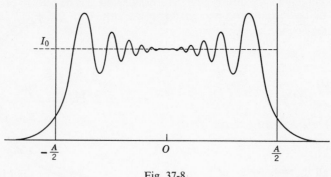

Fig. 37-8

Small s

This corresponds to: narrow slit, large distance from the screen, and long wavelength. In this case, there never is a time when one end of the tube is at the upper part of the spiral while the other end is at the lower part. Therefore there will be a long region in the center of the pattern in which the intensity will change very slowly, and fluctuations will arise only when we get far out to the sides, away from the center of the slit, so that the short tube starts to wind up on one end or the other of the spiral and the length of the line connecting the ends can change comparatively rapidly. This behavior is similar to that of the Fraunhofer pattern from a single slit, and in fact the Fraunhofer pattern does correspond to the limiting case of this type.

Intermediate s

The qualitative discussion of this case can be quite difficult. However, the quantitative determination of the intensity distribution is quite easy, involving, as it does, only the measuring of lengths of lines, squaring them, and using (37-20).

Exercises

37-1. Suppose that light of wavelength 5000 angstroms is incident upon a slit whose width is 0.1 millimeter. Using the Cornu spiral, calculate and make a plot of the intensity distribution on a screen located 2.5 millimeters from the slit.

37-2. Discuss the details of how the Cornu spiral can be used to obtain the Fresnel diffraction pattern from: (*a*) an opaque strip, (*b*) a double slit similar to that of Fig. 36-6.

38 Hamiltonian of a charged particle in an external field

We recall that the force on a charge q in an electromagnetic field is given by (19-34) as

$$\mathbf{F} = q(\mathbf{E} + \mathbf{v} \times \mathbf{B}) \tag{38-1}$$

This force is an important example of a *velocity-dependent force*. For many purposes, particularly in the development of the quantum mechanical description of the interactions among charged particles and electromagnetic fields, it is desirable to describe the system in the Lagrangian and Hamiltonian formulations of mechanics.

In (7-32) we found that the equations of motion could be written

$$\frac{d}{dt}\left(\frac{\partial T}{\partial \dot{q}_j}\right) - \frac{\partial T}{\partial q_j} = Q_j \tag{38-2}$$

with $j = 1, 2, \ldots, n$, where n is the total number of independent generalized coordinates. In (38-2) T is the kinetic energy, and the generalized forces Q_j are found from the fact that the work done in a virtual displacement of the system can be written $\sum_j Q_j \, \delta q_j$.

The force (38-1) is not conservative in the usual sense, but it is evident that if the forces can be derived from a generalized potential $U(q_j, \dot{q}_j)$ such that

$$Q_j = -\frac{\partial U}{\partial q_j} + \frac{d}{dt}\left(\frac{\partial U}{\partial \dot{q}_j}\right) \tag{38-3}$$

we can define a Lagrangian function $L = T - U$, so that the equations of motion (38-2) can be written in the usual form

$$\frac{d}{dt}\left(\frac{\partial L}{\partial \dot{q}_j}\right) - \frac{\partial L}{\partial q_j} = 0 \tag{38-4}$$

If we write the fields in terms of the potentials as given by (31-5) and (31-7), and insert them into (38-1), we obtain

$$\mathbf{F} = q\left(-\operatorname{grad} \phi - \frac{\partial \mathbf{A}}{\partial t} + \mathbf{v} \times \operatorname{curl} \mathbf{A}\right) \tag{38-5}$$

We shall consider the x component of (38-5) in order to show that we can find a generalized potential U. If we use (1-18) and (1-30), we get

$$(\mathbf{v} \times \operatorname{curl} \mathbf{A})_x = v_y(\operatorname{curl} \mathbf{A})_z - v_z(\operatorname{curl} \mathbf{A})_y$$

$$= v_y\left(\frac{\partial A_y}{\partial x} - \frac{\partial A_x}{\partial y}\right) - v_z\left(\frac{\partial A_x}{\partial z} - \frac{\partial A_z}{\partial x}\right)$$

$$= v_y\frac{\partial A_y}{\partial x} + v_z\frac{\partial A_z}{\partial x} + v_x\frac{\partial A_x}{\partial x} - v_x\frac{\partial A_x}{\partial x} - v_y\frac{\partial A_x}{\partial y} - v_z\frac{\partial A_x}{\partial z} \quad (38\text{-}6)$$

after adding and subtracting the term $v_x(\partial A_x/\partial x)$.

Now let us consider the total time rate of change of A_x. Since A_x depends on position as well as on time, it will change because of its explicit time dependence and, in addition, because the motion of the particle changes the spatial location at which we wish to evaluate A_x. Therefore

$$\frac{dA_x}{dt} = \frac{\partial A_x}{\partial t} + \frac{\partial A_x}{\partial x}\frac{dx}{dt} + \frac{\partial A_x}{\partial y}\frac{dy}{dt} + \frac{\partial A_x}{\partial z}\frac{dz}{dt}$$

$$= \frac{\partial A_x}{\partial t} + v_x\frac{\partial A_x}{\partial x} + v_y\frac{\partial A_x}{\partial y} + v_z\frac{\partial A_x}{\partial z} \quad (38\text{-}7)$$

If we combine (38-6) and (38-7), we find that

$$(\mathbf{v} \times \operatorname{curl} \mathbf{A})_x = v_x\frac{\partial A_x}{\partial x} + v_y\frac{\partial A_y}{\partial x} + v_z\frac{\partial A_z}{\partial x} - \frac{dA_x}{dt} + \frac{\partial A_x}{\partial t}$$

$$= \frac{\partial}{\partial x}(\mathbf{v} \cdot \mathbf{A}) - \frac{dA_x}{dt} + \frac{\partial A_x}{\partial t} \quad (38\text{-}8)$$

The last step was possible because the q_j and $\dot{q}_j$ are independent variables in the Lagrangian formulation.

Substituting (38-8) into (38-5), we find that

$$F_x = q\left[-\frac{\partial \phi}{\partial x} - \frac{\partial A_x}{\partial t} + (\mathbf{v} \times \operatorname{curl} \mathbf{A})_x\right]$$

$$= q\left[-\frac{\partial \phi}{\partial x} + \frac{\partial}{\partial x}(\mathbf{v} \cdot \mathbf{A}) - \frac{dA_x}{dt}\right] \quad (38\text{-}9)$$

Since $\mathbf{A} = \mathbf{A}(x, y, z, t)$ and is independent of $\mathbf{v}$, we can write

$$A_x = \frac{\partial}{\partial v_x}(\mathbf{v} \cdot \mathbf{A})$$

Then (38-9) can be written

$$F_x = q\left\{-\frac{\partial}{\partial x}(\phi - \mathbf{v} \cdot \mathbf{A}) - \frac{d}{dt}\left[\frac{\partial}{\partial v_x}(\mathbf{v} \cdot \mathbf{A})\right]\right\}$$

$$= q\left\{-\frac{\partial}{\partial x}(\phi - \mathbf{v} \cdot \mathbf{A}) + \frac{d}{dt}\left[\frac{\partial}{\partial v_x}(\phi - \mathbf{v} \cdot \mathbf{A})\right]\right\} \quad (38\text{-}10)$$

because ϕ is also independent of v_x. If we define

$$U = q(\phi - \mathbf{v} \cdot \mathbf{A}) \quad (38\text{-}11)$$

we can write (38-10) as

$$F_x = -\frac{\partial U}{\partial x} + \frac{d}{dt}\left(\frac{\partial U}{\partial v_x}\right)$$

which is of the desired form (38-3). Since we would find corresponding results for F_y and F_z, we see that the Lagrangian L corresponding to (38-1) is

$$L = T - U = \tfrac{1}{2}mv^2 - q\phi + q\mathbf{v} \cdot \mathbf{A} \quad (38\text{-}12)$$

We can note here that, if in addition to being subject to the electromagnetic field, the particle is subject to conservative forces given by the potential V and to non-conservative forces Q_j, we can define

$$L = T - U - V = \tfrac{1}{2}mv^2 - V - q\phi + q\mathbf{v} \cdot \mathbf{A} \quad (38\text{-}13)$$

and the equations of motion will be

$$\frac{d}{dt}\left(\frac{\partial L}{\partial \dot{q}_j}\right) - \frac{\partial L}{\partial q_j} = Q_j$$

For simplicity, however, we shall continue to assume that the only forces are due to the electromagnetic field as given by ϕ and $\mathbf{A}$.

We proceed in the usual way to find the Hamiltonian. By definition, the generalized momenta are

$$p_x = \frac{\partial L}{\partial \dot{x}} = \frac{\partial L}{\partial v_x} = mv_x + qA_x$$

So that

$$\mathbf{p} = m\mathbf{v} + q\mathbf{A} \quad (38\text{-}14)$$

This interesting result shows that, in the presence of an electromagnetic field, the momentum is no longer simply equal to the product of the mass and velocity, but includes the vector potential as well. Using (38-12) and (38-14) in the definition (10-3) of the Hamiltonian function H, we find that

$$H = \sum_j p_j v_j - L = mv^2 + q\mathbf{v} \cdot \mathbf{A} - L = \tfrac{1}{2}mv^2 + q\phi$$

$$= T + q\phi = \text{total energy of the particle}$$

Since we still must express this in terms of the momentum, we use (38-14) and obtain

$$H = H(p_j, q_j) = \frac{1}{2m}(\mathbf{p} - q\mathbf{A})^2 + q\phi \tag{38-15}$$

which is our desired result.

One can now show that, when H is used in the Hamiltonian equations of motion,

$$\dot{p}_j = -\frac{\partial H}{\partial q_j} \quad \text{and} \quad \dot{q}_j = \frac{\partial H}{\partial p_j}$$

the resulting equations are equivalent to (38-1).

Application to theory of magnetic susceptibilities

Let us apply (38-15) to an electron in an atom. Since the Hamiltonian is numerically equal to the energy, we can expand the square in (38-15) to get for the electron energy the following expression

$$w = \frac{p^2}{2m} - \frac{e}{m}\mathbf{p} \cdot \mathbf{A} + \frac{e^2}{2m}\mathbf{A}^2 + e\phi = w_0 + \Delta w \tag{38-16}$$

where $w_0 = p^2/2m$ is the energy in the absence of an external field and Δw is the energy change due to the presence of the field.

Let us consider the atom containing this electron to be subject to a uniform induction $\mathbf{B} = B\hat{\mathbf{k}}$. We know from Exercise 25-3 that a vector potential for this case is

$$\mathbf{A} = \tfrac{1}{2}(\mathbf{B} \times \mathbf{r}) = \tfrac{1}{2}B(-y\hat{\mathbf{i}} + x\hat{\mathbf{j}}) \tag{38-17}$$

and that $\phi = 0$. Substituting (38-17) into (38-16), we obtain

$$\Delta w = -\frac{eB}{2m}(xp_y - yp_x) + \frac{e^2B^2}{8m}(x^2 + y^2)$$

$$= -\frac{eB}{2m}l_z + \frac{e^2B^2}{8m}(x^2 + y^2) = w_p + w_d \tag{38-18}$$

where $l_z = (\mathbf{r} \times \mathbf{p})_z = $ electronic angular momentum.

Let us consider the first term of (38-18). It can be written

$$w_p = -\frac{e}{2m}\mathbf{l} \cdot \mathbf{B} = -\boldsymbol{\mu} \cdot \mathbf{B} \tag{38-19}$$

and, by comparison with (23-15) which holds for the electric situation, we see that associated with the motion of the electron is a magnetic dipole moment given by

$$\mu = \frac{e}{2m} \mathbf{l} \tag{38-20}$$

Thus the magnetic moment and angular momentum are proportional; the constant of proportionality, $e/2m$ (or $q/2m$ for a general charge q), is called the classical gyromagnetic ratio. We note that, if the charge is positive, μ and $\mathbf{l}$ are in the same direction, while, if the charge is negative, as it is for the electron, μ and $\mathbf{l}$ are oppositely directed.

Let us now turn our attention to the second term of (38-18). If we sum it over all of the N electrons in a unit volume, we get the corresponding magnetic energy density arising from this term; the result is

$$u_{m,d} = \frac{e^2 B^2}{2m} \sum_i (x_i^2 + y_i^2) = \frac{e^2 B^2 N}{8m} (\overline{x^2} + \overline{y^2}) \tag{38-21}$$

and it involves the average squares of the x and y coordinates. In the simplest case, we can assume the electron positions within the atom to be symmetric, so that

$$\overline{x^2} = \overline{y^2} = \overline{z^2} = \tfrac{1}{3}\overline{r^2} \tag{38-22}$$

since $r^2 = x^2 + y^2 + z^2$. Then (38-21) becomes

$$u_{m,d} = \frac{Ne^2 \overline{r^2} B^2}{12m} \tag{38-23}$$

and is proportional to B^2.

An energy proportional to B^2 will arise when the moment is induced by the field. This effect was calculated in (23-12) for the electric problem; the analogous expression for the magnetic problem must be

$$u_m = -\tfrac{1}{2}\mathbf{M} \cdot \mathbf{B} = -\tfrac{1}{2}\chi_m \mathbf{H} \cdot \mathbf{B} \simeq -\frac{\chi_m B^2}{2\mu_0} \tag{38-24}$$

where we have used (25-4) and the justifiable approximation that $\mu \simeq \mu_0$. Comparing (38-23) and (38-24), we see that this *diamagnetic susceptibility* is

$$\chi_m = -\frac{N\mu_0 e^2 \overline{r^2}}{6m} \tag{38-25}$$

The induced diamagnetic moment is opposite to the field since χ_m is negative. Since $\overline{r^2} \neq 0$, $\chi_m \neq 0$ always; hence all atoms should have this induced diamagnetic moment. This is not observed for all atoms because in many cases the average angular momentum of the electrons along a given axis is different from zero, and a *paramagnetic moment*, arising from (38-20), can also be present. When both moments exist, the paramagnetic one is generally much larger; then the diamagnetic contribution to the over-all atomic moment is negligible.

Exercise

38-1. Verify the statements in the paragraph following (38-15).

Index